The ENVIRONMENT
of MEDICAL PRACTICE

The
ENVIRONMENT *of*
MEDICAL PRACTICE

Edited by

R. B. ROBINS, M.D.

Member, Board of Trustees, American Medical Association
Chief of Staff, Ouachita County Hospital, Camden, Arkansas

YEAR BOOK MEDICAL PUBLISHERS, INC.
35 EAST WACKER DRIVE • CHICAGO

Preface

FOR THE PAST FEW YEARS the editor has noted that many young physicians are completing their internships and residencies and beginning their practices with inadequate knowledge of the socio-economic-ethical phases of the practice of medicine. It has also been noticeable that medical school curriculums have little to offer in this area. Full-time professors are interested in the scientific side of medicine, often to the neglect of the social, economic, and ethical considerations of medical practice.

The House of Delegates of the American Medical Association, at the New York City meeting in June, 1961, being aware of this situation, suggested that each medical school "develop and present a required course in ethics and socio-economic principles, and that each state board of medical examiners include questions on ethics and proper socio-economic practices in all examinations for license."

Hence, I was stimulated to edit a small volume on these phases of the practice of medicine so that medical students, interns, residents, physicians, and the public could have assembled under one cover basic background material in this area.

Each author has special knowledge and experience in his particular field. We are grateful to each essayist for the time, interest, and effort expended in producing this book.

R. B. ROBINS, M.D.
Editor

Table of Contents

1. The Human Side of Medicine

A GENERATION AGO we had only a few specific remedies for diseases. Many diagnostic measures now in common use were not known or had not been perfected. The family doctor had to rely on his own wisdom and close observation, together

9

with his knowledge of the personal and familial traits of his patients. He was much more likely to consider his patient as a whole person and not just as a "case" of a certain disease. His patients regarded him as a sort of honorary member of their families and depended on him for advice about many different sorts of problems—from Johnny's broken arm to Mary's marital difficulties.

The spectacular advances in diagnosis and therapy have inevitably led to an increase in specialists and to a greater dependence on hospital care in time of illness. As a result, it is harder for the individual doctor to stay close to his individual patient. The greater emphasis on the scientific side of medicine has, it must be admitted, served to de-emphasize the human side—the art of medicine. Many patients feel that they are not getting the individual attention they crave. Consequently, a great many people are becoming increasingly resentful and critical of the whole medical profession. They seem to take for granted the extra years of life they may now anticipate, the freedom from infectious diseases that took such heavy toll of their ancestors, and the dramatic results of modern surgical advances.

Both patients and doctors are human beings with human faults and weaknesses but also with human virtues. While it is admittedly much harder to see another's viewpoint than one's own, it will be helpful to both the medical man and the layman to try to exchange viewpoints occasionally. In this chapter, we will do our best to portray the human side of both patient and doctor, with the hope that each may gain a better understanding of the other's point of view.

The Patient's Human Side

In a lecture to Harvard medical students in 1945, a well-known writer, the late Ben Ames Williams, described admirably the patient's viewpoint (1). He began by saying that the word *panic* is derived from the Greek god Pan, who aroused fear in human beings wherever he appeared. The modern prototype of this god, Mr. Williams told the Harvard students, is the doctor.

The lesson that every doctor most needs to learn is that his patients are afraid. . . . Your success in quieting your patient's fear of you and his fear for himself will in many cases do more for him than all the medical knowledge accumulated through the ages.

Mr. Williams gave some excellent advice on how the physician can help to dispel the patient's fears:

In a large proportion of cases, the good that the doctor can do the patient is determined within a few minutes after their first meeting. . . . The most successful doctor is one who supplements his professional competence with what salesmen call a good approach.

One excellent suggestion was that the doctor report to the patient as soon as possible the results of laboratory or x-ray studies. He also advised the physician to present as hopeful an outlook of the patient's illness as he honestly can.

While not all patients are as afraid of doctors as Mr. Williams must have been, there is no doubt that most of them have some degree of anxiety in connection with their illness and are in need of sympathy and understanding. Often the reassurance a doctor can give—especially after a careful examination—will give the patient more relief from a tension headache or a spastic colon than will a prescription for an analgesic or antispasmodic medication. Such reassurance can often be afforded by a simple explanation of the patient's symptoms. He can be told, for example, enough about the working of the autonomic nervous system to give him an understanding of the role played by emotional stress in causing his stomach-ache.

THE DOCTOR'S HUMAN SIDE

The doctor, too, has his human side. At the end of a trying day—especially if he has been up half the night before—it is not easy for him to appear calm and sympathetic and understanding. It requires real self-control to force his mind to concentrate on the patient's symptoms when he is aching with fatigue. It is also hard for him not to react negatively to a disagreeable patient or a hostile family.

Sir William Osler was not only a great clinician. He also knew, perhaps better than any other doctor who ever lived, how to interpret his profession to its own members. In one of his most famous addresses ("Aequanimitas") he stated his belief that the most important quality for a doctor to cultivate is imperturbability—"the quality that is most appreciated by the laity, though often misunderstood by them." He defined imperturbability, or *aequanimitas,* as "coolness and presence of mind under all circumstances, calmness under storm, clearness of judgment in moments of grave peril." Because a doctor, to be most effective, has to steel his emotions, his patients often think he is not truly sympathetic. His is the kind of sympathy that makes him look for means to relieve suffering instead of expending itself in pitying the sufferer.

Factors Responsible for Deterioration of the Doctor-Patient Relationship

The failure of both doctors and patients to appreciate each other's human side is one of the major reasons for the public disfavor into which the medical profession has fallen. It may be pertinent to discuss frankly, and as fairly as our own human nature will permit, some of the other factors responsible for deterioration of the doctor-patient relationship.

The Greater Cost of Sickness

Although doctors' fees have not risen nearly as rapidly as the cost of living, the cost of hospital care and of many new drugs has risen much faster. Since the doctor is the central figure in medical care, he gets much of the blame for the total increase in the expense of being sick.

Two important facts are overlooked by those who deplore the high cost of illness: (1) The average hospital stay now is very much shorter than it was a generation ago. Therefore, while the cost per day may seem higher, the cost per illness is usually much less than in years past. (2) Many infectious diseases that were responsible for long periods of disability, great medical expense, and many untimely deaths in the older generation—typhoid, dysentery, diphtheria, and tuberculosis, for example—have virtually been eliminated by preventive medicine or can be cured quickly by modern remedies. It is difficult to estimate the economic savings brought about by preventive medicine, but these should be considered in reckoning the over-all cost of medical care.

The Increasing Complexity of Modern Medicine

The trend to specialization and group practice has led to a more impersonal relation between doctor and patient. The responsibility for making appointments and talking to the patient is usually left with a secretary or receptionist, who may give the wrong "image" of the doctor. Too often patients may get the impression of an "assembly-line" technic in some clinics.

The multiplication of mechanical gadgets and laboratory technics to aid in diagnosis and treatment has caused many doctors to neglect the essential history and physical examination of the patient. Even some psychiatrists are apt to rely on shock therapy as a short-cut in the treatment of anxiety states or depressive reactions, without giving the patient the opportunity to talk out his troubles to an understanding listener and counselor.

The dramatic response to the so-called wonder drugs has

led people to expect a quick cure for every disease and to be impatient if it is not attained. As a sort of corollary, doctors themselves sometimes rely too much on these drugs and use them without proper indication, thus adding to the cost of medical care.

Overemphasis on Research in Medical Education

Our medical schools must bear some responsibility for the deterioration of the doctor-patient relationship. The tremendous increase in funds available for research grants to medical schools has resulted inevitably in greater emphasis on research, at the expense of clinical teaching and patient care. Many medical leaders have expressed concern over this development. For example, in the Chairman's Address to the Section on Gastroenterology, delivered at the 1960 meeting of the American Medical Association, Dr. Joseph B. Kirsner said:

The current glamour of "basic research" notwithstanding, there also must be renewed attention to the patient as a person. There is a definite danger, with the present emphasis upon research and the apparent de-emphasis of professional skills and teaching ability, that instruction in clinical medicine will deteriorate.

Pressure for Government Control of Medicine

Perhaps the chief cause for the public's changed attitude toward the medical profession is the relentless pressure for government control of medical practice and other health services. For at least a quarter-century various groups and individuals—many of them government employees—have sought to provide by legislation the American equivalent of the British National Health Service. In their campaign they have deliberately tried to create an unfavorable image of the private practitioner of medicine.

Even though the medical profession is far from perfect, it will be a sad day for the American public if it falls for these deliberate distortions of the image of medicine and votes to sacrifice the private doctor-patient relationship for tax-paid medical care. Government red tape and the demands of malingerers and hypochondriacs would mean that even the best-intentioned physician would have no time to practice the *art* of medicine—and that is where medicine's human side is found.

METHODS OF STRENGTHENING THE HUMAN SIDE OF MEDICINE

To a great extent, the means for reversing the deterioration in the relationship between patient and physician lie in the hands of the medical profession. By applying these methods, doctors would inevitably strengthen the human side of medicine and would do much to improve the medical profession's poor public relations.

Teaching Medical Students the Art of Medicine

Our medical schools should renew their emphasis on the art of medicine, beginning with the evaluation of the applicant for admission. The principles of medical ethics should be instilled into the student from the beginning of the clinical years, by example as well as precept. Every medical school should have on its faculty at least one broadly trained practitioner with a background of family practice. Such a man can teach the prospective physician the importance of such details as devoting a few minutes at the beginning of an interview with a new patient to getting acquainted. The mention of mutual friends or acquaintances helps to establish good rapport and lets the patient know that the doctor himself is a human being as well as a scientist. The wise practitioner seeks to gain the confidence of his new patient at the outset and to quiet, as far as possible, the fears of the patient and of his family.

Cooperation between the Specialist and the Family Doctor

Every patient needs a "family doctor" to whom he can turn for advice, instead of trying to diagnose his own ailments and select the specialist he thinks he needs. The specialist and the family doctor should work together in harmony. Each should respect the other and recognize that the patient's welfare is the goal of both.

Instead of attempting to do major surgery or to treat ailments requiring highly specialized knowledge or equipment, general practitioners should refer patients to competent specialists. If feasible, however, the family doctor should visit his referred patients while they are in the hospital. The specialist can learn much from the general practitioner, and he can learn from the specialist. The patient should benefit by an exchange of ideas.

Consideration for the Patient's Time and Money

One of the commonest complaints heard about doctors is that patients have to wait too long for appointments made well in advance. Because minutes and hours are so precious to the busy physician, he often fails to realize that many patients value their time as highly as he does his own. It is obviously impossible for a physician to foresee how many emergencies will arise during a day, or how long he will need to devote to each patient. By making only a reasonable number of appointments, however, and by setting aside an extra amount of time for new patients, the doctor should normally be able to keep pretty close to his schedule. When a schedule is unavoidably disrupted, a tactful explanation by the wise secretary almost universally brings the willing understanding and cooperation of the patient.

While "the laborer is worthy of his hire," a conscientious doctor will not profiteer on a patient's illness, nor take advantage of an insurance company by overcharging. He will also respect the hospital's rights and will not abuse the interests of the Blue Cross and Blue Shield associations by ordering unnecessary tests or prolonged hospital stays. He should explain unusually high charges to the patient and his family.

A careful history and physical examination will often eliminate the necessity for many expensive studies. As evidence for this statement, the experience of two different clinics in the same medical center may be cited.

In the private clinic, where patients bear the full cost of their medical care, they are interviewed and examined by seasoned clinicians, who then order the tests they consider necessary. In the outpatient clinic, where no charges are made for the doctors' services, patients are "worked up" by fourth-year medical students, supervised by young practitioners. Although in one year the number of patients registered in each clinic was almost exactly equal, more than twice as many x-ray examinations were ordered in the outpatient clinic as in the private clinic.

Consideration for the Patient's Emergency Needs

A doctor should always arrange for a substitute to "cover" for him when he leaves town or is off duty, even for only an afternoon. While a partnership or group practice automatically takes care of this situation, the solo practitioner should also show this consideration for his patients. When a patient is seriously ill, it is sometimes advisable for the physician to cancel a nonessential trip. Young doctors often fail to realize what an important role the patient's confidence in his own personal physician plays in his recovery. One simple test of this fact is to compare the blood pressure readings taken by a strange doctor and by the patient's own physician.

County medical societies can render a most worthwhile service by arranging to have a doctor readily available for emergency calls at any time, day or night. A newcomer in a community, or a patient whose doctor is temporarily out of reach, is understandably upset if he cannot secure a doctor with reasonable promptness. The existence of such a service, and the means of obtaining it, should be given adequate publicity in each community where it is available.

Consideration for the Patient's Family

In his efforts to allay the patient's fears and give him moral support, the physician should not forget the patient's family, but should keep them informed of the patient's course. If the illness is a serious one, it is far kinder to let the family know the true prospects than to soothe them with false hopes. It is also well to suggest a consultation with another physician, especially if there is any question about the diagnosis or treatment.

After a patient's death, the physician should not fail to have a talk with one or more members of the family. He can offer real comfort to the relatives by assuring them that everything humanly possible was done for the deceased one. In many cases where the cause of death is uncertain, the family will be grateful to the doctor for suggesting that an autopsy be performed to provide an answer to the questions in their minds.

Good Citizenship and Religious Faith

An excellent way for a doctor to show his human side is to be a good citizen, as well as a competent professional man.

He should welcome opportunities to speak to lay groups, nurses, and students, and should not shrink from serving in his church or in community organizations, such as Chambers of Commerce and boards of education.

Finally, a doctor should not be ashamed to show his religious faith. He may well heed the words of the late Dr. Henry Christian (3) in an address to the students of Jefferson Medical College many years ago:

> The medical man should be an exemplar in his community of the worthy life. His dealings all must be upright and honest. His habits free from criticism. He will need the support of a true religion. . . . The believing physician often can bring into perfection a cure not otherwise obtainable. There is no place in the profession of medicine for the agnostic, the atheist. Man needs a religion and particularly when he is sick.

CONCLUSION

An excellent guide for the doctor who desires to cultivate the human side of medicine is Dr. Francis W. Peabody's classic *Doctor and Patient,* especially the chapter on "The Care of the Patient." This little book, together with Osler's *Aequanimitas and Other Essays,* will prove valuable additions to the physician's library. Two quotations from Dr. Peabody's book form an appropriate conclusion for this chapter:

> Any reorganization of the medical profession that threatens the personal bond between doctor and patient is to be viewed with suspicion, even if the object appears at first sight to be more thorough and careful practice. With the exception of the relationship that one may have with a member of one's family, or with the priest, there is no human bond that is closer than that between physician and patient (or patient's family), and attempts to substitute the methods of machine or organization, be they ever so efficient, are bound to fail (4, p. 3).

In the final sentence of the essay on "The Care of the Patient," Dr. Peabody summed up the whole matter of the human side of medicine: *"The secret of the care of the patient is in caring for the patient"* (4, p. 57).

REFERENCES

1. Williams, Ben Ames: The Greeks had a word for it, New England J. Med. 233:427, 1945.
2. Kirsner, Joseph B.: On specialization and gastroenterology, J.A.M.A. 174:1606, 1960.
3. Christian, Henry A.: The fruition of the clinician (William Potter Memorial Lecture) Jefferson M. Coll. Alumni Bull. 2:4, 1938.
4. Peabody, Francis W.: *Doctor and Patient* (New York: The Macmillan Co., 1939).

GEORGE M. FISTER, M.D.

President for 1962–63 of the American Medical Association, Dr. Fister has been on the AMA Board of Trustees since 1957 and is a former chairman of its Council on Legislative Activities. He received his medical degree at Rush Medical College, Chicago, interned in Henry Ford Hospital, Detroit, and after study abroad in his chosen field of urology, he returned to Utah, where he has been in practice in Ogden since 1928. He is a clinical lecturer in surgery at the University of Utah College of Medicine and is active in the cause of medical education. He holds numerous positions in professional organizations concerned with the public welfare.

2. The Physician's Place in Public Affairs

THE TITLES Physician, Doctor of Medicine and M.D. have different meanings for different people. Yet, one fundamental meaning represents the only real difference between a physician and the other people of his community—his work of caring for the sick and the prevention of disease. He has a diploma from a college of medicine, a license to practice his profession, probable membership in several medical societies, but he is simply one individual in a community of hundreds or thousands.

Theodore Roosevelt once said, "Every man is, first, a citizen of some community." Today, this is perhaps more true of the physician than it is of other men in an age of mobility, because a physician's presence is expected as part of the service of a community. Too, a physician needs the stable elements of a community upon which to base his practice. Not only his professional life but his personal life as well are dependent on the community in which he lives. Citizenship antedated his professional work and will probably postdate it.

In the past, the physician was a leader of thought and action in his community because of his learning and his human relationships. Social changes, however, have altered both medical practice and the community and have fostered specialization, which in turn has led to a narrowing of interest for many people, including the physician. Ivory towers have become almost as common as split-level houses. Yet now, more than ever before in history, we need the trained minds of professional groups directed at today's problems at both the local and the national levels.

Perhaps we should leave the old-fashioned picture of the American physician in the attic of the past and shape a new one from the incredibly rapid advances of medicine and the social and economic changes of our times. We have a sound base from which to start in the revised Principles of Medical Ethics adopted by the American Medical Association's House of Delegates at the annual meeting in June, 1957. Section 10 of those principles reads:

The honored ideals of the medical profession imply that the responsibilities of the physician extend not only to the individual, but also to society where these responsibilities deserve his interest and participation in activities which have the purpose of improving both the health and the well-being of the individual and the community.

We have another sound base in the most important document ever signed by mankind: "We hold these truths to be self-evident, that all men are created equal . . . and for the support of this declaration with a firm reliance on the protection of a Divine Providence, we mutually pledge to each other our lives, our fortunes, and sacred honor."

This guiding statement is from the Declaration of Independence. Six members of the medical profession were among the original signers of that document. By doing so, they indicated that their place as physicians in public affairs was a recognized privilege. To date, there has been no change in this basic philosophy; what change that has occurred has been in the nature of the problems that require study and action. Our shaping of a new picture of the American physician should contain the foundation appreciation that all men are equal, that the physician must labor with humility to demonstrate his faith in mankind and his ability to share as an equal in life's struggles.

Like others in his home town, the physician is engaged in a competitive profession, competing with his fellow physicians. He appreciates success and experiences failures according to his ability. His position is open to any other person who would sacrifice and work to obtain it. In addition, he, too, has a family responsibility. He is a man among men. Common sense should be sufficient reason for his interest in his home town. Above all, the physician should stand shoulder to shoulder with his fellowmen and assume his proportionate share of civic responsibility. Membership in a medical association does not relieve him of membership in his church, chamber of commerce, civic clubs and hospital staffs. Neither does it lighten his duties as a citizen. Here in America, along with all citizens, the physician is a free man, an individual with a station in life of his own choosing.

Dr. Edgar Lee Dessen, Director of the United States Chamber of Commerce, has compiled a list of common objections to civic brotherhood and commented upon them in parenthesis:

1. Costs too much. (The physician's station in his home town is such that any objection to dues or contributions to civic organizations is particularly inflammatory to Mr. Average Citizen.)

2. Not professional or ethical. (Is it professional to be an isolated clique in the community? Is it ethical to forget that one is first a citizen, next a physician? AMA is very clear on this point.)

3. Too busy. (All successful men are too busy, but does that mean they should deny their talents to the community? If you honestly lack the time to participate actively, don't withhold your moral and financial support of community activities. Others can then handle your share of community betterment and civic duty while you are not available.)

4. The community organizations often accept members of "fringe professions" or even out-and-out quacks. (Perhaps they do. They will accept anyone interested in the betterment of his community. Wouldn't it be a sad commentary if the so-called undesirables were interested and the physicians not? And is it better for the fringe professions to speak for the professional group on community problems or the physicians themselves?)

5. I never got any business, directly or indirectly, from such organizations. (These are not "scratch-my-back-I-scratch-yours" organizations. You obviously make a living in the community, or you wouldn't stay there. You must enjoy living in the community, or you wouldn't be there. No man ever succeeded in any business or profession in the middle of the Sahara Desert.)

6. Physicians make their contributions to their communities through clinics and charity services and should not be called upon to give more. (Probably the most frequent and most pernicious of all objections. Free medical care for those unable to pay is our proud heritage and responsibility. Let us not cheapen our heritage by bargaining with it nor shirk our responsibility by underestimating it.)

In the principles of the Declaration of Independence, the founding fathers of this country asked for freedom and the opportunity for individual initiative. They considered it the proper function of government to be the protection of man, not to provide for him. In the Principles of Medical Ethics of the American Medical Association, physicians are guided into the kind of professional service which makes individual initiative possible and rewarding for all.

The education of a physician should have taught him to accept more of the world's responsibilities, not less, to offer to his patient not only his technical skill, but also his advice in human relationships. The quality of his advice depends upon how well he understands and handles his responsibilities as a citizen. At the present time, every student in a medical school receives excellent scientific training and at the time of graduation, is well qualified to render excellent medical care. If the student either before or after graduation does not give adequate attention to public affairs, he may lose the element most essential to the best patient care—his professional freedom.

The physician's place in public affairs must include a sincere and active interest in civic and city management problems at the grass roots level for here is where decisions are made that affect the individual, family, and community. It is influence for the betterment of mankind at this level that accumulates into a unity of action that reaches throughout the state, the nation and into international areas. If the physician leaves his community's decisions to others, he should be satisfied with the results and not deliver, in the hospital dressing room, a soapbox oration condemning community affairs. In addition to his participation in golf, tennis, fishing, etc., he should arrange for an equal contribution of time to the Chamber of Commerce, P.T.A., and church of his choice, various cultural activities and political groups. A long drive on the fairway of a golf course does not relieve him of participation in the hard drive for funds for the Community Chest.

Naturally, the physician's wife and family would have a matching keen interest and devotion to public affairs. A family response frequently indicates that there has been a home study made of the problems. For example, if a problem is one that would take freedom from the individual, the physician's wife can carry an educated program to persons and areas not readily available to the physician.

Further, the maturing family can be made aware of the future burden of our national debt, the conflict of national control versus freedom of the individual, the very question of peace or war which will be won or lost by what is now the younger generation. If the present adult generation seriously and honestly considers the national give-away program, the overloaded indebtedness, the national budget that never seems to be in balance, the loss of individual, family, community, and state initiatives to the innumerable federal bureaus, these same individuals would not only vote for the preservation of the freedom of the individual, but they would demand it.

Ours is a nation where freedom of the individual has been the source of its progress and strength. But never in our history, except perhaps at the time of the signing of the Declaration of Independence, has it been so necessary for every individual to participate actively in state and national affairs. Why? Because there are pressures, either willingly pursued or accepted through a false philosophy, which could change this nation from one of individual freedom to one of federal control. Subsidies, bureaus, and regulations, when correctly labeled, mean in varying degrees a socialistic state.

The medical profession, along with many other free enterprises and professions, is feeling this pressure. Even though America's physicians are providing the people of this nation with the best medical care in the world, there are determined efforts being made to transfer medical care from individual responsibility to government. This would bring a third party between the patient and his physician, a central government with power to dictate, regulate, and control the patient, the physician, and the hospital. Of the three, the individual patient would incur the greater loss, the very basis of satisfactory medical care, the free choice of physician.

What type of medical care can the patient expect if he must follow regulations as to his choice of physician or hospital, if his history and records of treatment are open to survey or approval by government employees, if the prescribing of drugs must follow governmental direction, if the number of hospital days is controlled by surveys made by so-called utilization committees?

The doctor won't suffer except perhaps mentally through not being able to do his best. But the patient must survive the cumbersome results of being treated by both his doctor and his government. He must survive confusion, massive paperwork, requests, approvals, disapprovals, waiting periods, overcrowded hospitals and overworked doctors. He will continue to hope, but he will find that his increased tax money has failed to provide him with the adequate medical care which he has now come to expect. It is the individual who is at stake, not the physician.

Because the physician has a dedicated concern for the welfare of the patient, he must have a sincere interest in public affairs, regardless of his place in the field of medicine. His interest must be demonstrated by public service with the firm conviction that he need never apologize for his activity and concern in political issues, whether they involve medicine or national affairs.

The Hon. Walter H. Judd, in an address at Jefferson Medical College in 1958, clearly indicated the physician's responsibilities when he stated:

> What we know as doctors about the practice of medicine should and must influence our thinking and our activities as citizens. We must work both as individuals and as members of groups which we join and support because they are dedicated to causes in which we believe; religious groups, civic groups, political groups. Often one finds doctors unwilling or too preoccupied to work in political organizations; yet, if you are to expand your influence in public affairs, you must participate in politics for politics determine government, and government determines the conditions of your lives.

National or international service clubs have an excellent record of devotion to the principle of freedom and the opportunity for individual initiative. The physician, if invited, should become not only a member of a service club, but an active member. He should be more than a mere "joiner" of any organization, for membership without work can mean dissatisfaction and loss of interest, while membership with work can produce surprising results.

In Phoenix, Arizona, the physicians launched an automobile seat belt campaign that put these straps in thousands of autos and made them standard equipment in every Arizona highway patrol car. They then joined with the state pharmaceutical association in waging war on accidental poisoning and in publishing a booklet on home safety. The booklet was so successful that there have been over two million reprints distributed in this and foreign countries. More recently, they helped establish a home for the aged.

In Decatur, Illinois, six new schools were built largely because of the County Medical Society's eleventh-hour support of a construction bond issue which was being threatened with defeat at the Decatur polls. The doctors, their wives and P.T.A. teams saved the day by distributing 5,000 leaflets financed by the medical society. The leaflets simply cited school expansion as necessary to good health and a better future for local youngsters. Inspired by this success, Decatur physicians went on to rally public support for a sewer bond issue, and then for a dam to raise the level of Lake Decatur. All three measures won by wide vote margins.

In Omaha, Nebraska, the Omaha–Douglas County Medical Society members supported their community United Fund Drive in a notable fashion. They marched into a campaign kickoff dinner meeting clad in football uniforms, played Dixieland jazz, sang and danced. They raised $11,000 for the fund and won their way into the hearts of the community.

New York's Bronx County Medical Society was successful in a hard fought campaign to persuade city officials to eliminate a creek as a serious health hazard. They have also been active in many other directions, including smoke abatement, safety programs, vote-and-register drives, free vitamins for the needy aged, better police and fire protection, improved public transportation and emergency ambulance service.

The Bronx Medical Society has worked in and through its Chamber of Commerce. No single lay organization has worked more closely with physicians in community affairs than the local Chamber of Commerce. Such liaison forms the backbone of community activities for many County Medical Societies. It is the basis for a recent decision of the Oakland, California, Chamber of Commerce to create a permanent place on its board of directors for a medical representative. It is the reason that a West Virginia Chamber "Business–Education Day" had physicians of the Parkersburg Academy of Medicine taking over high school classes to inform youngsters what the profession was all about. It was responsible for a Good Citizenship citation awarded to the Orleans Parish Medical Society by the New Orleans Chamber of Commerce for promoting a get-out-the-vote compaign.

The American Medical Association's biennial surveys of constituent county medical society activities have indicated representative physicians' interest and activity not only in blood banks, disease control programs, and graduate education, but also in civil defense, chambers of commerce, public education, politics, human relations, United Funds, and other community affairs.

Physicians as individuals have and will continue to have a marked influence on local and national affairs. But as groups or organizations, they can never hope to be any more effective than the strength provided by the individual members permits. And here is the paradox. Some otherwise active physicians seem to lose their individuality when they become members of groups or organizations. Yet, they have by far the highest average educational level in any community; they are above average in intelligence, or they would not have survived the high selectivity of the physician's training program; they have been accorded a prestige unique in American life. The voices of these physicians are needed to answer Dr. Leonard W. Larson, president of the AMA when he said in an address on July 27, 1961:

The pace of medical progress continues to quicken. Furthermore, both physicians and patients are involved in a changing pattern of relationships, changing methods of organization and financing of medical service. Medicine, in short, is caught up not only in the role of scientific advancement, but the whole current of social, economic, and political change affecting our nation and the entire world.

Individuals, whether in business, labor, or profession, have found it necessary for many reasons to form associations, for educational effectiveness, for conservation of time, for the proper opportunity for open discussion by the members which leads to the formation of policy representing the accumulation of wisdom of the individual members.

The participation of individual physicians and their families in civic affairs provides the opportunity for American medicine to maintain or improve the so-called "doctor image." But it is the association of physicians organized as the county medical society, at the grassroots level, that is the keystone to successful programs, be they local, state or national. Active interest in the county medical society indicates the pathways to active interest in other civic affairs.

Encouragement for the formation of and active interest in county and state medical associations was one of the primary aims of the American Medical Association. Perhaps the founders of organized medicine saw something of the future complexities of medical service and the changes in social and economic philosophies. Undoubtedly, they realized that physicians working alone could not do what physicians could accomplish by working together. They knew that, while each physician must render individual service for the welfare of the patient, there should also be service through organized groups, without losing sight of the fact that the practice of medicine is an art achieved through science and enriched by civic responsibility. They built upon the principle that dedicated service can control the environment for the practice of medicine.

Dr. Paul Mitchell, of Corsicana, Texas, in an address before the Navaro County Medical Society, stated:

> We must accomplish our end by working together within the body of organized medicine. Medicine has not lost by making its philosophies and politics, conclusions, and recommendations in unison. We have not failed by representation, but we can fail by lack of it. Medicine will attain its greatness in the public esteem only when medicine deserves it.

So together with the civic responsibility of the individual comes the equally important civic responsibility of the group. The county medical society, the state society and AMA represent the accumulated wisdom of the individuals who form the policies for the organizations. In turn, the organizations represent and act for the individual.

This was set into motion in 1847 in Philadelphia, where 250 physicians formed the American Medical Association. These doctors were concerned about the poor quality of medical education in the United States, the traffic in patent medicines and the lack of a code of ethics for physicians. They further felt that a national association of physicians was needed to unite the medical societies already existing, to foster the formation of new ones, and to lead the crusade for better medical care for the American people.

While the original membership was small, it began its growth on a firm foundation as expressed in Article 2 of the AMA Constitution: "The objects of the Association are to promote the science and art of medicine and the betterment of public health." This was 114 years ago. It is interesting to note that the objectives of this organization in 1847 and restated in 1961 were all directed toward the improvement of medical care for the patient.

Of the original aims set forth at the founding of AMA,

what have been the results? The quality of both medical education and medical care in the United States is now the highest in the world. The traffic in patent medicines and narcotics is under adequate control, and the American Medical Association continues its vigorous fight against quacks. The adherence to the Code of Ethics for each and every member of the Association continues to be a major function. The increase in membership to approximately 180,000 indicates the faith that the physicians have in these principles.

Membership in AMA is one of the primary areas of public service open to all physicians who are members of their respective county and state medical societies. In addition, the Woman's Auxiliary of the AMA offers membership to all physician's wives, creating an amalgamation of efforts aimed at increasingly better medical care, and better understanding between the public and American medicine.

The ultimate results of physician participation in public affairs, regardless of his avenue of approach, will be created by each individual physician through his honesty, his ethics, his devotion to patient care, his thirst for knowledge in scientific achievement and human relations and, above all, through his service to humanity carried forward as an area of freedom.

There is one pathway of civic affairs that all persons and their representative organizations can follow, not only with a sense of duty, but also with a desire to serve, and that pathway leads into plain, ordinary politics. By politics is meant a belief in the fundamental precepts set forth by a party, group, or an individual. Everyone in the nation should be proud to contribute his efforts and support to the political party or viewpoint of his choice, to follow the elections and insure that those elected serve their fellow men.

Here are seven "basics" of citizenship which are recommended for every physician who takes his civic responsibility seriously:

The doctor's primary duty as a citizen is to be the guide and source of authority in all health matters relating to his community. This is an all-year-round civic responsibility which his training and experience have qualified him to handle better than any other person in the community.

The doctor should openly identify with the party of his choice, and vote regularly at all elections.

The doctor should make an investment in democracy by contributing liberally financially to the party of his choice.

The doctor should encourage patients and others with whom he comes in contact to register and vote in all elections.

The doctor should keep informed on candidates and issues and let others know where he stands politically.

The doctor can help candidates of his choice by such means as displaying campaign literature in his waiting room.

The doctor should devote as much time as his professional duties permit to working for good government and for the political party of his choice.

In addition, he can register his thoughts and opinions in print by writing letters to his local newspapers. He can help develop candidates for future elections by encouraging promising young persons to fully develop their potential, and by helping them financially. He can change his attitude to a positive one regarding politics, politicians, and other physicians active in public affairs. This will help get better people into politics.

The physician need never fear that an honest interest in the political aspect of civic affairs will be resented by his patients or his fellow citizens. This is America, where the voice of freedom still speaks, where the destiny of the nation is dependent on the dignity and the degree of participation of its people in politics, for those elected to office direct the course of the nation.

In his comprehensive study of the history of AMA legislative activity, Jonathan D. Wirtschafter, Portland, Oregon, points out that soon after its founding, the American Medical Association learned that there were vital problems under consideration by the Congress that affected the health and welfare of the people. The leadership, devoted to the objectives established by the founders, were convinced that active participation was necessary in Washington to assist the Congress on national health problems. In 1900, a national committee on medical legislation was formed as a permanent part of AMA.

In 1901, Association president, Dr. Charles Reed, at the annual meeting, outlined various types of legislation that were needed: (1) a national bureau of health, (2) greater sanitary measures along the nation's waterways, (3) a study of medicinal flora with government research funds, (4) a pure food law and (5) a change in the status of military surgeons. He also stated: "Every physician should in a perfectly respectable sense become an active, working politician."

By 1907, AMA through the Council on Legislation, representing 135,000 physicians with 2,000 county societies, had been influential in two important national decisions made by the President and Congress: (1) the appointment of Col. W. C. Gorgas of the U.S. Army to full authority as a member of the Panama Canal Commission to combat the sanitation problem that was almost prohibiting the building of the canal, and (2) the passage by Congress of the Pure Food and Drug Act which was signed into law in 1906 by President Roosevelt.

These are but a few of the accomplishments realized during the first ten years of work by AMA's Committee on Legislation. Nearly fifty years later, when the Murray-Wagner-Dingell bill for socialized medical care was introduced into Congress, members of AMA had developed a long-standing, active interest in legislation. They recognized this area of responsibility for American medicine—the responsibility to study, analyze and assist the members of Congress in whatever matters concerned the health of the American people. They also realized that their strength in national legislation lay at the state and local levels. This was proved early when, in support of the appointment of Col. Gorgas to the Panama Canal Commission, fourteen hundred telegrams from Association members arrived at the White House within forty-eight hours.

Here is one of the most important civic responsibilities of each physician as well as each medical society—definite and ultimate assistance at the local level. AMA has given vigorous support to sound medical legislation and an equally vigorous opposition to measures it believes would lower the quality of medical care or would not be in the best public interest. AMA will continue to take the lead in stimulating and coordinating through its multiple services all member physicians, specialty groups and those with related interests.

In personal correspondence, Dr. Jack Redman suggests:

Now is the time for each of us to become, and to stay, involved to the very extent of our abilities in intra and extramedical civic activities; to be seen and heard as active, dynamic citizens of our respective communities, our states, our Nation; to be seen and heard as active, dynamic members of the profession of Medicine, telling the story that is ours alone to tell, ever striving to enhance the art and the science of ministering to the people.

To the extent we are willing to meet the challenges of today and tomorrow as active citizens; to the extent that we are willing to rededicate our lives to the precepts of our fathers and fore-fathers; to the extent that we are willing to become really in-volved in day-to-day American living; we shall, with God's help, be able to add our share to the preservation of our Republic and to her fight for peace.

Each individual physician must contribute his best if he is to be worthy of the title Doctor of Medicine. He must, if the title is to mean one thing to all people, rather than different things to different people. He must, if he is to demonstrate his faith in mankind and his ability to share as an equal in life's struggles.

Josiah Gilbert Holland, in his "The Days Demand," set forth a pattern when he wrote:

God give us men! A time like this demands strong minds—great hearts—true faith and ready hands!
Men whom the lust of office does not kill.

Men whom spoils of office cannot buy.

Men who possess opinions and a will.

Men who have honor; men who will not lie.

Men who can stand before a demagogue and damn his treacherous flatteries without winking.

Tall men sun crowned, who live above the fog in public duty and in private thinking.

SAMUEL R. GERBER, M.D.

For the past 25 years Dr. Gerber has served Cleveland and Cuyahoga County, Ohio as coroner. President of the American Academy of Forensic Sciences in 1961–1962, his interests in forensic medicine have led to international activities, such as invitations to lecture at Oxford University and the London College Hospital. Dr. Gerber is a past-president of the National Association of Coroners and has been Secretary of that organization since 1943; he has also been Executive Secretary of the Ohio Coroners' Association since 1939.

3. The Physician's Relations with the Medicolegal Officer

WHEN DEATHS OCCUR under circumstances that may incur legal problems, official investigations must be conducted to determine the medical and the legal facets of causation. The authority for conducting such investigations usually is vested in the office of Coroner or Medical Examiner.

Although there is diversity in statutes governing the administration of either office in various jurisdictions, all are charged with the same responsibility: to determine the *mode, manner* and *cause* of death, in compliance with demands imposed by the legal implications. In view of this similarity in objectives and the variations in the laws and diversity of the methods of administration, this brief treatise shall be limited to general consideration of the fundamental relationship of the physician to the achievement of justice in medicolegal problems. It is

37

hoped that readers will gain some concept of the direct influence of the treating physician on the rights of individuals and the community in the administration of civil and criminal laws.

The determination of the mode, manner and cause of death is merely one focus of consideration in the many problems that require interrelation of the disciplines of law and medicine; however, in nearly all jurisdictions in the United States, official medicolegal investigations are instigated only when death occurs. Therefore, *medicolegal officer* shall be used here as an inclusive term to designate the offices of both coroner and medical examiner. Certainly, the manner in which the duties are discharged has greater significance than the name. This sentiment was expressed in a report of an American Medical Association Committee to Study the Relationship of Law and Medicine:

Comment.—Obviously the name under which the medical investigator operates has little or no bearing on the effectiveness with which his public duties are discharged. If the law requires first that he be professionally competent and second that he have both the authority and the facilities for the conduct of such investigations as are required in the interest of public welfare, the name of his office is inconsequential (1, p. 578).

Certainly, *authority* and *facilities* for conducting investigations and professional *competency* of the investigator are crucial factors in affording opportunity for effective administration of medicolegal offices; however, a most basic factor is the *cooperation of physicians.*

Unfortunately, many physicians do not recognize the need for accuracy in certification of deaths in cases in which the legal as well as the medical cause of death must be established. The significance of the legal implications is extraneous to his usual focus of attention. He may not fully comprehend the consequences and sequelae of deaths affecting the safety and welfare of the community. Every citizen ought to assume some responsibility for the safety and welfare of the community.

The physician is not exempt from this obligation. On the contrary, he must recognize that by virtue of his profession he has particular responsibilities that should not be disregarded and cannot be delegated to others.

It is quite natural for a physician to recognize that his professional duty encompasses obligation to the community as well as responsibility to the individual patient when a communicable disease is suspected. Problems that might evolve from inaccurate certification of death in such cases are apparent to him because primarily they are medical in nature. If his attention were directed to the socio-economic problems that may ensue, he would be equally cautious concerning inaccurate certification of deaths in cases which have legal implications.

Erroneously certifying a death to have resulted from natural causes, when some form of violence was involved, obstructs the administration of justice in a multitude of diversified problems. Whether the violence was suicidal, homicidal or accidental in nature, an erroneous certification of the cause of death in each instance has a significant effect on the social and economic welfare of the community. Consequences of the failure to recognize murder has been stressed more frequently than some of the other effects. It is a common misconception that "nice people do not commit murder." The physician who does not realize that homicide may masquerade as suicide or accident, or who is oblivious to the socio-economic implications of suicides and accidents, repudiates his moral obligation to the community and to the legal heirs of the decedent. The ramifications of just settlement of claims for compensation for injury or death must be considered.

The implications of lack of discernment displayed in inaccurate certification of these deaths were stated succinctly by the Committee to Study the Relationship of Medicine and Law in conclusion:

The ineffectual manner in which medical knowledge and skill

are utilized in the administration of justice in many jurisdictions in the United States undoubtedly predisposes to:

(a) The nonrecognition of murder.
(b) The unjust accusation of innocent persons.
(c) The improper evaluation of medical evidence bearing on the circumstances in which fatal injuries were incurred.
(d) Failure to acquire medical evidence which would be useful in the apprehension of criminals.
(e) Failure to acquire medical evidence essential to the administration of civil justice.
(f) Ignorance of certain otherwise preventable hazards to public health, and
(g) The impairment of the value of vital statistics (1, p. 583).

Authority for conducting medicolegal investigations is decreed generally by state laws. Therefore, throughout the United States there is considerable variance in designation of types of deaths to be investigated and the extent of the authority of medicolegal offices. In many states, there is dire need for modernization of these laws to provide the legal framework for effective medicolegal investigations. Various groups (1–3) have formulated suggestions to guide legislators in revising the laws in their jurisdictions. Laws directing the administration of this and many other government functions cannot be strictly uniform throughout the United States since such factors as population density, transportation and communication facilities and availability of competent personnel must be considered. However, there is general agreement that any death involving history, evidence or suspicion that violence might have been a significant factor in causation, or whenever the cause of death is obscure, a medicolegal investigation should be conducted to establish the legal as well as the medical factors of causation, i.e., the mode and manner and the anatomic diagnoses.

The National Association of Coroners (2) adopted the following resolution in 1949:

We, the coroners of the various counties of the various states throughout the United States, . . . do hereby resolve that we will sponsor the adoption of a Uniform Bill—(1) defining the jurisdiction of the coroner and (2) providing for performance of autopsies—to be introduced in the various State Legislatures throughout the United States; said bill or proposal to read as follows:

When any person shall die as a result of criminal or other violent means, or by casualty, or by suicide, or suddenly when in apparent health, or in any suspicious or unusual manner, the physician called in attendance shall immediately notify the office of coroner of the known facts concerning the time, place, manner and circumstances of such death, and any other information which may be required pursuant of this act. In such cases, if request for cremation is made, the funeral director called in attendance shall notify the coroner immediately.

And, in respect to autopsies, we recommend that a bill containing the following language, in substance, be introduced in the various state legislatures of the United States:

The coroner or his deputy may, if he deems it necessary, go to the dead body and take charge of the same. If, in the opinion of the coroner, or in the absence of the coroner, his deputy coroner, an autopsy is deemed necessary, the coroner or deputy coroner shall perform or cause an autopsy to be performed by a physician competent in the performance of autopsies. A detailed description of the observations written during the progress of the autopsy or as soon thereafter as may be reasonably possible and the conclusions drawn therefrom shall be filed in the office of the coroner.

And, we further recommend the adoption of a bill containing the following language:

It shall be the duty of any citizen who may become aware of the death of any such person to report such death forthwith to the coroner of the County in which such person died. Any person who shall willfully neglect or refuse to report such death or who without written order from the coroner shall willfully touch or remove or disturb the clothing or any article upon or near such body, shall be fined not more than $500.00 nor less than $25.00, or suffer imprisonment of not more than one year or less than one month, or both, such fine and imprisonment at the discretion of the Court.

Prototypes for these recommendations were in the statutes of New Jersey (4) and Ohio (5) and recommendations of the

American Medical Association (1, p. 582). More recently the National Committee on Vital and Health Statistics released recommendations of the Subcommittee on the Medical Certification of Medicolegal Cases that deaths occurring under the following conditions should be investigated by medicolegal authorities (6, p. 15):

1. *Deaths due to violence.*—All deaths due to violence (whether homicide, suicide, or accidentally inflicted injuries) in which an external cause or agent contributes to the death. The term "violence" includes mechanical trauma, chemical, thermal, radiational, electrical, and other forms of injury due to external agents that lead to death.

2. *Deaths occurring under suspicious or unusual circumstances.*—All deaths in which the circumstances leading to death, or in which the absence of detailed or specific information, raise suspicion of traumatic injury or poisoning as the cause of death.

3. *Deaths due to industrial diseases and injuries.*—All deaths in which an injury or disease contracted during employment is suspected to have caused or contributed to death whether or not the individual had been receiving treatment for such a disease or injury. The terms "industrial injury" and industrial disease" are intended to apply only to those cases covered by industrial or workmen's compensation laws.

4. *Sudden and unexpected natural deaths.*—All deaths occurring unexpectedly where the deceased was not under medical treatment for the disease or condition believed to be the cause of death.

5. *Deaths without medical attendance.*—All deaths in which the deceased was never seen by a physician, or in which the physician treating a patient did not see the patient within 10 days prior to death. In this instance, the referral to the coroner or medical examiner does not mean necessarily that he will decide to take jurisdiction of the case.

6. *Deaths occurring while in custody of the law.*—All deaths occurring in police detention areas or in permanent correctional institutions, except those known to have resulted from natural disease under treatment by the medical staff of the institution.

7. *Deaths associated with diagnostic, therapeutic, and anesthetic procedures.*—All deaths that occur during or as a result of diagnostic, therapeutic, and anesthetic procedures, including

deaths from misadventures during immunization procedures. Such deaths should be reported irrespective of the elapsed time if the procedure was associated with the death. These deaths should not be reported as an accident or a homicide unless there is evidence of criminal intent. However, the circumstances of the death should be described in broad terms. In view of the number of such cases now being litigated, it is believed that official investigations will materially aid all parties concerned by providing impartial, objective, medical evidence relative to the case.

8. *Maternal deaths associated with abortion.*—All deaths of females in which there has been an abortion or suspicion of abortion. This should include cases in which there was no pregnancy, if there is evidence that procedures were initiated to bring about an abortion.

9. *Deaths from diseases thought to be of a contagious nature.* All deaths in which the local health authority believes a confirmation of the cause of death by an autopsy will materially assist in the control of the disease, for example, typhoid. In these cases, the medicolegal officer acts as the agent of the local health department and only upon its official request.

The medicolegal office serves so many interests of the medical and legal professions that members of both professions should actively support efforts to improve its standards of practice. There is particular need for cooperation of the professions through their state and local associations to influence the enactment of suitable legislation to provide for effective medicolegal investigations. The interrelationship of law and medicine in these offices is so involved that neither profession can equate all of the problems nor recognize all of the implications.

In view of the diversity in the laws of the various states, each physician must acquire practical knowledge of the regulations of the jurisdiction in which he practices. He should consult the local medicolegal officer for specific directives concerning the cases to be reported, the mechanics of reporting and the type of information required. He must respect the jurisdiction and authority of the medicolegal officer, established by law. If he considers the law unsatisfactory in these aspects, he should strive to obtain the necessary revisions. If he finds that the medicolegal officer is incompetent or negligent in performance of his duties, he has recourse to suitable action to replace him. However, he should bear in mind that experience has demonstrated that adequate legislation is often a prerequisite to recruitment of competent personnel; and unprejudiced appraisal of ineffectual medicolegal offices will reveal most frequently that the fundamental predisposing factor lies in the failure of the law to provide for sufficient authority or jurisdiction. However, whether or not the current laws and regulations need revision, they must be observed until the necessary changes are effected.

After the physician has a concept of *when, why and how to report a death* to the medicolegal officer, the next area of consideration is: *What are his obligations to the patient and to the medicolegal investigation?*

Until the patient is pronounced dead, the physician's primary obligation is to strive to alleviate suffering and prolong life, but he should also give attention to recognizing and preserving evidence that might be significant in the investigation to determine the mode and manner of death. Certainly, when confronted with a case of apparent sudden death, the physician's first concern must be to ascertain by *thorough examination* that the person actually is dead. There have been instances in which a doctor has pronounced an individual to be dead after only a cursory examination, and subsequently it was proved that the person actually was alive at that time. In such cases the physician exposes himself to legal action charging negligence.

Whether this examination is conducted at the place of death or in an emergency room in a hospital, every possible precaution should be exercised to avoid unnecessary disturbance or destruction of potential evidence. It should be remembered that, although dirt and debris constitute anathemas to doctors and nurses, these may be blessings in disguise to official investigators to whom they have considerable significance. Therefore, if the individual is dead on arrival, or death appears immediately imminent, undressing and bathing serves no medical purpose and may hinder or obstruct the investigation.

If the examination is conducted at the place of death, the physician should not move or handle anything unless it is necessary to do so in order to examine the body satisfactorily; in which event, he should be able to describe the original position. He should be aware of the significance of, and be able to recall and report accurately, pertinent facts concerning the position of the body, the presence, shade and site of livor mortis, the presence and extent of rigor mortis, as well as any evidence of violence.

The private physician should resist temptation to assume the role of detective and should avoid expressing his personal opinions concerning the mode and manner of death to anyone except the official investigators. He must realize that appearances may be deceiving, and only a thorough investigation into all of the circumstances can disclose the true facts. Failure to follow this advice may result in embarrassment for the physician and confusion in the progress of the investigation.

In some states, certification of death is not accepted from a physician who has not been in attendance prior to death. As an explanation of *what constitutes attendance upon the deceased,* it was the recommendation of the Subcommittee on the Medical Certification of Medicolegal Cases that:

The term "physician in attendance upon the deceased" should be defined as the physician who treated the deceased for the illness or condition which led to death. It is highly desirable that the physician personally examine the deceased prior to preparing the medical certification of cause of death if he was not present when death occurred in order to be reasonably certain that death resulted from natural causes and from the illness or condition for which the patient was being treated.

It is recommended further that when death occurs more than

10 days after the deceased was last seen by a physician, the case should be reported to the coroner or medical examiner. For deaths occurring within 10 days after the last visit, the physician should be authorized to certify the cause of death provided that he views the body after death. However, the physician should be allowed to refer the case to the coroner or medical examiner, if he prefers.

It is not intended to suggest that because cases are referred to the medicolegal officer that he will exercise jurisdiction in every case. Rather, by prompt notice of the fact of death and the circumstances, the medicolegal officer will be able to determine whether there is a need to investigate the case or return it to the physician (6, p. 6).

Experienced medicolegal officers can cite a number of cases in which a physician carelessly certified death as due to a chronic condition for which he was treating the patient, and it has been discovered that death was hastened by a suicidal or homicidal act or by accidental means. The examination of the dead body must be equally objective in observation of signs and symptoms as any examination of the living patient.

In most states the law requires that the medical officer must be notified immediately upon the occurrence of death in any case wherein evidence existed or suspicions were aroused, prior to death or subsequently, to indicate that an act of violence might be involved. The fact that the physician treating the patient for an extended period believes that death resulted from complications or conditions apparently unrelated to trauma does *not* alter his obligation to report the death and *the history or suspicion of violence*. He must realize that, when there is any history of violence, legal problems usually arise; therefore, the certification of death must be intelligible from a legal as well as a medical viewpoint.

Investigations would be expedited if all cases of critical injury, including poisoning, were reported to the medicolegal officer or other law enforcement officers when death appears imminent in order that official investigations might be initiated promptly. Time is a crucial factor influencing success or failure in such investigations. A lapse of time affords the opportunity for intentional or unwitting obliteration of significant evidence and clues.

Laws in some jurisdictions require that whenever a physician treats a patient who has sustained a gunshot wound or wounds inflicted by other weapons, he must promptly notify the law enforcement officers. An example is the following, from the Ohio Revised Code (Sec. 2917.44):

Report of wound with deadly weapon.—Whoever is involved in any manner in a circumstance in which a person sustains a gunshot wound, or any wound which has been inflicted by a deadly weapon of any kind, shall, as soon as possible, notify the sheriff of the county or, if within a municipality, the police department of such municipality, or the state highway patrol within areas of its jurisdiction; provided that nothing contained in this section shall be construed as requiring an attorney, a clergyman or priest, a husband or wife, or a physician to make a report to a sheriff or police department of any matters which, if reported, would constitute a violation of a confidential relationship existing between the attorney and his client, or between the clergyman or priest and his communicant or penitent, or between husband and wife, or between the physician and his patient, except that any physician who shall treat, or be called upon to treat, any such wound shall make a report setting forth a description of the wounded person, his name and address, if known, and a description of the nature and location of such wound.

No person who makes a report in good faith with a view of complying with the requirements of this section shall, by reason thereof, have violated any confidential relationship, or be held to answer for the betrayal of a professional secret, or be held liable in damages to any person.

Any such report to the sheriff or the police department may be made in person, by telephone, or in writing.

Whoever violates this section shall be fined not more than one thousand dollars or imprisoned not more than six months, or both.

Such reporting does not violate the legal privilege or concept of medical ethics in regard to physician-patient relationship. An expressed Opinion of the AMA Judicial Council (7, sec. 9) reads:

A physician may not reveal the confidences entrusted to him in the course of medical attendance, or the deficiencies he may observe in the character of patients, *unless he is required to do so by law or unless it becomes necessary in order to protect the welfare of the individual or of the community* [emphasis added].

The physician's responsibility to the patient and to the community requires that he shall recognize evidence and voluntarily supply any information that may aid in the apprehension of an assailant or any person involved in a criminal act.

Bullets recovered from wounds must be removed as carefully as possible and saved, taking all precautions to preserve the integrity of the evidence, i.e., (1) avoiding unnecessary mutilation of significant markings, during and subsequent to the operation; (2) recording name of patient, date, time and place of operation, site and appearance of wound, name of physician who removed bullet, and names of witnesses present at operation; (3) placing the bullet in a protective container and sealing; and (4) keeping it in a locked place until submitted to proper authority, at which time a signed receipt should be obtained.

Similar precautions should be observed in regard to evidence removed from other wounds. Such evidence might consist of particles of glass, wood, metal or other debris. Factors of great significance to investigators are frequently overlooked by the physicians, e.g., external appearance of wounds, including presence and extent of evidence of contact or near-contact gunshot, size, shape and course of wounds. Destruction of such evidence by surgery complicates the investigation. The physician should be aware of the significance of such evidence, should examine all wounds critically and objectively and describe his observations accurately in his records. Of course, there is the possibility that bullets may have been removed before the patient consults the doctor for treatment. If the physician suspects this has happened, he ought to inform the authorities of this possibility.

The physician's responsibility in medicolegal cases includes his obligation to appear as a witness. Physicians are subject to subpoena and are not excused because of their professional duties. If respectfully approached, courts usually will attempt to schedule the physician's testimony to be given at a convenient time. In many states (5) the medicolegal officer is empowered to subpoena witnesses. A physician called as a witness may be required to give medical evidence in a case involving death, if he was the attending physician before or at the time of death. This evidence may be either oral or documentary. The documentary evidence usually consists of a medical report and notes or memoranda made at the time of treatment or pronouncement of death. Oral evidence is that information which has not been reduced to writing but of which the physician has personal knowledge. It should be emphasized that well-kept records are a fundamental prerequisite to satisfactory testimony. The attention given to indoctrination of the physician as a witness in the current literature is sufficiently abundant that only the most basic principles bear stating here. Every physician should familiarize himself with courtroom procedure before being called as a witness. Pre-trial conferences are strongly recommended. The physician must recognize the necessity to present medical evidence in simple and concise terms, to be dignified without appearing arrogant and to be respectful.

SUMMARY

The physician's responsibility to the medicolegal officer can be summarized in two areas: *What the attending physician should know* and *what the attending physician should do*.

What the Attending Physician Should Know

1. Specific laws of state and local jurisdiction which define *the cases to be referred for medicolegal investigations.*

2. The mechanics of reporting prescribed by the immediate medicolegal officer.

3. Information routinely required by medicolegal authority.

4. Types of supplementary information pertinent to medicolegal investigations.

5. The potentialities and limitations extant in the immediate locality for effective medicolegal investigations.

6. Statistics from coroners' and medical examiners' offices in jurisdictions of various sizes in the United States demonstrate the validity of the frequently quoted estimate that 20–30 per cent of all deaths occur under circumstances that require an integration of the medical and legal aspects to accurately determine the cause, mode and manner of death. The effectiveness with which such official investigations are conducted will be markedly influenced by the quality of cooperation displayed by the attending physician.

What the Attending Physician Should Do

1. Cooperate fully, promptly and voluntarily with the medicolegal officer and comply with all laws and regulations.

2. Develop an awareness of the significance of legal aspects and exercise constant alertness to recognition of medicolegal implications.

3. Give attention to the recognition and preservation of evidence.

4. Avoid assuming the role of detective.

5. Render all possible assistance in achieving justice.

6. Recognize responsibility as a member of the medical profession to aid in efforts to improve standards of medicolegal practice in his community.

REFERENCES

1. American Medical Association: Report of the Committee to Study the Relationship of Law and Medicine, J.A.M.A. 125:578, 1944.

2. Gerber, S. R. (Ed.): Proceedings of 1949 Convention, National Association of Coroners, p. viii.
3. National Municipal League: Model post-mortem act, 1954.
4. New Jersey Statutes Annotated 40:21, 1927.
5. Ohio Revised Code, Sec. 313.11–313.13, 1945.
6. National Committee on Vital and Health Statistics: *Medical Certification of Medicolegal Cases* (USPHS Publ. No. 810). Washington, D. C.: Government Printing Office, 1960.
7. AMA Judicial Council: *Principles of Medical Ethics,* Special Edition J.A.M.A., June 7, 1958.

SUPPLEMENTARY READING

Books

Adelson, L., *et al.*: *Physician in the Courtroom* (Cleveland: Western Reserve University Press, 1954).

Curran, W. J.: *Law and Medicine* (Boston: Little, Brown & Company, 1960).

Shartel, B., and Plant, M. L.: *The Law of Medical Practice* (Springfield, Ill.: C C Thomas, 1959).

Mant, A. K.: *Forensic Medicine* (Chicago: Year Book Publishers, Inc., 1960).

Camps, F. E., and Purchase, W. B.: *Practical Forensic Medicine* (New York: The Macmillan Company, 1957).

Journals

Journal of the Forensic Society, S. S. Kind, Ed., (Yorkshire, England: Rossett Holt).

Journal of Forensic Medicine (Johannesburg, South Africa: Juta & Company, Ltd.)

Journal of Forensic Sciences, official publication of the American Academy of Forensic Sciences (Mundelein, Ill.: Callaghan & Company).

Medicine, Sciences and the Law, F. E. Camps, Ed., official publication of the British Academy of Forensic Sciences (London: Sweet & Maxwell, Ltd.).

Other publications

Adelson, L.: Possible neurological mechanisms responsible for sudden death with minimal anatomical findings, J. Forensic Medicine 1:39, 1953.

Adelson, L.: Medical evidence in fatal gunshot injuries, Am. J. Clin. Path. 23:758, 1953.

Adelson, L.: Some medicolegal observations on infanticide, J. Forensic Sciences 4:60, 1959.

Adelson, L.: Slaughter of the innocents, New England J. Med. 264:1345, 1961.

Cowan, M. E.: Trace evidence: tremendous trivia, Postgrad. Med. 31: A-66, 1962.

Gerber, S. R.: Adequate medical examinations in unexpected and violent deaths, J.A.M.A. 138:1190, 1948.

Gerber, S. R.: The role of the coroner in motor vehicle deaths, Clin. orthop. 9:3, 1957.

Kulowski, J.: Needed: wide medical interest in motorist casualties, J. Kansas M. Soc., Nov., 1955.

Lewis, S. K.: The medical examinership as a career, J. Iowa M. Soc., Feb., 1961.

Steuer, A.: The judge looks at the impartial doctor, Postgrad. Med. 26: A-52, 1959.

Trauma (Albany, N. Y.: Matthew Bender Company).

A. C. OFFUTT, M.D.

Dr. Offutt is the Indiana State Health Commissioner. After receiving his medical education at Indiana University School of Medicine, he served in the Army with a medical battalion; he was later graduated from the Medical Field Service School in Carlisle, Pa., where he became an instructor before going overseas during World War II. Dr. Offutt is a past-president of the Middle States Branch of the American Public Health Association, has just completed a 3-year term as Secretary-Treasurer of the Association of State and Territorial Health Officers, and is now vice-president of that Association.

4. The Physician's Relations with the Health Department

THE PHYSICIAN, in his daily practice, works with many official and voluntary agencies operating in the health field. For several reasons, the organization with which he has the most frequent and intimate contact, the health department, is the one about which he is frequently poorly informed. This is difficult to explain since history indicates that health departments throughout the United States were, for the most part, established at the insistence of organized medicine. If one will study the early development of state departments of health, he will discover that groups of practicing physicians worked long and patiently to convince the public and legislators that the ills of a community were different from those of the individual. The physicians reasoned that a governmental agency, managed by

53

professional people with special skills and authority and charged with specific responsibilities, could achieve results in the improvement of total community health beyond those that could be achieved by the "one-to-one" approach characterizing the relationship between private physician and patient.

In order that people may enjoy the best health possible and in order that the physician may more effectively deal with the problems of his patients, the health department engages in specific activities, which, because of their nature, cannot be satisfactorily resolved on an individual basis. Even though there are some slight variations in the programs as a result of specific community needs, the basic functions of well-organized and professionally staffed health departments are fairly uniform throughout the country.

HEALTH DEPARTMENT FUNCTIONS

Vital Statistics

Collecting, recording, and analyzing the incidence of disease and the factors surrounding births and deaths are extremely important in assessing the health situation of a community and in planning programs pertinent to those needs. The dissemination of information resulting from the recording of vital facts can be of great assistance to the physician in anticipating some of the problems that he will face in his private practice. The creation of a number of state health departments resulted from the importance placed upon this information by organized medical groups and their encouragement of the establishment of a state agency to perform this function. The value of vital records is proportionately related to the completeness of the reporting of disease, births and deaths; and the completeness of the reporting is determined by the practicing physician's understanding of the importance of such information to himself and his community.

The reporting of births, deaths, and certain diseases is required by law. Birth- and death-reporting throughout the country is practically 100 per cent complete. On the other hand, the reported cases of disease in many instances represent only a small percentage of the actual occurrence. The use made of the records of births and deaths by the public as well as by the health department is generally understood. Perhaps this accounts for the conscientious manner in which these facts are reported. Should health departments make it clear that reported instances of disease are essential for other purposes than providing data for statistical compilation, and if physicians realized that information gained from the compilation and analysis of such data had far-reaching implications in their practice, it is quite possible that requirements related to disease-reporting would be scrupulously followed.

Communicable Disease Control

In addition to the reporting of communicable diseases just discussed, there are other relationships in this area between the health department and the physician from which both benefit. The health department is in a position to supply information concerning the immunization status of a given community as well as current information on new agents and methods of immunization. The health officer frequently is in a position to alert physicians to a disease that may threaten a community and to work with the medical society in developing plans to protect the community. In the event that a disease does reach epidemic proportions, the health department and the physicians working together represent a formidable team to resolve the problem.

Environmental Sanitation

The relationship between sanitation and disease was one of the major facts that added impetus to the public health movement. The close relationship between environment and health still exists, but the nature of the problems and, consequently, the functions of the health department have changed somewhat during recent years. Promoting the establishment of centralized water supplies and sewage systems and policing the production of milk and other food products played a major role in removing the filth-borne diseases—typhoid, diarrhea, etc.—as a threat to the life and health of people. In recent years urban sprawl, making centralization of public services in sanitation most difficult to achieve—the provision of safe water supplies, adequate sewage disposal, garbage collection and the like—has challenged the health department. Even newer problems resulting from scientific and technological advances have created new areas of concern for the official public health agencies. Most progressive health departments are now engaged in efforts to protect the public against air pollution, radiologic hazards, dangerous food additives, and pesticides. The practicing physician is interested in these problems because they represent a threat to the health of his patient. As an individual, however, he may be helpless to institute corrective measures. Working with the health department, the possibility of removing or reducing these health threats becomes a reality. The health department's patient is the community and not its individual members.

Laboratory Services

The practice of medicine is greatly enhanced by having complete laboratory services available. There are several private resources within the average community from which the physician may secure such services. In some instances it is not feasible for other than the health department to make certain laboratory services available. When this situation exists, the local health department should provide these services directly. In those instances where this is not practicable, and frequently this is the case, such needs should be met by the state health department. The health department must depend on organized medicine to help determine the type of services needed and the conditions under which they are made available. In addition to servicing the needs of physicians, health departments must have at their command facilities capable of doing tests on water, milk and food.

Maternal and Child Health

The practicing physician stands to benefit materially in those instances in which a public health program for mothers and infants is developed jointly by the health department and organized medicine. The great majority of health officers hold that a properly developed and administered program in this area enhances the relationship between the doctor and his patient. Activities of the health department in providing pre- and postnatal instruction for expectant mothers are indicated when situations exist which preclude such education being provided through private practice. The development of an acceptable school health program which includes the referral of discovered defects back to the private physician or dentist is an activity of the health department beneficial to both the community and the physician. The official health agency's program relating to nutrition, immunization, and other good health procedures represents another area of cooperation from which everyone concerned stands to benefit.

Health Education

The education of the public concerning the health problems and needs of a community represents one of the major activities of a well-organized official health agency. The health officer and his staff are frequently in a more acceptable position to engage in such programs than are individual physicians or the medical association. Promotional and educational programs concerning immunization, securing continuous medical supervision, periodic medical examinations, etc., properly can be carried on by the health department. The health department is also in position to work closely with school officials in constructing the health curriculum and determining the content of the school health education program. By working with various community groups—such as voluntary health agencies, community service agencies and others—the health department can help mobilize support for those measures that will result in improved public health. It is extremely important that the medical association assist the health officer and his staff in determining the nature and objectives of the educational program.

Chronic Disease Control

Efforts to control chronic disease represent one of the newer programs of health departments. Although the control of the chronic diseases presents one of the greatest challenges ever faced in public health, the method of approaching the problem has not been fully determined. For this reason, effective operations in this area will depend on the willingness of organized medicine and public health workers to determine the appropriate role of the health department in this difficult and complex area of health. The solution will require the best thinking of both groups in the area of primary and secondary prevention. The care of the individual with a chronic disease challenges the ingenuity of all. Hospital care, nursing home care, and home care of the chronically ill require understanding and close cooperation between the medical profession and the health department.

Summary of Main Functions

The activities just described, in a very general way, are typical of most health departments throughout the United

States, but peculiarities in needs and customs of various communities result in slight variations in public health programs.

Although the activities of the average health department are many and varied, by grouping these activities into two major categories, the interdependence of the practicing physician and the official health agency is brought more sharply into focus. In this way the benefits to be derived by both through harmonious and cooperative relationships are more readily discernible. For purposes of discussion, consider the activities of public health as classifiable under the broad categories of *epidemiology* and *health education.*

One of the unique contributions to the effective practice of medicine made by the official health agency is through the various activities that can be considered essential to the epidemiologic effort. Information gained from epidemiologic studies can provide the physician with a better understanding of the health and disease situation in the community where he practices and result in supportive services which will enable him to render the most appropriate preventive care to his patients.

The control of communicable disease depends on the interchange of information between the physician and the health department, the discovery of the sources and routes of transmission, and the determination of methods of eliminating either these sources or routes. The laboratory services, the investigation made by the health officer and other specialists of the health department, and the conclusions that result are essential in a disease control program.

The recounting of an actual occurrence will illustrate how the epidemiologic efforts of a health department are dependent on effective communication between practicing physicians and the department and the mutual aid that appertains.

A state health department suddenly became aware, from the reports of individual physicians through a local health department, of a number of cases of typhoid fever centered in one area.

One reported typhoid fever case was enough to cause concern; but when, within a period of two weeks, three such cases were reported, the health department went into action. Local physicians were contacted, and it was soon discovered that there were not three cases but thirteen. Public health physicians, nurses, sanitarians, sanitary engineers, and health educators from the state health department came to the aid of the local department. Their activities were not directed toward the individual who was suffering from the disease. His treatment and care were the responsibility of his family physician. However, the public health workers were concerned as to the source of each individual's infection and how further spread of the disease might be prevented.

Discussions were held with the local medical society as to the course to be followed in the investigation and emergency procedures to be inaugurated. Patients were interviewed for the purpose of discovering a lead to the source of the disease. Many possible sources had to be considered and eliminated. The presence of a carrier who, in some manner, had come in contact with those who were ill represented one possibility. Water, various foods, common eating places, different types of dairy products, etc., all came under suspicion and had to be investigated. While the investigation continued, new cases were reported and the geographical area involved expanded. Educational programs were instigated to alert the public and to encourage people to take indicated precautions.

As a result of interviews by physicians and nurses, a number of different foods and their sources had to be investigated by the engineers and sanitarians. One by one these items were cleared of suspicion. Two months after the health department entered the picture, and after many more individuals had become ill with typhoid fever, all possibilities had been checked out. The possibility of a carrier, water and foods, except cheese, had been cleared. Finally evidence proved that one batch of cheese, made on a given day in one plant, had been contaminated with the organism causing the outbreak.

It is evident from this account that the time devoted to this investigation and the various skills required to carry it through to a successful conclusion required the organized effort of a public health team and practicing physicians. It is also apparent that the efforts of each group did not duplicate but complemented and supplemented the others.

The second major function under which the activities of the health department may be categorized is health education. In a sense the educational program of the health department is the only ethical form of advertising available to the medical profession. The health department uses its facilities and skills to educate the community to seek and take advantage of competent medical care, to avoid falling prey to charlatans and misleading advertising. It can inform the people, through the various communicative channels, of specific threats to health and measures to be followed in protecting themselves. The busy physician hardly has time to educate the community about the threats to health, the importance of good nutrition, of immunization, etc. After attempting to educate one stubborn patient, it is doubtful that he would be inclined or have the time to assume the job of imparting knowledge to the public. The primary role of the physician in a community health education program is that of working with the health department in determining the needs, objectives and the nature of such effort. Such assistance from the medical association is not only accepted but sincerely appreciated by the health department.

SOME MISCONCEPTIONS CONCERNING RELATIONSHIPS BETWEEN PHYSICIANS AND HEALTH DEPARTMENTS

In the past, and to some degree in recent years, there have been occasional discordant notes in the relationship between the physician and the health department. Since these have usually resulted from misunderstanding rather than true differences in philosophy, the conflicts are being gradually resolved. As a result of improved understanding, the public, the physician, and the health department have benefited materially. Examples of these misconceptions follow.

Public Health and Socialized Medicine

A few physicians have labored under the impression that public health is a step toward socialized medicine and that workers in the field hold socialistic beliefs. On the other hand, many leading physicians, including those speaking for the American Medical Association, have stated: "The best bulwark against socialized medicine is a good health department." It should be remembered that health officers have been educated in the same medical schools from which the practicing physicians received their medical training. Both groups have developed their appreciation for medical ethics from common sources of information and indoctrination. The activities and policies of most health departments of this country are controlled by boards of health. Physicians are members of these boards and are frequently in a majority and, consequently, in position to help determine policy and program.

The medical profession gave birth to the health department concept, and there is little danger of infringement upon private practice by the health department when organized medicine assumes its responsibility for the development and progress of the official health agency.

Health Officer: Bureaucrat or Specialist?

To some physicians who have not had many close associations with the health department, it represents a bureaucratic agency interfering in the medical field. To them the department exists to fulfill certain legal and necessary requirements that are only slightly related to medicine. Even the necessary function of registering births and deaths loses some of its acceptability when associated with what they consider useless accumulation of morbidity statistics. When the practicing physician considers the health officer as a specialist in preventive medicine and turns to him for consultation in this highly technical field, just as he turns to other specialists, if his request is then handled effectively and expeditiously, differences are well on the way to resolution.

The busy practicing physician is hard-pressed to keep abreast of the changes that are occurring in the broad field of medicine. He turns to specialists and consultants when he feels that he is beyond his proper scope of activity. Present day health problems being what they are, the generalists recognize the need for the specialist in community health just as they recognize the need for available consultation in other areas of individual medical practice.

It frequently has been pointed out that the public health physician is a specialist in the field of preventive medicine and public health. He and his professional and technical staff and the practicing physician can integrate their mutual interests and activities to effect better health protection for all the people.

Need for Knowledge of Medical Practice

In some instances the health department has considered the practitioner uncooperative and unwilling to provide required reports and the answers to simple requests. This is not necessarily so, and it would be well for the health department to develop a much keener perception of the modern practice of medicine. As this is done, it is quite possible that it would be discovered that a substantial number of physicians are already applying some of the recommended public health technics. Without such first-hand knowledge about medical practice and the extent to which given technics are adhered to by the practitioners in a community, unjust criticism will result in a considerable waste of public health resources.

IMPROVING RELATIONSHIPS BETWEEN PHYSICIANS AND THE HEALTH DEPARTMENT

During the developmental years of public health, the relationship between the physician and the health department generally has been good. As a result, remarkable success has been achieved in the battle against the contagious and infectious diseases and the various environmental hazards that threatened the health and life of people.

Today's major problems and their solutions demand the closest possible cooperation between the private practice of medicine and the health department. The problems of prevention of the present, whether they be those nurtured by new environmental hazards or those that have their origin in hereditary or constitutional disorders, cannot be dealt with successfully unless the efforts of the practicing physician and the public health worker represent coordinated endeavor.

In order that their cooperation may not be left to chance and the public be denied the type of health service that medical and related sciences have made available, the physician and the health department must understand their relationships and responsibilities to each other.

The practicing physician should become acquainted with the laws, rules, and regulations that relate to his responsibility for providing information to the health department. He should also acquaint himself with the various services available to him through the official health agency. Special laboratory services, aid in the care of indigent patients, consultation concerning special problems of preventive medicine, and educational materials are all available to the physician from the health department and can be of inestimable value in his practice. Practicing physicians should accept the responsibility of serving on the official board of health or become members of advisory committees to the department. In this way they will be in a better position to help develop public health policies for the community, help determine the program of the department, advise, and constructively criticize concerning the operations of the official health agency.

The health officer should become well acquainted with the medical community in which his department functions. He should develop an intimate knowledge of the climate of medical opinion and practice of the community he serves. In addition, the health officer should participate in the affairs of the medical association. He should inform the practicing physician of the various responsibilities that, as an individual, he has to the public health agency and to the public in general. It is more essential, however, that the importance of these obligations be explained. When physicians are convinced that the value received in services to themselves and their patients justifies the effort expended, few will fail to report vital events, to provide requested information or to fulfill other such obligations. When the health department provides expert consultation upon the special request of the physician, makes available appropriate and necessary laboratory services, engages in significant epidemiologic studies and, by other action, demonstrates that the health department considers service to the private physician and his patients one of its main duties, strong bonds develop between the department and the physician.

The success of a public health program is dependent, to a large extent, upon the support of the medical profession. A health department that commands the respect of all segments of the community, including organized medicine, is a strong department. A strong health department, with a quality staff, serves the community well and renders valuable service to the physician and his patients.

THOMAS STEWART HAMILTON, M.D.

President of the American Hospital Association for 1962, Dr. Hamilton is Executive Director of Hartford, Connecticut, Hospital. His work in hospital administration began soon after he took his M.D. at Wayne University College of Medicine in 1939; he served as Assistant Director of Massachusetts General Hospital, as Executive Officer, Sixth Army General Hospital, and as Director of Newton-Wellesley Hospital in Massachusetts before going to Hartford in 1954. His allied positions have included Chairman of the AHA Council on Professional Practice, advisor on nursing education to AHA and USPHS, and service on the Joint Commission on Accreditation of Hospitals and the AMA Committee on Internships.

5. Hospital-Physician Relations

At the beginning of the twentieth century, a physician could know nearly all there was to know about medicine and carry with him most of the tools he needed in his practice. But as the knowledge and tools grew in volume and complexity, it became necessary for the physician to specialize and to depend on other individuals and institutions for help in caring for his patients. He turned to the hospital and, in so doing, completely altered the character of the hospital. Within the last three-quarters of a century the hospital has changed from a place oriented toward supportive nursing care to a center of health care for the community and a center of the physician's professional life.

66

The word hospital is derived from the Latin words *hospes,* meaning guest, and *hospitium,* the place where guests are received. The French *hospice,* originally an inn kept by religious orders for travelers, eventually housed the poor, infirm, incurable or insane. Today's general hospital has evolved as the place for temporarily housing the acutely ill, requiring specialized medical and nursing care.

Until nearly the end of the nineteenth century, the hospitals remained institutions for nursing care, primarily of the indigent, the military and merchant seamen; physicians continued to give medical care in the home or office. But the medical revolution of the late nineteenth and early twentieth centuries made hospitals essential to all and produced the present interdependence between hospital and physician.

Today hospital and physician are essential to each other. Theoretically, the doctor could do without the hospital, if he were willing and financially able to assemble the necessary ancillary personnel and equipment (in effect, to develop his own individual hospital), but in a time of highly complex and expensive skills and equipment, this is impractical and unwise. The people and equipment must be supplied on a broader community basis and the hospital becomes the mechanism.

Thus the physician cannot practice the best medicine today without the hospital's centralized collection of personnel, services and equipment. The hospital never could provide care without the physician's scientific and technical knowledge.

Because they are so linked, the physician must understand both the workings of the hospital and his relationship and responsibility to it.

The physician, to say the least, has a complicated relationship with the hospital: (1) as a physician who treats his patients there, (2) as a teacher, a student and, often, as a researcher, (3) as a member of the organized medical staff and

(4) as a member of the community which supports and which benefits from the hospital.

THE HOSPITAL

A hospital has been variously defined as a health team, as people, as a restaurant providing food for special needs, as a laundry, as a power plant, as a pharmacy, as an educational institution, as a workshop for physicians, as a research center, and as a center for community health. It is each of these and all of these and more.

It is difficult to find a simple definition of a hospital, but the following is perhaps useful:

A hospital is an establishment offering services, facilities and beds for use beyond 24 hours for two or more non-related individuals requiring diagnosis, treatment or care for illness, injury, deformity, infirmity, abnormality or pregnancy, and regularly making available at least (1) clinical laboratory services, (2) diagnostic x-ray services and (3) treatment facilities for (a) surgery or (b) obstetrical care or (c) other definitive medical treatment of similar extent.

Hospitals may be described in many ways, such as type of service, length of stay, ownership, etc.

Type of service.—A general hospital treats patients of all ages, usually for all types of illness. Of the more than 25 million patients admitted to hospitals each year, more than 90 per cent are cared for in general hospitals. Most of these are referred to as community hospitals.

A specialty hospital cares for patients with specific diseases or conditions, such as mental illness or tuberculosis, or for patients in certain age groups, such as children or elderly persons.

Length of stay.—Hospitals may be either short-term or long-term, depending on the average length of stay of the patients. Many specialty hospitals are long-term; general hospitals are usually short-term, although there is a growing trend toward having both short- and long-term facilities in the same environment.

Ownership.—There are three major types of ownership: voluntary-nonprofit (operated by a church or nonprofit association); governmental (operated by the federal, state or local government) and proprietary (operated for profit by an individual, partnership or corporation).

Hospital Functions

To the practicing physician, the hospital's major function may appear to be that of a workshop for his practice. However, it is far more.

Traditionally hospitals have had three functions: care of patients, education and training of physicians and other health personnel, and research. Just as three-legged stools have been replaced by four-legged chairs, the hospital's tripartite responsibility has expanded to include responsibility for improvement of the community health. As the hospital came to occupy a more central role in medical care, the community began to expect more from it than just after-the-fact therapeutics. It came to expect preventive care, finally looking to the hospital and its staff as overseers of the community's health.

Patient care, education and medical research all contribute to the community's health, but unless they are set within a broader pattern of public and preventive health, they lose a good deal of their effectiveness. Responsibility for total community health adds stability to the other three functions, providing the proper milieu for their discharge.

The physician increasingly uses the hospital to treat all of his patients, not just those who must be admitted as inpatients. More and more doctors are meeting their patients at the hospital—to set a broken arm, to have diagnostic tests made, to care for dozens of ailments once treated at home or in the office.

The hospital supplies the doctor with an increasing number of his tools, particularly the expensive and complicated ones. Only through grouping under one roof can a community afford the equipment necessary to the practice of modern medicine. The hospital, for instance, can afford to assemble the necessary team of skilled persons and equipment for open heart surgery. The physician cannot.

Many recent medical advances have themselves resulted from research in the hospital, both large university hospitals and smaller community hospitals. Additionally the hospital plays a major role in the education of physicians and other health personnel. The physician's part in the provision of training and his participation in research will be outlined below.

This question of education has raised major conflicts within medicine and within the community. The traditional "town-and-gown" conflict of the university occurs also in medical education, affecting the hospital in the performance of its duties.

Russell A. Nelson, M.D., director of the Johns Hopkins Hospital, Baltimore, has pointed out that the "town" expects service from the hospital, while the "gown"—the medical school and hospital faculty—desires to raise the academic, scholastic and scientific content of medicine. This conflict must be resolved if the interest of the total community is to be served. It can be resolved if the university teaching hospital is viewed as "primarily an instrument of education and secondarily one of community service," Dr. Nelson believes. In an era of complex medicine, education is vital; the university teaching hospital should serve as the center from which medical education radiates.

But medical education should continue throughout the doctor's lifetime. So it is essential to good patient care that education in some form be carried out in every hospital. The universities and their hospitals cannot do the job alone. They can set patterns, offer the stimuli and the guidelines, but the bulk of physicians must find most of their continuing education close to home. Every hospital must be a teaching hospital.

Hospital-approval Programs

A number of systems exist with the aim of assuring and upgrading the quality of services provided in the hospital. While some of these approvals are governmental, most are of a voluntary nature, growing out of a long tradition of self-government, self-action and self-control on the part of physicians and hospitals.

Historically in this country, the state has existed primarily to provide minimal services and protection to the individual person or group. However, there now appears to be a move away from this position toward one of placing more responsibility upon collective society. Increasingly institutions are being designed to serve the public and increasingly they are being subjected to scrutiny by the public for assurance that its interests are being protected. If the public is dissatisfied with what it sees in its institutions, it demands controls. If these controls are not imposed by the institutions themselves, the public will demand that controls come from government.

So far, hospitals have exerted sufficient control over themselves to assure the public that they have its interests at heart. Only through licensure has government yet exerted much control, and this is still rather minimal. However, for this self-control to continue, hospitals and physicians must voluntarily participate in approval and certification programs, support them and be willing to place themselves under the scrutiny of the approving bodies.

Licensing laws for hospitals vary from state to state but generally deal with fire safety, structural and space features and sanitation. While some states long have had hospital licensure, the real growth in such laws occurred after World War II. A provision of the Hospital Survey and Construction (Hill-Burton) Act of 1946, under which many hospitals have been built, required that each state develop standards for hospitals to be built with federal funds.

In addition, the American Hospital Association, the U.S. Public Health Service and other national organizations developed a model comprehensive hospital licensing law, which has been enacted by a number of states. Some states do not have complete hospital licensing laws, although in each, hospitals are regulated by the state through other methods (for instance, approval by the department of welfare before hospitals are reimbursed by it).

The American Hospital Association annually registers hospitals which meet 11 basic requirements dealing with size, facilities and staff. This registration program is quantitative rather than qualitative. It provides a census of hospitals, not a measure of the quality of care provided. The latter is done by the Joint Commission on Accreditation of Hospitals.

The accreditation program is probably the best known and most important of the hospital approval systems. The Commission, established in 1952, has the objective of evaluating and raising the standards of patient care in hospitals. It is sponsored and financed by the American College of Physicians, the American College of Surgeons, the American Hospital Association and the American Medical Association.

Participation is voluntary, with the hospital making application for survey by one of the Joint Commission's staff, all of whom are physicians. That the program is important and successful is borne out by the fact that more than half of all American hospitals are now accredited.

To qualify for survey, a hospital must have at least 25 beds, have been in operation for at least 12 months and be listed by the American Hospital Association. A hospital may be accredited for one year, after which it must be re-surveyed; for three years, after which it is surveyed as soon as possible; or not at all. A hospital may receive a one-year accreditation only twice.

The surveyor personally investigates all phases of hospital operation, comparing its activities with Commission standards for methods of procedure. Standards are those considered necessary to insure high quality medical care and are based on a set of underlying principles.

These principles, as outlined by the Joint Commission, briefly sum up the components of a good hospital.

I. Administration

Physical plant.—The buildings of the hospital must be constructed and arranged to insure the safety of the patient and promote his welfare.

Governing body.—The governing body has the legal and moral responsibility for the conduct of the hospital as an institution. It is responsible to the patient, the community, and the sponsoring organization. Its official representative is the chief administrative officer of the hospital.

Facilities for the following services.—Dietary, medical records, pharmacy or drug room, clinical laboratory and pathological services, radiology and medical library.

II. Medical Staff

The medical staff is responsible to the patient and to the governing body of the hospital for the quality of all medical care provided to patients in the hospital and for the ethical and professional practices of its members.

III. Nursing

There must be a graduate registered nurse on duty at all times and professional nursing care must be available for all patients at all times.

The standards spell out the procedures for maintaining these principles, and range from emergency lighting in operating, delivery and emergency rooms, to the data required in medical records. All have but one aim—to insure that quality of care is maintained and continually improved.

Other voluntary approval systems concerning hospitals are those covering educational programs. The American Medical Association approves internships and residencies offered in hospitals, as well as hospital educational programs for medical technologists, x-ray technicians, medical records librarians, occupational and physical therapists.

Educational programs for professional nurses, practical nurses, dietitians, and nurse anesthetists are approved by their respective national organizations.

Still another type of self-control exists in the hospital associations—state, regional and national—which hospitals voluntarily join. Increasingly these associations are setting up self-regulatory programs; for instance, policies on pricing of hospital services; planning for hospital facilities on a regional basis; recommending and supporting utilization committees in individual hospitals; cooperating with Blue Cross Plans in examining and reducing costs.

Each of these programs compels the hospital to constantly evaluate its services, thus helping to improve them. Further, they offer assurance to the public that hospitals are interested in meeting their obligations as public institutions.

Hospital Organization

Within the hospital system, hospitals fall into two major classifications—private and public. Because the majority of hospitals are private, and specifically nonprofit, voluntary, the remainder of this chapter will deal with this type of community hospital.

However, it might be pointed out that some district hospitals, while legally governmental entities, frequently have a large measure of individual autonomy, even to the extent of a non-political governing body.

The *governing body* is legally and morally responsible for the conduct of the hospital as an institution. It is responsible to the patient, the community, and the sponsoring organization. Its major function is to formulate and establish policies governing the management of the hospital.

The board delegates to the hospital's medical staff responsibility for medical practice, and to the administrator the internal operation of the hospital.

Composed of public-spirited citizens, the board carries out its duties through committees. The most common standing committees are executive, investment or finance, buildings and grounds, nominating, and joint conference.

The board's official representative is the *administrator,* the chief executive officer of the hospital. He is responsible for the total management of the hospital and for seeing that the policies of the board are carried out. He is responsible for the hospital's physical and financial assets, for personnel, and for maintaining liaison among the governing body, the medical staff, the nursing staff, and all other departments of the hospital.

Formerly many administrators were physicians, nurses or individuals recruited directly from the business world. Few had any specific training in hospital administration. In recent years, a number of universities have begun offering courses in hospital administration, designed to provide the prospective administrator with a thorough grounding in the complex business of running a hospital.

THE MEDICAL STAFF

The hospital's *medical staff* is responsible for the quality of all medical care rendered in the hospital and for the ethical and professional practices of its members. In addition to physicians, the medical staff frequently includes dentists, psychologists, biochemists, and other professionals.

The staff's major functions are:

1. Clinical or professional care of patients.

2. Administration of medical staff affairs, including determination of medical policies, and recommendations to the governing board on medical staff appointments and other professional matters.

3. Review, analysis, appraisal, and control of clinical work.

4. Education, particularly of staff members.

5. Research and its promotion.

Clinical Care

Clinical care of the patient is the primary function of the medical and dental staff individually and collectively. Members of the medical staff must assure the governing board that they are providing the best possible care. The hospital is responsible for providing facilities and personnel.

Administration of Medical Affairs

The board of governors places the responsibility for medical matters on the medical staff, which sets up its own organizational system to carry out its various duties. A necessary component is the establishment of bylaws, which clearly define the purposes of the medical staff, its system of organization, and its method of functioning. While technically an extension of the governing body's bylaws and requiring approval of the board, the medical staff bylaws are developed by the staff itself as a self-governing body. The bylaws might be termed the medical staff's constitution.

In addition to the bylaws, the organized medical staff sets up rules and regulations of practice which are observed by all physicians practicing in the hospital. They deal with such matters as admitting procedures, use of operating rooms, consultations, writing of orders, and medical records.

To be effective, the rules must carry with them self-activating sanctions which can be invoked without discretionary discipline by the staff. For instance: the rules may specify that medical records must be completed within 48 hours of the patient's discharge. If the physician fails to comply with this rule, he loses his privileges until such time as he does comply. Then he automatically regains privileges.

The granting of staff privileges is a grave responsibility and must be carefully considered and carried out.

In selecting a physician for staff privileges, it must be remembered that a license to practice medicine is not a guarantee of competence. It confers only a legal right to practice medicine in the state granting the license. It does not confer a legal right to practice medicine in any given institution. Most institutions are not required to give staff privileges to any and all licensed physicians. Furthermore, hospitals have a moral responsibility to insure that all practice within their confines is of the highest possible quality and in the best interest of the citizens of the community.

Privileges should be extended according to a physician's experience, judgment, ability and competence as evaluated by the medical staff's credentials committee and as recommended to the staff and the governing board. The board makes the appointment.

The Joint Commission on Accreditation of Hospitals has said concerning staff appointments, "Individual merit and competence should be the sole criteria for selection and under no circumstances should the accordance of staff membership or professional privileges in a hospital be dependent alone upon certification or membership in specialty societies."

Appointments are usually made on an annual basis and members are eligible for reappointment if they are approved by the staff and accepted by the governing board. Reappointment at the end of the year is usual, although not automatic. The hospital, because of its right of selection, may simply choose not to reappoint, and the physician can usually do nothing about it. However, if an appointment is terminated before the end of the year (and sometimes upon failure of reappointment), the physician has recourse according to the method set forth in the medical staff's bylaws. Each staff, as an independent body, sets up its own methods of appeal.

The privileges granted must be carefully spelled out in making the appointment and must depend on the physician's training and experience. He must be judged fully competent in his area of performance before being granted any privileges. They should be reviewed at least annually.

On the basis of this review, through which a physician's attainments are regularly assessed by his peers, he is advanced and his abilities are compared to those of his colleagues. The regular review is also a demonstration of medical staff responsibility for medical care in the hospital and in the community, through the delineation of privileges of the physicians.

A senior position on the staff of an accredited hospital is accepted by the public as a sign of medical excellence.

Provisions should be made in the bylaws for promotion of staff members to insure that younger men have an opportunity to progress. Some type of rule should be set forth for retirement from active staff participation, although not from clinical practice. This assures the hospital of continuing vigor in its medical staff and prevents the development of closed monopolistic control of the staff by a small group of men.

There are several categories of staff membership, determined on the basis of professional qualifications and demonstrated ability.

All physicians are responsible for the clinical care of their own patients, but the group particularly responsible for evaluating and maintaining the quality of care rendered in the hospital is the *active medical staff*. In addition, the active medical staff transacts all staff business and carries certain teaching duties. Generally only active staff members may vote and hold office.

Other categories of staff usually include:

Honorary staff.—Former active staff members, retired or

emeritus, and other physicians whom the active staff wishes to honor.

Consulting staff.—Recognized specialists willing to give their services in such a capacity. They may also be members of the active staff.

Associate staff.—Physicians who use the hospital infrequently and those less experienced undergoing a trial period before being considered for appointment to the active staff. They are appointed and assigned to departments in the same manner as active members.

Courtesy staff.—Physicians who wish to attend patients in the hospital but who are for any of several reasons not members of the active or associate staff. A physician usually holds an active staff appointment at only one hospital and courtesy appointments at others.

The organizational structure of the medical staff varies according to the size and activities of the hospital. In most, the staff is headed by a president or chief of staff, elected annually. The president is responsible for the business of staff, but not for supervision of clinical work unless he is also chief of staff. The chief serves as the professional or clinical head of the medical staff, being responsible for the functioning of the clinical organization and for supervising all clinical work.

Other officers of the medical staff are vice president, secretary and treasurer.

The staff is usually organized into committees, the number and kinds depending on the size of the staff and the activities of the hospital.

Executive committee.—Usually composed of the medical staff officers, the departmental heads and two members-at-large, this committee transacts the business of the staff. It refers matters to the whole staff only as the need arises, thus allowing staff meetings to be devoted to clinical discussion. In small hospitals, the executive committee may be the only committee, assuming the functions of all other committees.

The administrator is usually an ex officio member without vote.

Credentials committee.—Also called the qualifications committee, it reviews applications for appointment and re-appointment to all categories of the staff. It delineates the privileges to be extended to the physician and makes appropriate recommendations to the staff, which in turn makes them to the governing board for final action.

Joint conference committee.—This committee consists of an equal number from the medical staff and the governing board, with the administrator as an ex-officio member. A medico-administrative liaison committee, it serves as the official point of contact among the medical staff, the governing board, and the administrator. While it may make recommendations, it has no power in itself.

Departments.—In larger hospitals, departments may be set up to facilitate the supervision of clinical work. Each department performs within itself the duties of clinical review and appraisal.

Each department is headed by the departmental member best qualified in training and experience. In a general hospital, the most common departments are medicine, surgery, obstetrics and gynecology, pediatrics, radiology and pathology.

Review, Appraisal of Clinical Work

Review, analysis, appraisal and control of the clinical work in the hospital are carried out through a series of review committees, commonly including medical records, tissue, medical audit, and utilization. These committees may cover the whole hospital or individual departments, depending on the medical staff organization.

Only physicians are capable of judging medical practice. Patients and hospital personnel may learn to recognize good practice, but only the physician can accurately evaluate its quality.

The opinions of individual physicians vary, so there must be group—or committee-participation in evaluating clinical practice.

The Joint Commission on Accreditation of Hospitals has said, "To judge the work of a colleague on a fair, unbiased, impartial level calls for the intelligence and wisdom of a Solomon. That this is so well done in thousands of hospitals can be attributed to the integrity, effort and persistence of each member of the medical staff."

Each physician has a personal responsibility to make sure that his patient receives the best possible care. He also has a responsibility to see that all medical practice in the hospital is the best possible. By sitting on the evaluation and other committees, he carries out this latter duty.

It must be emphasized that these are evaluation and not policing committees. Their objective is improvement, not punishment.

The committees review and appraise the handling of a case or cases. From such review, errors in judgment are discovered and new methods of treatment or procedures may develop. The individual physician should be informed of the committee's findings regarding his work; however, anonymity should be maintained through coding before presenting findings to the whole staff. When committee findings are passed onto the medical staff, all members gain.

Occasionally, however, situations arise in which it becomes clear that a physician is making consistent and recurring errors. Then the doctors, as members of the review committee, must sit in judgment on their fellow physicians. This is certainly difficult to do, but proper organization of the staff makes it easier to carry out.

Furthermore, the acts are given credence by the fact that the ultimate authority to ratify or, in some cases, overrule the self-governing actions of the medical staff lies in a community-oriented governing board. The medical staff in such cases is acting as the self-governing agent of a community body—the board—rather than of a group of physicians with vested, self-serving interests.

All staff committees have the same goal: to assure, by evaluating and reviewing case records, that all medical care in the hospital is appropriate and of high quality. They look for errors which can be pointed out and thereby prevented in future treatment, and they, further, urge that appropriate new technics be undertaken.

A medical staff may set up all the customary committees, vary the pattern, or function as a committee of the whole. The important point is that the functions of appraisal and evaluation are carried out.

Medical records committee.—This committee has three duties: to review the patients' clinical records from the standpoint of completeness, legibility, and value as a medical document; to review and evaluate the quality of care as evidenced by the records, and to recommend to the administration policies and procedures concerning the medical records department.

The individual physician has direct responsibility for the records of each of his patients. He must include all pertinent information and keep the records up to date—sufficiently so that another physician could take over the patient's care at any time. He must complete the record within the established period after discharge.

The medical records department is charged with the responsibility of maintaining the records, keeping them accessible, and assisting the medical records committee in its review of the records and the compilation of various reports.

These monthly and yearly reports usually deal with cases admitted and discharged by category, with deaths by category and autopsies. These compilations provide a clear profile of the adequacy and correctness of medical treatment rendered in the hospital.

Autopsies should be performed in a minimum of 20 to 25 per cent of all deaths occurring in the hospital. Each staff member is expected to be actively interested in securing autopsy permission and should make every attempt to persuade the family to permit autopsy. Through autopsy, the correctness of the original diagnosis is checked and medical science is advanced. He must, in addition, be constantly alert to report to the medical examiner or coroner all deaths which might come within that official's jurisdiction.

Tissue committee.—This committee should always include representatives from the departments of surgery, obstetrics and gynecology, and pathology. It reviews all surgery, whether or not tissue is removed. Its chief activity is, however, the review of all tissue removed at surgery. It also must appraise the necessity for the operation and the adequacy of treatment.

Medical audit committee.—This is a relatively new committee and only about 5 per cent of hospitals have one. It compiles statistical analyses of all records of all discharged patients and evaluates in detail, selected records by category. It may cover the work done by the medical records and tissue committees or it may be limited to medical treatment.

The medical audit has been compared to the financial audit which hospitals produce regularly. The late Malcolm T. MacEachern, M.D., a leading authority on hospitals, once explained the need for regular medical audits by saying,

> If it is important to have an audit in dollars and cents, is it not more important to have an audit of the professional work of the hospital, an account of the medical care rendered in terms of lives saved, avoidable and unavoidable deaths, diseases arrested, and patients rehabilitated and restored to society as happy, healthy, productive people?

Utilization committee.—Again, only a few hospitals to date have this committee, but its use is spreading. Its aim is to assure that each patient receives the diagnostic and therapeutic services appropriate to his condition, no more and no less. Certain regulatory bodies, such as state insurance departments, are promoting these committees as a method of reducing unnecessary use of the hospital.

The committee appraises the necessity for admission; the length of stay, and the use of x-ray, laboratory, and other services. While interested in reducing over-utilization, it is equally interested in preventing under-utilization.

The committee should consist of representatives of each major department, and always the chiefs of pathology, radiology, and anesthesiology.

In addition to the committees specifically charged with the appraisal of the quality of care, a medical staff may have a number of other committees, such as infections, pharmacy and therapeutics, education and patient care.

Infections committee.—While this is a medical staff committee, it also includes representatives of the administration and nursing service, and when possible, of community health organizations, since the problem is not confined to the hospital itself.

The committee has two objectives: to establish controls against infections and to develop technics for discovering infections.

It should routinely review existing practices within the hospital, including dietary and food handling procedures; laundry practices; disposal of waste; traffic control; general and specific cleaning methods; air conditioning and ventilation and sterilization technics.

Additionally it should set up programs for educating all personnel in aseptic technics. It is especially important that physicians, by practice and precept, teach strict asepsis.

The committee should appraise the use of antibiotics in the hospital. The Joint Commission on Accreditation of Hospitals has found in its surveys that the infection rate in most hospitals where antibiotics are routinely ordered is higher than in those where they are not.

Pharmacy and therapeutics committee.—Consisting of the hospital pharmacist and physicians with knowledge and interest in pharmacotherapeutics, this committee assists in the formulation of policies regarding the evaluation, selection, procurement, distribution, use, safety procedures, and other matters relating to drugs in the hospital.

It serves as an advisory group on the choice of drugs to be placed on the formulary or drug list of the hospital, evaluates clinical data concerning new drugs, and decides what drugs are to be stocked on the nursing unit floors and by other services.

If a formulary system is adopted, this committee is responsible for it. This system has been recommended by the American Hospital Association and the American Society of Hospital Pharmacists.

The formulary is the compilation or list of pharmaceuticals accepted for use in the hospital, after consideration by the committee. The system provides for the procuring and prescribing of drugs under either their nonproprietary or proprietary names, although the nonproprietary designation is preferred for use in dispensing and administering. Under the system, the medical staff member agrees that he will authorize the pharmacist to dispense and the nurse to administer the drug he has prescribed under its nonproprietary name. The physician may, by so requesting, however, have any specific drug he wishes administered to his patient.

This system of using nonproprietary designations and of stocking in the pharmacy only selected drugs (as decided by the medical staff's pharmacy and therapeutics committee and approved by the staff), has been criticized by the American Medical Association as being "restrictive beyond the needs of good hospital administration" and "an invasion of the professional prerogatives of the physician" in determining the needs of the patients. The American Hospital Association and the American Society of Hospital Pharmacists believe, however, that the system offers a program for sound and rational drug usage in the hospital in an era of increased multiplicity and potency of drugs.

Education

Staff committees do not function independently; they report regularly to both the executive committee and the whole medical staff. Since their functions are primarily those of upgrading care, they necessarily must tell—or more accurately, teach—the medical staff what they have found. Thus the fourth function of the medical staff—education.

It has been said over and over that a physician's education never ends, and with the rapid and constant advances of medical science, this is truer today than ever. Individually and collectively, physicians must learn and must teach.

Continuing education of the practicing physician at the local level, once the primary responsibility of the county medical society, has moved into the hospital. Here is another factor in the centralization of the physician's life in the hospital. It has become the doctor's classroom as well as his workshop.

Staff meetings and clinical conferences are the most common educational devices. Each hospital has its own pattern of meetings as determined by the medical staff bylaws. The most common are monthly meetings of the whole staff or monthly departmental and clinicopathologic conferences.

The bylaws of each medical staff outline attendance requirements. Most require that at least half of the active staff be present at each meeting and that each staff member attend at least half of the meetings. The major portion of each meeting is devoted to review of current or recent cases.

Ward rounds and clinicopathologic conferences are other teaching devices. Through them, the physician has the opportunity to evaluate his own work and to receive the evaluation of his peers.

Another method that may be classified as educational is consultation. Each medical staff lists in its rules and regulations those cases in which consultations are mandatory. Basically consultation is required to protect the patient, but it also serves as an excellent means of education.

Procedures most often listed as requiring consultation are: all first Caesarean sections; all curettages or other procedures by which a known or suspected pregnancy may be interrupted; all sterilizations; major surgical cases in which the patient is considered a bad risk, and cases in which the diagnosis is obscure or in which there is doubt as to the best therapeutic measures to be adopted.

Still other educational devices are up-to-date medical libraries, guest speakers, symposia and postgraduate short courses sponsored in cooperation with other hospitals and county medical societies.

The pursuit of excellence in medicine is never-ending; therefore, all physicians have an obligation to participate in educational programs—either as student or teacher. Only through education can the physician expect to remain competent in this era of rapid medical advance.

In addition to the continuing education of the practicing physician, there is another educational responsibility of the medical staff and the hospital—that of new physicians, nurses and other paramedical personnel.

If a hospital has an internship or residency program, the medical staff members have the key roles in the instruction and training of these new physicians. The primary purpose of an internship or residency is education, not service; and interns and residents should not be expected to provide any service except that which is a part of their education.

The members of the medical staff must cover all service aspects of the hospital, including the care of ward patients, the emergency department and weekend duty. The staff may organize this service in any of a number of ways, but it must not depend entirely on interns and residents.

The internship and residency are essential parts of a physician's education, following medical school and preceding the actual practice of medicine. At present there are more than 12,000 approved internships and more than 28,000 residencies in United States hospitals. Each year about 25 per cent of the internships and 15 per cent of the residencies go unfilled, even though graduates of foreign schools fill some of them.

The graduates of foreign schools present a special problem and a special opportunity in education. In the past, these men were not infrequently used largely in a service capacity; however, within recent years, through the efforts of the American Medical Association, the American Hospital Association, the Association of American Medical Colleges and the Federation of State Medical Boards of the United States, programs for foreign graduates have become more truly educational. The main objective of training these men in the United States is to prepare them for return to their own countries where they will assist in upgrading medical care around the world. They can carry out that duty only if they are well-trained.

Hospitals and their medical staffs which use interns and residents largely in service capacities are failing to meet their educational responsibilities. Together physicians and hospitals must work out staffing patterns that will free interns and residents from service and provide them with the education they need and deserve.

In accepting staff membership in hospitals with interns and residents, physicians must be prepared to carry out their educational duties, as well as their regular service duties. Participation in the educational programs benefits the teacher-physician; he is led to alertness and learning by the constant scrutiny and inquisitiveness of his students.

Physicians must also participate in the education of nurses, dietitians, x-ray technicians and other health personnel who receive part or all of their training in hospitals. They will soon be depending on these very students to provide care for their patients.

Education, then, is a constant process in all hospitals—"teaching" and "non-teaching." The distinction between "teaching," which applies to hospitals associated with undergraduate medical education, and "non-teaching" is unfortunate, since it implies that no teaching occurs except in medical school-affiliated hospitals. Actually it occurs in every hospital worthy of the name.

Research

The fifth function of the medical staff—research—is closely allied to patient care and education; it is the basis on which all medical science progresses.

As with "teaching" hospitals, there is an inclination to refer to "research" hospitals, usually meaning the large medical center or the university-affiliated hospital. But research is something that every hospital can carry on, provided it has personnel who are interested and funds available.

Hospitals, the journal of the American Hospital Association, has editorialized, "A hospital with a research project is a richer hospital. But many hospitals have been unable to thus enrich themselves because of a lack of funds." However, funds are available, particularly from foundations, if hospitals will but make the effort to search them out.

Research in a hospital falls into three major categories: medicine, administration, facilities. Medical research may be divided into three types: applied, basic, and clinical; administrative research deals primarily with the management of hospitals and the interpersonal relations of hospital employees; facilities research includes planning, design and construction and development of equipment.

Every hospital and its medical staff carries out applied medical research in the compilation and analysis of medical records statistics. It is a simplified form of research, to be sure, but out of it may come a new fact, a new idea or a new trend that ultimately advances medicine.

Basic research, such as cellular studies, and clinical studies, such as those involving the testing of new drugs, may be carried out in any hospital with laboratory facilities and interested investigators.

Research may be carried out by a hospital individually or in cooperation with some other organization—a larger hospital, a university, or a drug firm.

The medical staffs of all hospitals have the responsibility to promote research, whether it is conducted in their own hospital or another.

A small hospital setting up an organized research program must tailor it to its own circumstances. Before embarking on a program, a hospital must decide just exactly what kind it wants, depending on its needs, the individual capacities of the investigators, and the space, facilities and financing available. The key to success is the presence of research-minded and trained individuals to direct and conduct it. The farther from a university campus the closer the research should be to the practicing physician. To put it another way, if research is outside the immediate field of interest of most of the medical staff, its value is remote.

The doctor's prime responsibility in organizing a research program lies in his support and enthusiasm for it and in his ability to help convince the governing board of the need for research. The governing board holds the key to a research program since it is responsible for financing. Funds for research are available from many sources, both public and private, and the governing body and the medical staff together can obtain the funds.

Once a hospital has decided on research, the first step is the organization of research committees by the governing board and the medical staff. In some cases, this may be a joint committee. The members are responsible for the program, making the final decisions about projects and assignment of investigators.

The major portion of research must necessarily be conducted in large well-financed, equipped and staffed institutions, but the smaller community hospital can make an important contribution.

A case in point is Memorial Hospital of Natrona County, Casper, Wyoming, a 245-bed county hospital, which is actively pursuing several areas of research, including studies in blood fats, the ultra-low frequency ballistocardiograph, and the prevention of primary attacks of rheumatic fever. While carrying out a research program, this hospital is also fulfilling its role as a community health center.

The rheumatic fever project is a striking example of cooperation among the hospital, physicians, and the community. With the cooperation of volunteers from PTA groups, daily inspections are made of school children for streptococcic nose and throat infections. The hospital provides the laboratory facilities; the hospital pathologist directs the program; several groups, including the hospital finance it, and a group of Casper physicians oversee the whole.

It was the first successful attempt at reducing first attacks of rheumatic fever in a civilian population, though various military programs preceded it, and it has been widely hailed in medical circles as an outstanding example of physician-hospital-community cooperation on a research program, with community health aspects.

Clearly, the small hospital can contribute in two ways— by conducting research within its confines or by promoting an interest in research generally. Research is basic to improved patient care; physicians must support it in all possible ways if they are to carry out their duty toward their patients and society as a whole.

PHYSICIAN'S PERSONAL RESPONSIBILITIES

We have seen that the responsibilities of the medical staff lie in five areas: patient care; administration of medical staff activities; appraisal and review of clinical work; education, and research. The success of the medical staff in meeting these goals is determined finally by its members; the staff, after all, consists only of individuals working separately and together.

This problem of working as a member of a team is one of the most difficult faced by the physician in the hospital. He is not trained to work in an organization. His education from the beginning has taught him to think for himself and to be skeptical. He is the epitome of the individual, yet in the hospital he is thrust into one of society's most complex organizations and expected to function on the one hand as a team member and on the other as his same old independent self.

Further, the physician, just as everyone else, is inclined to see only the specifics that personally concern him, namely his own patients. The hospital, as a social institution, has a broader view. It is dedicated to the welfare of the whole community, and the doctor and his patients are, in the final analysis, only a part of the community. Thus the physician, while maintaining a major interest in his own patients, must at times subjugate his own interests to those of the whole. As a citizen of the community, he also has a responsibility to take an active role in assuring its welfare.

Thus the physician has three major responsibilities: to his patients as their physician; to the hospital as a member of the medical staff, and to the community as a citizen.

There are six specific responsibilities facing the physician practicing in the hospital. If he carries them out, he will have served his patients, his hospital, and his community. They are:

1. *To admit, treat and discharge his patients in accordance with his best knowledge and ability and the hospital and medical staff rules and regulations.*—Working in accordance with his own best knowledge and ability is—or should be—second nature to the physician. Working within the hospital and medical staff rules and regulations takes some adapting and adjusting.

But if the doctor, as a logical individual, realizes that each of the rules has a sensible reason behind it, he will be able to work within them with no difficulty. And if a rule is not sensible, the doctor must work for its correction through the medical staff organization. Rules and regulations are made to protect the patient, to improve care, and to facilitate the operation of a complex institution. They are not made for the mere sake of making rules. The physician as a member of a group must necessarily adhere to them.

2. *To function within the limitations of the clinical privileges granted to him.*—The days of the doctor's independence began to diminish when the amount of knowledge available to him grew beyond one man's ability to comprehend and retain it all. Now he must be willing to have his activities limited to those for which he has proven his capabilities. No longer can he "decide to specialize" and then drift into a specialty. In an era of complex medicine, complex education and training are required.

The doctor must conform to standards of practice set by his peers. The hospital medical staff, through its staff bylaws, determines and maintains its standards. They are usually in addition to standards of the state licensing board or a national specialty body. The doctor must be willing to have his colleagues survey his work and then work within the bounds of the standards set by them.

Only by limiting his work to those areas in which he is truly competent, can the physician be sure that he is providing the best care to those individuals for whom he is responsible.

3. *To participate in the medical staff functions assigned to him.*—This means that the physician must teach, provide care for the indigent, consult, or sit on committees as requested by the medical staff. As a member of an organization, he has the responsibility to see that its goals are met. He cannot expect to reap the benefits of membership without doing some of the work. Only by participating himself can he expect other doctors to do so, and only through the participation of all can the quality of medical care be maintained at its highest possible level.

4. *To participate in teaching and educational programs of staff and other health personnel.*—Again, the physician has several responsibilities: to himself and his patients to learn all he can about medicine; to the community to insure that medical personnel will be properly trained and available in the present and future; and to the community and all the patients in the hospital to protect them from unqualified and incompetent treatment.

5. *To acquaint himself to some degree with the governing board's problems in all phases of hospital operation.*—Running a hospital is a complicated business and involves far more than the practice of medicine: financing, personnel, construction, maintenance, purchasing and endless other matters. Because the hospital provides the physician with his place of work, with much of his equipment, and with trained personnel to assist him, the physician has an obligation to the hospital. He can meet this obligation in part by understanding the institution. By understanding the problems, the doctor may help solve some of them, but if he is unable to do that, he at least understands.

6. *To explain to patients and the public the policies of the hospital and support them.*—What the physician does and does not do frequently influences the patient's and the public's attitudes toward the hospital. Many people do not understand hospitals; they are afraid of them; they dislike them. Yet

everyone expects the hospital to be there ready and waiting when illness or emergency strikes. The hospital can exist as a community institution only so long as the community supports it financially and morally.

If the physician belittles the hospital, complains about its service, blames all medical costs on the hospital, the public follows, accepting the physician as the expert on medical care. As indicated before, the doctor has an obligation to the hospital and he can meet it by developing a loyalty to his hospital. Because he is in constant personal contact with many individuals, he has an excellent opportunity to explain the hospital to them.

The doctor receives much support in his practice from the hospital; he must return that support himself and attempt to gain further support from his patients, friends and the public.

Hospitals and physicians are intimately related in a common goal—the improvement and preservation of the health of the people. Neither can meet the goal alone; they cannot exist without each other, although they still seem to view themselves as separate entities. Dr. John P. Bowler said a decade ago that the greatest field for the future advance in health lies in closer cooperation between the physician and the hospital. Both must press toward this goal of closer cooperation if they are to function in the best interests of the public they both serve.

Hospitals and physicians are inseparable and they must recognize this fact and deal with it. As Philip D. Bonnet, M.D., administrator of Massachusetts Memorial Hospitals, Boston, has observed, "Without the hospital today, a physician is relatively helpless to deal with severe illness. Without the physician, the hospital is not a hospital, and in fact, has no purpose."

R. B. ROBINS, M.D.

*Founder of the Robins Clinic, which was
established in 1937 in Camden, Arkansas,
Dr. Robins is also Chief of Staff, Ouachita
County Hospital, Arkansas. He received
his M.D. from the University of Chicago
in 1925 and was subsequently Professor
of Medical Economics at the University
of Arkansas School of Medicine. His work
in medical organizations include a term
as President of the American Academy of
General Practice, which he helped to
found in 1947. He is a member of the
Board of Trustees and a former
vice-president of the American Medical
Association.*

6. Medical Organizations and Their Purposes

THE COUNTY MEDICAL SOCIETY

THE COUNTY MEDICAL SOCIETY is the basic unit of medical organization, and the essential purposes of these local societies are to aid in the spread of scientific knowledge, to foster better relations among the doctors on a community level and to promote the public health at the community level.

Every young graduate in medicine should associate himself in membership with his local county medical society, regularly attend the meetings and keep himself alerted to scientific progress in the field of medicine. Membership in the county medical society is basic to membership in the state medical society and the American Medical Association. Thus, it is noted that the American Medical Association is organized from the bottom up rather than from the top down.

AMERICAN MEDICAL ASSOCIATION

Organization

The American Medical Association, known to many people as AMA, is the national organization of the physicians of America. It has as its major concern the health and medical care of Americans. Its objective is to promote the science and art of medicine and the betterment of public health.

Back in the early days of America, formalized medical education was practically nonexistent. Medical quackery and traffic in patent medicines ran rampant. The medicine man vied with the medical doctor for patients' attention.

Reputable physicians were seriously concerned about the state of medical affairs, and 250 of them met in Philadelphia in 1847 and formed the American Medical Association to improve medical education, promote higher medical ethics and reduce quackery. From this simple beginning, AMA has grown to a large national organization with over 180,000 members.

The American Medical Association is a confederation of 53 state and territorial medical associations and more than 1,900 county medical societies. It is organized along the lines of the government of the United States (see the accompanying chart), with authority for national policies and activities flowing up through the county and state societies to the Association. The individual physician remains its most important unit.

AMA's Congress, called the House of Delegates, is composed of 216 members. These are elected delegates from the states (one delegate per 1,000 members in a state) and the specialty sections. Twice a year this House of Delegates meets to establish broad policies and programs.

Delegated by the House to implement policies established by the House between sessions is an elected nine-member

AMERICAN MEDICAL ASSOCIATION

Organizational Chart

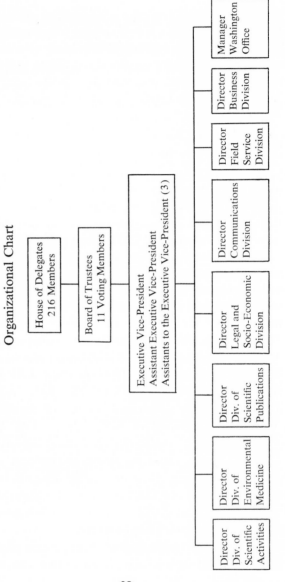

Board of Trustees. The chief administrative officer of day-to-day activities of AMA is its Executive Vice-President.

With headquarters in a nine-story newly remodeled building at 535 North Dearborn Street in Chicago, AMA employs a staff of around 700 people to carry out its many activities. There is also a small staff of people in Washington to run the Washington office of the Association.

To accomplish its work efficiently, AMA has organized its headquarters staff into seven divisions, encompassing: scientific activities, scientific publications, environmental medicine, legal and socio-economic matters, field service, communications, and business.

Meetings

When a physician receives his M.D. degree, he has only begun his education. He must study constantly throughout life to keep abreast of the rapid progress in medicine. To aid physicians in this staggering task, AMA uses every medium possible to convey new data on discoveries, drugs and devices to its members. When a doctor hangs a sign on his door saying he has gone to an AMA meeting, he is off on a search for new ways to care for his patients. In the summer and in the late fall two huge postgraduate meetings offer fantastic educational opportunities. These meetings have hundreds of lectures, exhibits, films, television programs and other demonstrations which the doctor may attend, returning to his patients better armed to fight disease. Throughout the year countless scientific seminars, symposia and other meetings are held on specific topics by AMA councils and committees.

Publications

Since 1883 the *Journal of the American Medical Association,* called JAMA, has been the most widely circulated medical journal in the world. It is published each week, and it culls from hundreds of manuscripts those of the greatest interest to all practicing physicians. JAMA also "reads" hundreds of foreign medical journals for physicians, abstracting significant articles. Important information on other medical subjects and news from medical organizations also appears.

As medicine has become more specialized, AMA has developed ten monthly specialty journals to meet demands from members for information on developments in these limited fields. AMA's first specialty journal was the *Archives of Internal Medicine*. Today the list includes: *American Journal of Diseases of Children, Archives of Neurology, Archives of General Psychiatry, Archives of Dermatology, Archives of Surgery, Archives of Ophthalmology, Archives of Otolaryngology, Archives of Pathology,* and *Archives of Environmental Medicine*.

With the growth of insurance programs, group practice, a variety of payment mechanisms, and new tax laws that require more detailed record-keeping, the physician has had to learn more and more about the non-scientific side of medicine. Much as he might like to concern himself only with patient-care, he has found that he must keep informed about the socio-economic side, the legal side, even the political side, of medicine for his patients' as well as for his own sake. Not long ago a new publication was created to communicate this information as simply and quickly as possible. *The AMA News* is a biweekly newspaper of American medicine.

Because the public has been increasingly interested in health and medical information, AMA publishes a monthly magazine called *Today's Health*. Born in 1922 as an authentic educational health magazine titled *Hygeia,* it was rechristened *Today's Health* in 1950, and in recent years its contents have broadened so that today it is a "magazine for the American family." With readership now running into the millions, *Today's Health* concentrates on those subjects most vital to the general public—good nutrition, basic medical information, child development, recreation and general health education.

For his annual dues the physician receives a free copy of JAMA each week, a specialty journal of his choice each month, *AMA News* every other week, and a reception room copy of *Today's Health* monthly. These are just a few tangible benefits of membership in AMA.

Each physician knows that he can rely upon the products advertised in AMA publications, since high standards for ad copy are maintained.

Scientific Problems

Over the years the American Medical Association has become the center of information on scientific medicine. Into it pours a never-ending stream of scientific information, which must be sifted, evaluated and categorized, as well as communicated to physicians.

Supervising this informational activity are formalized work-teams of physicians—councils and committees of practicing physicians. But AMA is more than a vast clearinghouse on scientific medicine. As medical problems arise, it must exert leadership to solve them. Each council or committee, with the help of permanent staff members at headquarters, deals with problems in its given area, whether related to drugs, physical medicine, foods and nutrition, pesticides, research or a number of other equally important but non-scientific subjects.

Today the spectrum of sciences which play an important part in medicine and health is increasingly wide. Some specific examples of how these councils work to achieve better medicine will now be given.

BETTER-EDUCATED DOCTORS.—Through its Council on Medical Education and Hospitals, AMA has achieved one of its original aims—that of improving medical educational standards in the United States, to insure that every medical graduate is properly trained. The old "diploma mills" of years ago have vanished. Today every medical school is accredited by AMA, and the Association's efforts now include evaluation of intern and residency training programs, evaluation of training programs for allied professions, such as medical technologists and medical record librarians, as well as cooperation with other national groups in improving hospital standards.

SAFE, RELIABLE DRUGS.—Since 1905 AMA's Council on Drugs has labored to make sure that new drugs are not only safe but properly labeled to protect the patient and the doctor. It has worked to stamp out quackery and misleading advertising. AMA efforts paved the way for the establishment of the Federal Food and Drug Administration, which oversees drug manufacture. AMA provides physicians with information as speedily as possible on new drugs and works on special problems related to the use of drugs in patient care.

ENRICHED BREAD AND BABY FOODS.—AMA's Council on Foods and Nutrition has over the years studied and helped put enriched bread and baby foods as well as vitamin-D-fortified milk on the grocer's shelves. Through its efforts doctors and the public are given the latest nutritional findings that affect medicine and health. The Council also provides medical recommendations on how to control weight.

AIR FILTERS AND ARTIFICIAL RESPIRATION.—Classes of apparatus and technics used in modern diagnosis and treatment, such as air filters for asthma sufferers, are evaluated by AMA's Council on Physics. Study of new methods of artificial respiration is just one more activity under way.

CHEMICAL POISONS.—Under study are more than a quarter million chemical products used in home and industry which are potentially dangerous. AMA's Committee on Toxicology has gathered voluminous information for physicians on poison therapy, worked for passage of a more adequate labeling law for such chemicals, and now is conducting a public educational campaign on ways to reduce accidental poisonings.

Medicine and Modern Living

Where and how people live and work has a great effect on health. AMA's Division of Environmental Medicine takes a vital interest in rural and industrial health problems, preventive medicine and military medicine.

The Council on Occupational Health, for example, works with industry to control health hazards on the job, such as air pollution and exposure to chemical irritants. Within its scope are continuing studies on workmen's compensation, rehabilitation of disabled workers, and aviation medicine.

The Council on National Security deals with medical military affairs to assure the best care for servicemen and the best utilization of medical manpower in the services. Its second responsibility is the alerting of physicians and the public to the importance of preparing for any emergency resulting from a national disaster.

Helping rural communities improve their health environment is the job of the Council on Rural Health.

Medicine More than Medication

Though a nation has good doctors, medical facilities and medical care programs, efforts must be made to give every person access to good medical and hospital care, no matter where he lives and regardless of his ability to pay. Studying the ever-increasing problems related to the non-scientific side of medicine are the councils and committees in the Legal and Socio-Economic Division. For example, committees of the Council on Medical Service probe questions in the following areas and develop recommended action programs.

Insurance and prepayment plans: aiming at wider coverage for all age groups.

Hospital construction: studies of legislation and new trends in hospital construction, with an eye toward the most efficient types of construction and financing.

Nursing homes: development of standards of construction of nursing homes to assure safe care for patients.

Indian and veterans medical care programs: making sure such population groups get top-notch care.

Indigent care: continuing study of existing and recommended programs for providing care for people who cannot pay their own medical bills.

Medical care for the aged: plans to assure good medical care for older people.

Maternal and child care: studies of ways to reduce maternal and neonatal deaths even further.

These are just a few of the areas in which this Council functions. Gathering and disseminating information on economic trends related to medicine is the job of AMA's Economic Research Department.

Medicolegal problems related to modern medicine are handled by the Legal Medicine Department. The Legal Medicine Department, for example, works actively in the application of medicine to crime detection. It has worked on a series of tests—chemical tests—for intoxication. Currently it is encouraging states to adopt a model AMA law requiring that coroners be physicians.

The physician who needs general information on a variety of legal questions can turn to the Committee on Medicolegal Problems and the Legal Medicine Department for assistance.

Carrying out one of the original purposes of AMA is the Department of Investigation, which wages constant war on medical quackery, serving as a source of information to government agencies and others to help bring quacks to justice. This department maintains one of the largest collections of nostrums and quack gadgets and medicines in the United States and helps educate the public about the dangers of quackery.

Communicating with Doctors and Public

With so vast an array of information to carry to physicians and to the public, AMA relies upon every medium of communication. In addition to its periodicals, hundreds of pamphlets, reports, and books on medical and related subjects are turned out each year. Some are beamed to the medical profession; others, such as "Your Family Health Record" and "Buyer's Guide to Health Insurance," are written for the public.

Many of these pamphlets, as well as other information, are provided by AMA through its Department of Health Education. This department also answers between 12,000 and 15,000 personal letters on health subjects each year.

Radio and television are used extensively to convey health information. Five-minute radio spots on historical medicine are part of the "Medical Milestones" series prepared by AMA. Television programs, often emanating directly from AMA's annual and clinical meetings, report on scientific achievements and medical affairs. Public service television shows carry AMA-produced films on health topics, medical careers or medicine in general.

Films are a widely used means of getting a message across, whether it be a scientific one for doctors or an educational one for the public on a health subject.

Making sure that newspapers and magazines carry accurate information on medicine are staff members of the Communications Division. Their services are also offered to radio and television producers, writers and editors of all types who want to produce accurate reports on medicine.

Exhibits, too, are developed to communicate with people. Exciting displays, such as AMA's "Transparent Twins," depicting the workings of the human body, are attracting nationwide attention.

Legislation

The American Medical Association works diligently to push passage of bills introduced in Congress which would provide proper solutions to particular health problems. Its interests extend from suggested legislation on reducing air pollution and the labeling of dangerous chemicals to mechanisms for providing medical care. AMA believes it a positive function to lobby on behalf of sound medical bills and to speak up on occasion to oppose medical bills which would lower the quality of American medical care or be incompatible with the free enterprise system.

Congressmen turn to AMA and its Washington office for information on a variety of subjects. AMA officers testify on request before congressional committees considering health legislation. When the Association sincerely believes pending legislation would be dangerous to good medical care, it enlists public support of its legislative position. These things it does on behalf of good medicine and health.

Field Service

One of the most recent divisions is the Field Service Division which was set up by AMA to serve state and county medical societies. Its core of representatives travel about the nation, keeping a sensitive finger on the national pulse, working with medical societies and allied groups to work out problems and develop sound health programs. They bring back to AMA a direct report on the thinking of the doctor and his medical society so that the Association can democratically reflect those views.

Business Division

For efficient operation, financial and record-keeping activities of AMA are integrated into a Business Division. To carry on the multitude of programs outlined only briefly in these pages, a great deal of money is needed. AMA is a non-profit organization. Its annual budget of over $17,000,000 comes from membership dues, sale of advertising in AMA publications, and sale of AMA publications to non-members, as well as sale of exhibit space at meetings. Membership dues contribute about one fifth of the annual income and about three fifths comes from advertising sales. Over 65 per cent of all expenditures are in the realm of scientific medicine.

Medicine Does Not Stand Still

No other field probably experiences such rapid changes as medicine. What is "new" today is outmoded tomorrow. America's major medical organization cannot stand still. Its programs and policies are constantly changing to reflect the times and the needs of the physicians and the public. The goal remains constant: the best medicine and health for America.

AMA is many things to many people. AMA is an employer and a property owner, a writer and publisher, an educator of physicians and the public. But above all, AMA is a servant of its physician-members while it stands firmly as a guardian of the public health.

There are numerous national and international medical organizations which are mostly specialty organizations. These will be found listed from issue to issue in the *Journal of the American Medical Association* under a listing called Meetings. The dates of the meetings and the addresses of the organizations are given in this listing.

THE AMERICAN ACADEMY OF GENERAL PRACTICE

The largest national medical organization is, of course, the American Medical Association, but the second largest is the

American Academy of General Practice. The author was one of the founders of this organization in 1947, served for the first three years as Speaker of its Congress of Delegates and was the fifth president.

It has more than 27,000 members, with chapters in every state. Its official magazine is published monthly and is called *GP*. It is publishing an abridged version of *GP,* called *Family Physician,* which is designed for the 37,000 non-members.

Young medical graduates have tended more and more toward specialization. In 1947 two out of every three active physicians were in general practice or part-time specialties. Today the ratio of GPs to full specialists is closer to 50-50. The Academy is interested in persuading more medical students to become general practitioners. The Academy requires its members to do a specified amount of postgraduate work each year in order to maintain membership in the organization.

The policies of the AAGP are determined by its Congress of Delegates, which is composed of two delegates from each state chapter.

The Academy preaches the concept that the man in the practice of medicine who comes closest to what the people seem to want is the competent general practitioner who can serve as medical counsel to the entire family. The competent general practitioner today can take care of 85 per cent of the illness that occurs and is able to distinguish the 15 per cent which needs to be referred to a competent specialist in a particular field. This service can be rendered to the people in a much more economical way. It is felt that more reliance on the family physician is the soundest approach to bringing down the cost of medical care.

Student American Medical Association

The Student American Medical Association (SAMA) was founded in Chicago in December, 1950, and it soon became the largest medical student organization in the world. Today the Association is composed of more than 60,000 active and affiliate members in 76 medical schools and hundreds of hospitals throughout the United States and its territories.

The Association is an autonomous organization operating independently, and except for the Executive Director and his staff, all officers, delegates and committee members are medical students, interns or residents. SAMA is governed by a House of Delegates, composed of members from component chapters, which meets annually and an Executive Council, elected by the House of Delegates to conduct official business in the interim period.

A full-time Executive Director and staff provide administrative services at the Executive Offices, located at 333 North Michigan Avenue, Chicago 1, Illinois.

The Constitution of the Association clearly defines the reason for its existence:

> The objects of this Association shall be to advance the profession of medicine, to contribute to the welfare and education of medical students, interns and residents, to familiarize its members with the purposes and ideals of organized medicine, and to prepare its members to meet the social, moral and ethical obligations of the profession of medicine.

THE WORLD MEDICAL ASSOCIATION

[This section of Chapter 6 was written by Dr. Louis H. Bauer, Consultant to the World Medical Association.—Ed.]

The World Medical Association came into being on September 10, 1947, in Paris. It is an organization of national medical associations. At present there are 56 such medical associations, comprising among them approximately 700,000 members.

Its aims are: to effect a closer liaison among the doctors of the world, to act as a center of information, to serve as a forum for discussion of international medical problems, to protect the honor and traditions of the medical profession, to act as spokesman for the medical profession before other international bodies, to raise the standards of health, medical care and medical education throughout the world and to improve international relations.

Its governing body is the General Assembly, which meets annually. It consists of the officers, delegates, alternate delegates and observers. The observers come not only from member associations but other national and international bodies. Voting strength is equal; each member association is allowed two voting delegates, regardless of the size of the member association. This provision appeals especially to the smaller associations, as they feel that any proposal is considered purely on its merits and not because of the voting strength of the proposing association.

The executive body is the Council. This consists of the President, the President-elect, the Treasurer and eleven elected members. Associated with the Council are Council committee members and Regional Secretaries (when they are not Council members).

There are the following regions, each having a Regional Secretary: Europe, Asia, North Pacific, Latin America, Australia and Indonesia. North America is handled by the General Secretariat. An African region has just been established but each country in that region reports to the General Secretariat through the Corresponding Secretary.

The Association has liaison with other international organizations, keeps track of their activities and informs them of medical opinion on various topics. The closest liaison is with the World Health Organization and the International Committee of the Red Cross.

The finances of the Association are derived from dues assessed on member associations in accordance with their size and financial status and from donations, mostly from supporting committees. The Association has had to operate on a limited budget but nevertheless has accomplished or is accomplishing numerous projects.

One of its most important activities has been in the field of medical education. WMA has sponsored two world conferences, one on undergraduate, the other on postgraduate medical education. They were both well attended, and publication of the Proceedings of both conferences has added to the medical libraries and schools of the world the only two books on world medical education.

The Association has also taken over the publication of *World Medical Periodicals*. The third edition is now under way. No medical library can do without it.

The *World Medical Journal* is a bimonthly, trilingual publication, giving news of medical events and conditions throughout the world.

In 1948, WMA adopted the Declaration of Geneva—an up-to-date version of the Hippocratic Oath—and in 1949 incorporated it in an International Code of Medical Ethics.

Wars and revolutions have resulted in many doctors losing all their medical credentials; WMA has established a Central Repository for Medical Credentials whose services are open to any doctor.

Much time is devoted to studies and surveys of the socioeconomic conditions affecting medical practice, and the Association has given support to several countries fighting further inroads by government into medical care.

At the present time WMA is working with the Red Cross to obtain international recognition for a new emblem to protect medical personnel and equipment used in civil defense, just as the Red Cross protects those attached to the Armed Forces.

Another project not yet complete is the drafting of an international code governing human experimentation.

One of the most effective actions of WMA has been the welding of the doctors of its member associations into a friendly, forceful unit so that when the Association speaks before other international bodies, it is listened to respectfully as voicing the opinion of the practicing profession.

WORLD HEALTH ORGANIZATION

[The material in this section of Chapter 6 is based on information furnished by Dr. H. van Zile Hyde, United States member, Executive Board, World Health Organization.—Ed.]

Historical Background

Although Europe has been exposed through the centuries to repeated incursions of pestilential disease from the East, it was not possible to inaugurate any rational defense measures until the turn of the century. Such action necessarily awaited a true and general understanding of the etiology and epidemiology of infectious disease.

Under the pressure of repeated waves of cholera, international sanitary conferences were convened intermittently during the latter part of the nineteenth century, starting in Paris in 1851. Attempts were made to reconcile the desire of some to create impenetrable quarantine barriers with the desire of others to keep international commerce moving without interference. Not until 1903 was it possible to develop a sanitary convention or treaty that defined generally acceptable quarantine practices. This was the first of a series of conventions that served as the basis of quarantine practices among signatory nations until 1946 when the whole matter was put on a more orderly and flexible basis by the incorporation of their functions among the other international responsibilities assigned to the World Health Organization.

In 1902 the countries of the Western Hemisphere established an office in Washington to collect and disseminate information on the international movement of epidemics. This became the Pan American Sanitary Bureau, which is now the administrative office of the Pan American Health Organization and serves the World Health Organization as its regional office for the Americas. The next significant step was the creation in Paris of the Office Internationale d'Hygiene Publique in 1907. These early organizations concerned themselves only with exchange of information on the international spread of communicable disease. After World War I the concept and scope of international health were expanded under the Health Organization of the newly created League of Nations. Although the United States, by virtue of its failure to join the League of Nations, was not a member, the Surgeon General of the Public Health Service played an active role as a member of the Council of the Office Internationale d'Hygiene Publique, which doubled as the technical advisory body to the League of Nations. The Rockefeller Foundation contributed substantially to its budget.

The League expanded the underlying concepts of international action in health to include the provision of certain services which could only be provided on an international basis. It developed international standards for biological products and internationally accepted minimal requirements for nutritional elements. Through seminars, conferences and expert committees it assisted in the development and initiation of programs for the control of malaria and the provision of medical services for rural populations. It sent advisory missions to Greece, China and Bolivia on request of these governments. Thus, by the time of World War II, there was a well-established tradition of international activity in the health field. This tradition indeed was so deeply entrenched that the three international health agencies existing at the time of the war continued their activities throughout its duration. The information available in the Office Internationale d'Hygiene Publique was of prime importance to the Allied Forces in reestablishing civil government in Germany. During the course of the war, the United Nations Relief and Rehabilitation Administration (UNRRA) assumed certain of the epidemiologic and quarantine functions of the League of Nations, while the staff of the League in Geneva continued to maintain statistical studies and records. UNRRA also provided technical assistance and supplies to war-devastated areas at the close of hostilities.

As part of the general postwar reorganization, new institutions were developed to carry on international activity on an expanded scale. The charter of the United Nations, which was adopted in San Francisco in 1945, provided for the establishment of "specialized agencies" in certain important fields, including health. These are autonomous agencies, based on their own separate treaties, coordinated in a very general way by the UN Economic and Social Council. The San Francisco Conference also adopted a joint declaration, submitted by the delegations of China and Brazil, calling for an "international conference to consider the scope of, and the appropriate machinery for, international action in the field of public health, and proposal for the establishment of a single international health organization of the United Nations."

In response to this declaration, 61 governments met in New York in June, 1946, in the International Health Conference, which wrote the constitution for the World Health Organization. The Conference also established an 18-nation Interim Commission to administer and develop international health activities, pending the 23 ratifications necessary to bring the WHO constitution into force and create WHO, which occurred in July, 1948. The International Health Conference further adopted a protocol providing for the absorption into WHO of the Office Internationale d'Hygiene Publique, the Health Organization of the League of Nations, and the Health Division of UNRRA. The WHO constitution made provision for the integration of the Pan American Sanitary Bureau as the regional office of WHO for the Americas. Thus a unified international health agency was created.

Objectives

The long-range, idealistic objective of WHO is broadly stated in its constitution as "the attainment by all peoples of the highest possible level of health," and health is defined as "a state of complete physical, mental and social well-being, not merely the absence of disease and infirmity."

The more immediate goals of the Organization are the mobilization of international resources to bring about the world-wide control of preventable disease, the universal development of competent indigenous national and local health services and the expansion and facilitation of medical research.

Structure and Membership

WHO is an intergovernmental agency, of which 105 independent governments are members (1961) and 4 dependent territories are associate members.

Organizationally, it includes the following chief elements: the World Health Assembly, the Executive Board, the Secretariat, Regional Committees and Offices, and Expert Panels and Committees.

THE WORLD HEALTH ASSEMBLY.—The Assembly, which is composed of delegations representing each of the members and associate members, meets annually, usually in Geneva, the site of WHO headquarters. The Assembly is the policy-making and governing body of the Organization. Its functions include the establishment of program priorities, the adoption of the annual program and budget, the adoption of the scale of contributions and the election of the Director-General. Delegations sent to the World Health Assembly are characteristically headed by the Minister or Director-General of Health. The United States delegation, which is appointed by the President and instructed by the Secretary of State, is normally headed by the Surgeon General of the Public Health Service and is broadly representative of the health professions. The delegation usually includes the president of the State and Territorial Health Officers Association, the president or other high official of the American Medical Association, a representative of nursing, sanitary engineering, dentistry and of a major voluntary health organization or private foundation.

THE EXECUTIVE BOARD.—Twenty-four governments are accorded the privilege by the Assembly of designating a health official to sit on the Executive Board, which meets twice annually. The United States member is appointed by the President with the advice and consent of the Senate and has always been an officer of the Public Health Service devoting full time to international health affairs. The Board is responsible for the implementation of the policies adopted by the Assembly. It carries out a detailed review of the proposed annual budget and program, making appropriate recommendations to the Assembly. It appoints the Regional Directors. It is also empowered to take emergency action on behalf of the Assembly.

THE SECRETARIAT.—The Secretariat is organized and appointed by the Director-General, who is the chief technical and administrative officer of the Organization. The Secretariat is composed of the professional, technical and administrative personnel required to direct the programs adopted by the Assembly. Exclusive of field personnel, it consists of some 1,000 persons of 64 nationalities, stationed at the headquarters in Geneva and at the six regional offices. The Directors-General have been nationals of Canada and Brazil, while the Deputy and Assistant Directors-General have been nationals of France, the United States, El Salvador, the Union of South Africa, the Soviet Union, and the United Kingdom.

THE REGIONAL COMMITTEES AND OFFICES.—WHO has a regional structure that is unique within world organizations. In each of six regions there is an intergovernmental committee composed of the WHO members and associate members of that region. There is also a Regional Office. These regions and the sites of their headquarters are: the Americas (Washington), Europe (Copenhagen), Africa (Brazzaville), the Eastern Mediterranean (Alexandria), Southeast Asia (New Delhi), and the Western Pacific (Manila). The Regional Committee meets annually to develop the program and budget for the ensuing year in the region and countries concerned, prior to its review by the Executive Board. It is also consulted by the Executive Board in regard to the selection and appointment of the Regional Director, who heads the office and directs the program in his region. The Regional Directors who have served thus far have been from the United States, Chile, Belgium, Egypt, the Netherlands, Portugal, India, Iran and China.

In the Americas the regional organization consists of the Pan American Health Organization which is composed of a Directing Council (the Regional Committee) and the Pan American Sanitary Bureau (the Regional Office). The PAHO has its own program—regionally financed—in addition to that which it carries out on behalf of WHO.

EXPERT PANELS AND COMMITTEES.—In some 38 technical fields WHO has set up panels of experts appointed from all parts of the world on the basis of their professional qualifications. The members of the Panels are consulted by correspondence and the Panels serve as the rosters from which Expert Committees are convened from time to time to advise on broad areas of activity or deal with special technical problems. Over 200 Expert Committee reports have been published, dealing with a wide range of subjects.

Program Activities

WHO activities fall into three major categories: assistance to governments, development and maintenance of central technical services, and the stimulation and support of research.

ASSISTANCE TO GOVERNMENTS.—WHO provides governments with expert consultants and visiting teachers, arranges international seminars and conferences, and conducts demonstrations of various types of health service. The Organization participates annually in some 600 projects, carried out by some 125 countries and territories. It awards approximately 1,000 fellowships annually for out-of-country study.

Prevention of communicable diseases constitutes a continuing heavy burden, particularly in the underdeveloped areas of the world. WHO presently assists annually some 250 projects directed at the control of malaria, the treponematoses, tuberculosis, trachoma, smallpox, leprosy and bilharziasis. Typical of such assistance are projects through which in 1961 WHO provided: to Burma, an epidemiologist, supplies and equipment to assist in setting up an epidemiological unit to determine the prevailing pattern of communicable diseases and plan appropriate control measures; to Morocco, an ophthalmologist and other consultants to assist in the control of conjunctivitis and trachoma through a program that provided treatment to 1,300,000 persons; to Paraguay, a leprologist to conduct an epidemiologic study and advise on the establishment of a leprosy control program; and, to Basutoland, two medical officers and public health nurses to assist in setting up a comprehensive national tuberculosis control program based on case-finding, contact-tracing and mass chemotherapy.

WHO's largest single program in the field of communicable disease is the world-wide malaria eradication campaign initiated in 1955. By 1961, seventeen countries or territories had eradicated malaria, 61 were conducting national eradication campaigns, and 20 others were preparing to embark on such campaigns. WHO carries out the central planning, maintains continuous evaluation, coordinates assistance provided by all governments and international agencies, conducts international conferences and training courses and supports research that is required in order to meet special problems encountered by the program, such as insect resistance, unusual cultural patterns and physical conditions.

WHO assists countries in strengthening national and local health services. Particular emphasis is given to maternal and child health, public health administration, environmental sanitation, mental health, nursing, nutrition, health education of the public, occupational health and, recently, radiation health.

CENTRAL TECHNICAL SERVICES.—WHO has developed a variety of central technical services which by their nature are of benefit to all governments. It organizes and supports international reference centers in established national laboratories to maintain agreed international standards and to facilitate research. Certain of these centers prepare, maintain and disseminate standard biological materials; others collect, exchange and study strains of organisms, such as the salmonella, shigella and escherichia, as well as poliomyelitis, influenza and other viruses. It supports an International Blood Group Reference Laboratory in London which provides typing services and maintains standard sera of all known blood types. It has organized networks of cooperating laboratories throughout the world which identify and follow the spread of influenza viruses, reporting centrally to London.

The International Pharmacopoeia, prepared by WHO, is widely used by Member Governments as the guide in developing national pharmacopoeias. WHO makes recommendations to governments concerning generic names for drugs, with a view to these names being kept in the public domain. By 1961, 640 names had been recommended and had been accepted by many countries, including the United States, as the generic names for the drugs concerned.

WHO has prepared and published the *International Statistical Classification of Diseases, Injuries, and Causes of Death,* which is widely used as the basis for mortality and morbidity statistics.

International Sanitary Regulations were adopted by the World Health Assembly in 1952 to govern national action in quarantine against smallpox, cholera, plague, yellow fever, typhus and relapsing fever. WHO broadcasts daily reports from Geneva and from a number of sub-centers on the current incidence of these diseases.

In addition to its official records WHO publishes the following.

The Bulletin of the World Health Organization, published monthly, contains original technical articles on subjects of international significance.

The Technical Report Series consists of the reports of Expert Committees.

Monographs each cover a specific health problem, such as poliomyelitis, cholera, plague, air pollution, water supply for rural areas and small communities, biology of the treponematoses, laboratory techniques in rabies and chemotherapy of malaria.

The Chronicle, published monthly, contains information on WHO's principal activities as well as summary reports of organizational meetings and of expert committee deliberations.

The Epidemiological and Vital Statistics Report, published monthly, contains statistics on births and deaths, incidence of notifiable disease and other epidemiologic and demographic information.

The International Digest of Health Legislation, published monthly, summarizes recent legislation of significance in a particular field, such as nursing, communicable diseases in schools, mental health, tuberculosis, etc.

Public Health Papers presents the ideas, observations and suggestions of individual specialists or special technical groups. Some of the subjects dealt with in this series have been psychiatric services and architecture, epidemiological methods in the study of mental disorders, health services in the USSR, aspects of public health nursing, ionizing radiation and health and the role of immunization in communicable disease control.

In addition to these publications, the Organization issues a number of special publications and official records. Among these are: *The First Ten Years of the World Health Organization,* a book issued in 1958 on the tenth anniversary of WHO; the *World Directory of Medical Schools; Medical Education; Annotated Bibliography,* (1945-1955); *World Directory of*

Dental Schools; and *The First Report on the World Health Situation* (1954-1956). The latter is a review of health conditions and services based on reports by national health services of 157 countries and territories. *The Second Report on the World Health Situation* will be published by WHO in 1962, and a *World Directory of Veterinary Schools* is in preparation.

Certain of the Organization's official records are of general use, particularly the annual reports of the Director-General and the reports of the World Health Assemblies.

MEDICAL RESEARCH.—WHO provides coordination, stimulation and support of international medical research, with special emphasis on research in communicable diseases, cancer, cardiovascular diseases, radiation medicine and human genetics. WHO's role is to provide research services such as standardization of nomenclature and techniques, maintenance of international reference centers, and provision of training for potential research scientists.

The Twelfth World Health Assembly in 1959 established an Advisory Committee on Medical Research which examines research proposals as to their suitability for WHO support and sets priorities for those which merit the Organization's support. WHO also seeks advice on research questions from outstanding scientists throughout the world who serve on its expert advisory panels. Examples of assistance in medical research include provision of consultants to advise on the BCG assay and a study of animal tuberculosis in relation to human disease, provision of technical services for assistance to research on the ecology of rabies and brucellosis, provision of consultants to advise on research in physical rehabilitation of leprosy patients and the chemotherapy and prevention of leprosy, and the provision of consultant service on the development of international reference centers for histopathology.

HARRY P. SMITH, M.D.

Dr. Smith is Professor Emeritus of Pathology, Columbia University. He now serves as Research Librarian of the American Society of Clinical Pathologists, an organization of which he was previously a President. He is also a Past President of the American Society for Experimental Pathology. He served for six years as a member of the Board of Governors of the College of American Pathologists, and was Secretary-Treasurer of that organization for two years. Dr. Smith is currently a member of the American Medical Association's Commission to Coordinate the Relationships of Medicine with Allied Health Professions and Services.

7. Paramedical Fields

THIS CHAPTER was designed to provide the reader with a brief survey of American health professions and services other than those performed by physicians themselves. There are many groups which collaborate with physicians in serving the needs of patients, and a much smaller number whose members practice independently. Independent practice, however, is a matter of degree. Dentists are independent in most respects. They have scientific training and are in the somewhat unique position of being engaged in practicing a clinical specialty without having prior training in other clinical specialties. Dentists have friendly relations with physicians; more and more they are being brought into close working relations with them. Pharmacy is an independent profession which serves physicians and their patients on the basis of written prescriptions.

In a different category entirely are the cults. They base their practice on dogma, not on scientific evidence. There are no ties between them and the medical profession. Optometrists are likewise independent in their practice, but they employ well-established principles of physics in fitting glasses. They are, however, not broadly trained in regard to diseases of the eye.

Many other paramedical groups do have close ties with the medical profession and are committed to close collaboration and teamwork. These categories include the nurses, medical technologists and x-ray technologists, for example. Their activities are largely technical, but the workers in question are coming more and more to assume responsibilities which require extensive scientific training and intimate familiarity with the methods and objectives of physicians. They are sometimes referred to as supporting technological groups, sometimes as "allied health professions."

Several of the allied professions will be analyzed in the sections which follow. They were selected from among many others because they illustrate certain principles involved in the delegation of responsibilities to non-physician workers. These principles will be summarized and discussed in a special section concerned with the coordination of activities so delegated.

VARIOUS PARAMEDICAL FIELDS

Nursing

Organized nursing existed in olden times, but usually in relation to leprosaria and pest houses or in relation to the infirmaries of almshouses. The care was largely custodial, and the nursing personnel was made up of members of ecclesiastical orders, of attendants recruited from the almshouses themselves, or from the lower servant classes of the communities. In any case, technical training was minimal, and was largely if not entirely secured on the job. Wealthy patients shunned the hospitals, for they preferred to be treated in their own homes.

Trends in nursing are closely dependent on trends in medical science and medical practice. The germ theory of disease, for example, was a concept of the very greatest importance in the organization of medical services. It formed the foundation of modern sanitation, both in hospitals and outside them. Along with the art and science of anesthesia, it formed the foundation of antiseptic surgery, of the modern operating room, of the modern hospital and of the nursing services related to them. The upper and middle classes now come to the hospitals in ever-increasing numbers for specialized types of diagnosis and therapy. Modern hygiene and sanitation likewise provided the scientific basis for the work of the public health nurse and the school nurse.

The new type of medical care requires special training for nurses who are to serve as leaders in public health nursing and in the modern hospital. This need was anticipated at the middle of the last century by Florence Nightingale, even before the germ theory had been established. She set new standards in nursing practice and initiated formal programs for the training of nurses. She was responsible for many of the modern traditions of nursing, and she has been the inspiration of nurses for over a century. The nurses who follow the Nightingale tradition are known as professional nurses, even though Miss Nightingale herself was opposed to the use of the term, on the ground that nursing is a calling, not a profession.

It may have been thought at the turn of the century that the professional nurse would eventually replace the non-professional variety altogether. Such has not been the case. By 1920, however, the professional group in the United States, with a membership of 150,000, had become as large as the non-professional group. From then on, both have increased rapidly, the non-professional slightly more rapidly than the professional. At present, approximately 500,000 professional nurses are actively engaged in nursing, 90% of them on a full-time basis. Each year, a new class of nearly 30,000 is trained. In contrast, the non-professional group now numbers somewhat over 600,000. It includes nearly 250,000 of a new category characterized by the fact that it, too, is now receiving formal training. This is the group known as practical nurses. It is growing more and more rapidly, currently at a rate of approximately 20,000 a year. Federal funds, supplemented by state funds, are being used to subsidize the educational programs for practical nurses. Governmental funds also provide fellowships and scholarships for graduate study by professional nurses.

The two types of "trained" nurse—the professional and the practical—are now subject to licensing laws in all of the 50 states of the Union, and likewise in the District of Columbia, Puerto Rico and the Virgin Islands. The professional nurses initiated their own campaign for licensure 60 years ago. Within two decades the campaign was largely won.

In recent years, the professional nurses have also supported the licensure of practical nurses. Changes in legislation are being made each year, but the professional nurses (12) support the thesis that "all persons who, for compensation, are engaged in the practice of nursing as defined in the law should be licensed."

Obviously, the stratification of trained nurses into two main categories involves jurisdictional problems. The matter is in a state of flux, but current policy of the professional nurses is set down in a pronouncement of the American Nurses' Association in 1955. It states, among other things (13):

1. The practice of professional nursing means the performance for compensation of any act in the observation, care, and counsel of the ill, injured, or infirm, or in the maintenance of health or prevention of illness of others, or in the supervision and teaching

of other personnel, or the administration of medications and treatments as prescribed by a licensed physician or dentist; requiring substantial specialized judgment and skill and based on knowledge and application of the principles of biological, physical and social science. The foregoing shall not be deemed to include acts of diagnosis or prescription of therapeutic or corrective measures.

2. The practice of practical nursing means the performance for compensation of selected acts in the care of the ill, injured, or infirm under the direction of a registered professional nurse or a licensed physician or a licensed dentist; and not requiring the substantial specialized skill, judgment, and knowledge required in professional nursing.

Perusal of the statutes of various states shows reasonably good conformity with the foregoing principles. However, there is less unanimity regarding methods of implementing the law. The Board of Directors of the American Nurses' Association (12) recommended:

There should be one nursing practice act in a state with provisions for licensing the practitioners of nursing.

There should be one licensing board for nursing in a state composed of licensed registered nurses qualified to carry out the functions of the board as provided in the law.

Exceptions to, or waiver of, certain requirements for licensure should be provided for a limited period of time when new licensure requirements are first made effective or when they are made mandatory. However, all candidates for whom these requirements are waived should be required to demonstrate competence by passing an examination before a license is granted.

In some of the states, the examining boards, both for professional and practical nursing, are made up exclusively of professional nurses, as recommended by the American Nurses' Association. In other states, however, the nurses share the responsibility with physicians, hospital administrators or practical nurses. In some cases, the law makes provision for advisory committees which include members of such categories. Obviously, the legislators are prone to spread the responsibility among several groups whenever convincing arguments are brought forward.

Licensure by the states is one of two main types. The first —true licensure—defines the field of professional practice and prohibits its practice by unlicensed individuals. We shall refer to this as a "mandatory" type of licensure, since that is the phrase commonly employed by nurses and technologists. The second type—a type commonly referred to by lawyers as state certification—is referred to by nurses and technologists as a "permissive" type of licensure. It does not define professional practice, nor does it prohibit its practice by unlicensed individuals. It merely confers upon the licensed individual the exclusive privilege of using certain designated titles such as "nurse," "registered nurse," "R.N.," "medical technologist," "clinical psychologist," etc.

Licensure by the states, both mandatory and permissive, is based in part upon examination of the candidate and in part upon educational attainment. The examinations for professional nurses are prepared by the National League for Nursing, but each state sets its own passing grade. Those individuals who wish to take the examination for professional nursing must have had high school education in almost all jurisdictions, followed by graduation from a school of nursing approved by the state. A total of 1,123 state-approved schools now exist. As stated already, they supply nearly 30,000 graduates annually. They are of three general types: (1) the diploma schools, with 3-year curricula. Of this type, 856 were owned and operated by hospitals as of 1960, and 35 were owned and operated by independent non-collegiate organizations having affiliations with hospitals, and designed exclusively for the training of nurses. The two types of diploma school graduated approximately 26,000 professional nurses in the year in question; (2) the schools operating associate degree programs, 42 in number, came into existence almost entirely within the past decade. They are operated by junior colleges, each having an affiliation with one or more hospitals. They graduate approximately 500 professional nurses a year. The programs are typically of two years' duration, with less hospital experience than in the diploma programs, but with more theoretical training; and (3) a second collegiate type of school, known as the university or senior collegiate type, operates a 4-year program leading to a baccalaureate degree. Emphasis is placed on broad training in arts and sciences, including physical, biological, psychological and sociological sciences. As in the associate degree programs, the amount of practical nursing experience is less than in the diploma programs. In some of the programs, "service" to the hospital is largely eliminated, and the students use the hospital for case studies of various types, typically in association with conferences and seminars. These baccalaureate programs, 190 in number, graduate a little over 4,000 professional nurses a year.

Statistics indicate (14) that the graduates of baccalaureate programs achieve higher scores on state board examinations than do individuals trained in the diploma program. The scores of those trained in associate degree programs are intermediate.

To the casual observer, it may seem strange that three distinct types of school, so different in educational standards, should exist side by side, each with the avowed purpose of providing basic professional education for nurses. But the reasons for this are to be found in history. The early programs, organized 60-80 years ago, were exclusively of the diploma type. They were designed to provide large numbers of nurses for private duty and for bedside nursing. As time went on, however, the evolution of medical practice made it necessary that nurses assume new responsibilities, both technical and administrative. Many of the graduate nurses entered into specialized forms of practice, i.e., as operating room nurses, psychiatric nurses and as public health nurses. Leaders of the nursing profession made the point repeatedly that the basic training, based on high school education, was not adequate for those who wished later on to specialize, nor was it adequate for those who wished eventually to become teachers or administrators. They insisted that the basic education should include collegiate education in the arts and sciences, especially in sociology and psychology. They succeeded over the past 60 years in securing the cooperation of an ever-increasing number of colleges and universities in setting up baccalaureate programs for nurses. Nevertheless, the diploma programs continued to supply nearly 90% of the professional nurses. Even so, it was generally agreed that a shortage of nurses has existed, up to the present day. More and more, the nurses have been drawn away from general bedside nursing into administration and into specialty nursing. It became increasingly evident that two distinct categories of trained nurse were needed, the professional nurse and the practical nurse. This became especially evident during World War II and during the years which followed. Federal funds were made available for advanced collegiate training of professional nurses. At present, approximately 2,500 graduate nurses are securing baccalaureate degrees each year, through deferred collegiate training. This is in addition to the 4,000 who are receiving such degrees in connection with their basic professional training in college-sponsored programs. An additional 1,200 are receiving master's degrees each year (7).

Progress in the training of practical nurses has been even more dramatic. Federal funds, supplemented with funds supplied at state and local levels, have permitted the establishment of numerous training programs for practical nurses. The practical nurses are taking over many of the routines of bedside nursing and are becoming extensively involved in providing certain types of private duty nursing, especially that related to chronic invalidism.

Serious questions are now being debated concerning the

future of the diploma schools for professional nurses. The attitude of the American Nurses' Association is clearly indicated by "Guide III" recently adopted. It states (20):

> To insure that, within the next 20-30 years, the education basic to the practice of nursing at the professional level, for those who then enter the profession, shall be secured in a program that provides the intellectual, technical and cultural components of both a professional and liberal education. Toward this end, the ANA shall promote the baccalaureate program so that in due course it becomes the basic educational foundation for professional nursing.

This implies a gradual abandonment of diploma programs for professional nurses. Indeed, the number being graduated from the diploma schools seems to be falling well below the earlier level of 30,000 a year. The collegiate programs for professional nurses have grown to the present level of 4,000. The training of practical nurses has also grown very rapidly, to the present level of about 20,000 a year. These two programs, the collegiate and the practical, may eventually usurp the field, except for the on-the-job training of nursing aides, orderlies, maids, ward clerks and other types of subsidiary workers. The basic dichotomy between collegiate and practical nurses, if it comes into full being, will render obsolete much of the earlier debate concerning policies of the diploma schools and the efforts to regulate them through programs of accreditation. In contrast, the matter of accreditation of schools of practical nursing is being debated. It may very well be a major problem of the future. In any case, the existence of two categories of trained nurse, the professional and the practical, is already a fact. It poses administrative problems which will be discussed in the section on the coordination of health services.

X-ray Technology

X-ray technicians comprise one of the largest of the technological groups in the health field. Data recently published by the U. S. Bureau of Labor Statistics (2) give a total count somewhat in excess of 60,000. According to the same source, approximately 15,000 of these are employed in hospitals. The latter figure may be even too low, for data published by the American Hospital Association (4) showed that the number employed by hospitals in 1958 was already somewhat in excess of that figure. The large number employed outside hospitals is not surprising when one reflects on the widespread use of x-rays in clinics, private offices and in screening programs for tuberculosis and cancer.

The evolution of radiology had its early beginnings shortly after the discovery of x-rays by Roentgen in the latter part of 1895. The importance of x-rays was recognized at once by forward-looking members of the medical profession. Within 15 years, x-ray equipment had come into widespread use, both in diagnosis and in therapy. At first, it had been thought by some that diagnostic radiology would be merely another branch of photography, and could be practiced successfully by laymen. It was soon found, however, that the practitioner must be a physician, for the practice of radiology requires extensive knowledge of anatomical structure and of disease mechanisms, in addition to the purely technical procedures involved. Moreover, the equipment was destined to become more complex and expensive. Use of the barium test meal, the angiogram and the fluoroscope requires medical experience and judgment. The same is true of the elaborate procedures now being employed in radiotherapy. For these reasons, the centralization of facilities has become essential and has progressed steadily over the past 50 years. Many physicians, and virtually all dentists, still have small diagnostic machines for use in their office practice, but they are used for limited purposes only.

The centralization of equipment has taken place in the offices of radiologists, in hospitals and clinics. The volume of work has grown so rapidly that technicians who assist physicians have come to outnumber the specialists in radiology in the ratio of five or ten to one, depending on location and type of practice.

The technicians who assist the physicians in the operation of x-ray departments are now recognized at their true worth as skilled members of the team of which the physician is the leader. This collaboration of skilled radiologists and technologists has been made possible by the development of training programs for radiologists and for x-ray technicians. The training of radiologists, like the training of other physician specialists, is being carried out in residency programs approved by the American Medical Association. The medical profession welcomed the creation of new x-ray facilities and the training of the physician specialists needed to operate them. Indeed, the American College of Surgeons insisted, over 40 years ago, that x-ray services be provided in hospitals if they were to meet the standards of their new program of hospital accreditation.

Standardization of the training of x-ray technicians at a high level has posed a problem which is more difficult in some respects. The creation of skilled technicians, committed to the principle of teamwork with radiologists, threatened the demise of the lay practitioners of the old order. Nevertheless, the Radiological Society of North America called related organizations into consultation and made a beginning. In 1922, their leaders instituted a program whereby x-ray technicians who had received adequate training could be certified by examination. Those who qualified pledged themselves to a code of ethics which, among other things, forbade independent practice. At about the same time, a group of well-trained technicians organized the national society now known as the American Society of X-ray Technicians.

The creation of a Registry by the Radiological Society of North America did not at once insure the establishment of standards for schools for x-ray technicians. As late as 1932, a radiologist stated that training standards were "chaotic."

The U. S. Army had instituted a training program for x-ray technicians during World War I, but commercial schools continued for a time to be virtually the only schools to provide for the training of civilian technicians. Some of the graduates of these schools opened offices and entered upon careers of independent practice. For that reason, many radiologists of that day were skeptical of registration, of formal training and of national organizations of x-ray technicians; they preferred on-the-job training. Evolution, however, required standardized training at a high level. Eventually, the American Society of X-ray Technicians and the Registry agreed on a program whereby the Registry would give its approval to schools which met certain minimal standards. When the Registry was reorganized and incorporated in 1937, 20 such schools had been approved. All of them were operated in hospitals or clinics by qualified radiologists. In 1943, the Registry was reorganized under joint sponsorship of the American College of Radiology and the American Society of X-ray Technicians. In the same year, the Council on Medical Education and Hospitals of the American Medical Association accepted an invitation to operate the program of accrediting the schools for x-ray technicians, with the College and the Registry as advisors. Minimum prerequisites for entry into the approved schools are still based on high school education, but the standards of professional education have gradually risen over the years, from a minimum of one year of professional training to the current level of two years under a radiologist. The number of approved schools rose from 310 schools in 1952, with approximately 1,150 graduates, to the 650 schools and 2,300 graduates in 1962. It seems unlikely that the 2-year requirement for AMA-approved schools, effective in 1962, will reduce the number graduating each year, for most of the schools had already adopted the 2-year program some years earlier. A few have specified collegiate training.

It is said that over 90% of those who graduate from AMA-approved schools of x-ray technology achieve certification by the Registry. In addition, the Registry certifies some who are trained through apprenticeship by recognized radiologists. The percentage so certified was quite high in the years prior to 1940, but is now only about 30% of those being certified. The failure rate of those informally trained is over twice that of those trained in AMA-approved schools.

It has been suggested that eventually registration will be limited to graduates of approved schools. The experience of other groups indicates, however, that undue rigidity along these lines may do injustice to other well-trained individuals, and may create estrangement and schism within the group.

The growth of x-ray technology since 1922 has been a credit to all concerned. The registered technicians are still a minority of the total, but the group is growing rapidly and is setting standards for the entire group. The early concern that registration and national organization of the technicians would create undue independence has not materialized. It is true that establishments operated independently by technicians still exist, but a survey made several years ago showed that none of these was operated by registered technicians. Officers of the American Society of X-ray Technicians have sought to foster cooperation and teamwork with radiologists, all in the interest of good medical practice. This has been achieved by voluntary means, with a minimum agitation for state licensure of x-ray technicians.

In concluding this section, note should be made of the fact that individuals trained primarily in physics have been employed in various programs dealing with the biological aspects of ionizing radiation. The U. S. Department of Labor estimates (2) that more than 700 health physicists (radiological physicists) are employed in connection with atomic energy installations and in connection with the shipment of materials and the disposal of radioactive waste. They are assisted by non-professional workers known as radiation monitors.

Certain large medical departments of radiology also employ physicists. These physicists assist physician specialists in radiology in the installation, maintenance and operation of the elaborate equipment now being used in the treatment of patients with ionizing radiation. They are especially helpful in localization and control of dosage desired by the radiologist. For somewhat over 10 years, the American Board of Radiology has operated a program for the examination and certification of physicists, on the basis of collegiate training at the M.S. or Ph.D. level plus a specified amount of training in biology and a specified amount of experience in an approved department of radiology. Thus far, 63 individuals have been certified in radiological physics, 14 in roentgen ray and gamma ray physics and 5 in medical nuclear physics (23).

Medical Technology

Medical laboratories serve a wide variety of purposes; their design and their organization vary accordingly. Service laboratories provide diagnostic and therapeutic services to patients; research laboratories, on the other hand, serve as an aid in solving problems of theory and technique. Admittedly, there is some overlap between the two types, but in the research laboratory the objectives are usually of a specialized nature and are pursued in depth, often over long periods of time. The ultimate costs are unpredictable. The service laboratory, in contrast, is organized in breadth, so as to provide a wide variety of services on a day-by-day basis, and to do so both quickly and economically.

The type of personnel in the research laboratory tends to differ from that in the service laboratory. In the basic science departments of the medical schools of the United States, a major portion of the research activity is carried out by Ph.D. scientists, usually in their individual research laboratories, of which a given department may have several. Much of the technical work is performed by the investigators themselves, or by their graduate students. In recent years, however, these investigators have employed technicians in ever-increasing numbers. Some of the technicians have had collegiate training in physics, chemistry or microbiology, but others—the laboratory assistants or laboratory aides—have lesser education and are assigned to perform specialized tasks of a limited nature, all the way from feeding animals to the operation of centrifuges, sterilizers and other types of equipment. The research laboratories of clinical departments also employ technicians and technical assistants of diversified educational backgrounds. As a rule, the research technician is trained individually, on the job, to perform the specific tasks in question, usually by the investigator under whom he serves. Rather rarely have research technicians had systematic training in schools of medical technology.

Service laboratories, organized in breadth, are often quite large, with divisions of clinical chemistry, clinical microbiology, hematology, anatomic pathology, etc. Their activities are closely related to the diversified activities of clinicians who need the assistance of the laboratory. The director and the assistant directors should be physicians, trained in disease mechanisms and in the practice of laboratory medicine. By virtue of such training they are able to assist the clinicians in recognizing and in utilizing the full combined potentialities of the various divisions of the laboratory. A finding in the microbiology division or in the chemical laboratory may call for prompt studies in serology or hematology, often on the same specimen. The physician specialist, properly trained in laboratory medicine, recognizes these opportunities; he consults his clinical colleagues and acts accordingly. The clinicians, in turn, call on him when occasion arises.

The service laboratory, with its emphasis on breadth, needs technologists who have been trained to perform a wide variety of procedures. As will be noted later, a laboratory in a large hospital may also use the services of technologists who have had intensive training in limited fields such as microbiology or clinical chemistry. All laboratories need a number of laboratory assistants or laboratory aides of lesser training, in order to clean glassware, to serve as messengers and to perform some of the simpler routine tests. In most laboratories, however, the basic strength of the technical staff resides in a large core of generalists, trained in one or more of the 776 schools of medical technology approved by the AMA Council on Medical Education and Hospitals. The education of such technologists includes training in hematology, clinical chemistry, clinical microbiology and tissue technique. The technologists thus trained have a grasp of the over-all functions of a laboratory organized in breadth, and are motivated to work toward common objectives. They can work across divisional lines when peak loads occur in one or another of the divisions. They can take turns in being on duty during the evening hours and on week ends and holidays; after all, a 40-hour week is only 25% of the total week, and patients may need laboratory services at any time. The laboratory of a small hospital will be expected to have a technologist on call at night and on week ends and holidays. The laboratory of a large hospital may operate a reduced shift of technical workers as late as midnight, and have one or more technologists on call after midnight. The evening shift completes the work initiated in the late afternoon hours and, like the midnight shift, performs new work of an emergency nature. These emergency procedures should be available at any time, and should include such things as blood sugar determinations, blood cultures and the arrangement for the services of the blood bank. The emergency procedures represent the irreducible minimum to which the variety of services can be curtailed during off-hours.

It is essential that the technologists who work at night or on week ends and holidays have broad training, as generalists, even though they may have eventually secured additional training in specialized fields. The generalist, on night duty, like the night-duty nurse, has a grasp of the over-all situation and, by virtue of experience and judgment, is able to meet routine demands and to know when to summon the physician director or one of his associates.

The technologists trained in breadth are the ones from whom most of the supervisory personnel are recruited. The head technologist of a service laboratory corresponds in many respects to the head nurse or the nurse supervisor. She looks after administrative detail, including work assignments and quality control, and is directly responsible to the physician director. She is constantly on the alert for matters which need the immediate personal attention of the latter. She is the one who integrates the work of technician specialists and technician generalists.

Specialization among technological workers does not conform to any set pattern. Nor are there any reliable statistics concerning the number of each type of technological specialist in the United States. Probably the largest segment of specialists is composed of generalists who develop special competence in one or another of the divisions of the field, either because of background training or because of special interest. The technologist now being trained as a generalist in an AMA-approved school has had a minimum of 3 years of preprofessional collegiate training which includes course-work in physics, chemistry and general biology. With this background, and with additional training as a technological generalist, she is in an ideal position to specialize in clinical chemistry, microbiology, serology, hematology or blood banking. Having been trained first as a generalist, she can continue, when necessary, to take night calls and to assist with peak loads in other divisions of the laboratory. Thus it is that good teamwork can be maintained throughout the entire technological staff—teamwork based on a community of training, of philosophy and of interest.

Another source of technical specialists is to be found in the academic centers. A few of the departments of biochemistry and microbiology of medical schools train technician specialists at the baccalaureate level, but most of them concentrate instead on the training of teachers and investigators at the Ph.D. level. Schools of agriculture support departments of biochemistry and microbiology, and the same is true of some colleges of arts and sciences. Many of their graduates secure employment with industry or as technicians in research laboratories associated with universities or governmental agencies. Some find their way into laboratories of clinical pathology. It is found, in most cases, that they are familiar with basic theory, but not with the procedures actually employed in such laboratories. They acquire this familiarity on the job, usually in a rather restricted field. These restrictions serve to set them apart from the technologists trained primarily as generalists. Furthermore, their lack of familiarity with emergency procedures outside their own restricted field makes it undesirable for them to take turns being on call at night and on week ends and holidays. This places an additional burden on the generalists, and tends to aggravate an element of estrangement. Experience indicates that good morale and good teamwork are most readily achieved when specialization, if any, is based on a broad foundation of professional tradition and training. This principle is similar to the one whereby specialization among nurses and physicians is based on broad foundations of professional training. Specialization, carried out in the absence of such a foundation, leads to undue fragmentation of effort and to a disruption of teamwork.

This section would not be complete without brief reference to accreditation of training programs in laboratory technology and to certification and licensure of individual workers in the field. Reference should be made first of all to the Council on Medical Education and Hospitals of the American Medical Association and its program of accreditation of schools of medical technology. That program was initiated, independently of AMA, in 1933, by the American Society of Clinical Pathologists. It was transferred to AMA in 1936, and is operated by the AMA Council on Medical Education and Hospitals. The Board of Schools of the American Society of Clinical Pathologists serves in an advisory capacity to the Council.

The Board of Registry of the American Society of Clinical Pathologists examines and certifies those graduates of AMA-approved schools who apply for certification. Thus far, slightly more than 42,000 have been certified, and this is thought to be approximately 90% of all graduates of AMA-approved schools. Of those certified during the past 30 years, approximately 32,000 still maintain registration, and about 25,000 are currently working in the field. The latter group comprises about 40% of all technical laboratory workers—a group which includes aides and assistants as well as technologists. A large segment of the certified technologists hold membership in the American Society of Medical Technologists, an organization which has an outstanding record in promoting sound educational and professional standards in the field of medical technology.

AMA-approved schools, 776 in number, are located in approved hospitals and are directed by physician specialists in clinical pathology, and assisted by technologists trained as teaching supervisors. From the very beginning, over 30 years ago, the schools have stressed breadth of training and experience in such fields as clinical chemistry, clinical microbiology, histologic technique and hematology. Programs for the training of cytotechnologists are also based on approval by the AMA Council on Medical Education and Hospitals. The Registry acts in cooperation with the American Association of Blood Banks to certify technological generalists who have received an additional year of special training in blood banking. The Registry also examines and certifies technical specialists in clinical chemistry, clinical microbiology and histologic technique, provided the candidates meet specified standards of education and experience. Several other registries, independently operated, have also certified technological and scientific workers in the laboratory field. One in clinical chemistry and one in microbiology certify specialists in their respective fields, a few at the Ph.D. level, others at the M.S. or B.S. levels.

Voluntary certification of the foregoing types has many advantages over the system of governmental licensure which prevails in certain parts of the United States. The voluntary approach provides standards of training which are adopted, tested and continually revised by experts, on the basis of experience. Governmental licensure, on the other hand, places in charge the governmental official, armed with regulations which tend to become rigid, bureaucratic and a focal point for political pressures. More often than not, licensure gives governmental sanction to the independent practice of laboratory medicine by technicians. The implied sanction of commercial laboratories calls, in turn, for the imposition of additional controls by the governmental agency. Regulations thus adopted commonly specify the qualifications of the director of the laboratory and of the various categories of technical worker. They commonly seek to establish separate categories of technologist, technician and laboratory aide, analogous in many respects to the various categories in the field of nursing. Experience in the field of laboratory medicine indicates that better working harmony, and better standards of performance, are achieved when functions, standards and qualifications are established on a voluntary basis by national organizations of technologists and clinical pathologists, not by governmental edict.

Physical and Occupational Therapy

The use of physical agents in the prevention and treatment of disabilities is properly the joint responsibility of physicians on the one hand and of qualified physical therapy technologists on the other. Massage and hydrotherapy had their early beginnings many centuries ago, sometimes under medical supervision, sometimes not. The more recent advent of equipment to provide ultraviolet light, galvanic current, diathermy and other "modalities" faced the physician with a new set of challenges. They also provided the charlatan with new opportunities to impress and exploit the trusting patient. The AMA Council on Physical Medicine, created in 1925, did much to combat extravagant claims for the new equipment and to promote sound medical leadership in the field in question. It helped in those early years to establish educational standards, thus supplementing similar efforts on the part of the technical workers and the physician specialists most directly involved.

The value of occupational therapy was recognized at an early date in connection with mental hospitals and in connection with hospitals for tuberculosis. In its simplest form it is "diversionary" or morale-building. In its present form, it also plays a vital role in restoring functional competence. A minor craft such as basket weaving can provide essential exercise for the muscles of the hands and forearms. Moreover, any patient with permanent impairment can be taught to make the best possible use of the capabilities which remain, often with the aid of the social worker, the vocational counselor, the speech therapist, the audiometrist and the physical therapist. Thus it is that occupational therapy has spread outward from the mental hospitals into general hospitals, and eventually into the complex rehabilitation centers which have been built in recent years. With each succeeding step, the teamwork of physicians and allied professional workers becomes more complex. Even in the general hospital and in office practice, each of these professional groups has its role. The hospital and the rehabilitation center bring them together into a coordinated team.

The systematic use of physical and occupational therapists, and the development of training programs for them, is largely a development of the past 45 years. Technological workers of both types were trained in limited numbers for service in the military hospitals of World War I. This was a stimulus to the modern developments in civilian life. Orthopedic surgeons were especially active in promoting and supporting the wartime programs. The technological groups themselves organized national societies: the American Occupational Therapy Association in 1917 and the American Physical Therapy Association in 1921. They undertook to develop educational and professional standards for their respective fields. They had the advice and assistance of orthopedic surgeons and of representatives of the new physician specialty now known as physical medicine or physiatry. The national organization of physiatrists, the American Congress of Physical Medicine and Rehabilitation, organized a Registry to examine and certify qualified physical therapists. The American Occupational Therapy Association organized a registry to examine and certify properly qualified occupational therapists.

In the mid-thirties, the accreditation of training programs in the two fields was transferred to the AMA Council on Medical Education and Hospitals. The Council now acts with advice of physician specialists and technologists. It now recognizes 42 schools for physical therapists and 31 schools for occupational therapists. The minimum training for entry into approved schools of physical therapy includes at least 2 years of collegiate training, followed by a minimum of 12 months of professional training. It is said that approximately 50% of current graduates have the baccalaureate degree. Approved schools for occupational therapists are based on a prerequisite of 4 years of collegiate training, including theoretical training in occupational therapy, plus a minimum of 36 weeks of hospital practice in the latter. During the year ending June 30, 1962, 682 students were graduated in physical therapy and 355 in occupational therapy (3). A perusal of earlier reports shows an apparent stabilization in numbers of graduates, but the number being graduated in physical therapy has actually declined perceptibly in the past 5 years, and the percentage decline in occupational therapy has been even more noticeable. This is disappointing in view of the fact that the need for additional numbers of physical and occupational therapists seems to be increasing steadily. It may well be that economic rewards have not kept pace with rewards available to college-trained workers who elect to pursue careers in other vocational fields.

Efforts are now being made to meet the shortage by training an ever-increasing number of subsidiary workers to perform some of the simpler routines. Precise figures are not available, but evidence indicates that several thousand such workers are currently employed in physical therapy in addition to approximately 10,000 active physical therapists trained in schools approved by the American Medical Association. Comparable figures for occupational therapists are thought to be smaller, approximately 6,000 graduates of AMA-approved schools and an equal number with lesser training.

The Baruch Foundation and the National Foundation for Infantile Paralysis did much to provide educational programs for physiatrists and their technical counterparts. This tended to provide a unified type of physician leadership. For a variety of reasons, however, the recruitment of specialists in physical medicine has not kept pace with the expansion of facilities and the recruitment of technological workers. For this reason, and for others, physiatrists provide the leadership in some institutions, while orthopedic surgeons or other clinical specialists provide the physician leadership in other institutions, often on a part-time basis. Indeed, divided leadership may exist within the same institution. Thus it is that the technological workers often have a minimum of real supervision. Frequently their responsibilities and prerogatives are vaguely defined. This has accelerated a trend toward autonomy, especially in connection with private office practice. The problem has not been as glaringly apparent in occupational therapy as in physical therapy, for the temptations of independent practice are greater in physical therapy. Moreover, cultists and charlatans have invaded the field of physical therapy in many portions of the United States. They appeal to state legislatures for licensure, sometimes of a type which would restrict the activities of physiatrists and physical therapists. The physical therapists, in self-defense, have sponsored legislation more acceptable to themselves. They have succeeded to a variable degree in about two thirds of the states. The legislation which they sponsor often goes well beyond that required for a defense against the aggressive activities of cultists and charlatans. It sometimes confers the privilege of working independently and of accepting patients referred by physicians. This constitutes autonomy of a rather high order. Moreover, autonomy and the concern over status tend to grow. Robert K. Merton, a sociologist, recently made the interesting remark (19) that "status-hunger grows by what it feeds upon; the appetite for status comes with eating." This remark was included in an article on nursing, but it might well apply to most professional fields.

Clinical Psychology

Clinical psychology is one of many subdivisions of the field of psychology. Some of the subdivisions are essentially of a scientific nature. However, two of them—clinical psychology and counseling psychology—deal rather extensively with professional practice. The training programs of these two branches are integral parts of collegiate departments of psychology, and are conducted at the graduate level. Programs in the two fields are accredited by the Committee on Evaluation of the American Psychological Association. Internship experience is acquired in approved agencies which are usually off campus. State licensure prevails in approximately one third of the states. There is some difference of opinion as to where to draw the dividing line between clinical psychology and psychiatry. Moreover, legal restrictions on use of the word psychology have interfered in some cases with the objectives of sociologists. This and related matters are discussed in an interesting paper by the sociologist, William J. Goode (6).

Other Paramedical Fields

Of the remaining paramedical fields, several are mentioned briefly in the introduction and in later sections of this chapter. Note has been made to the effect that optometry is an independent profession. Its practitioners deal directly with the public. It is said that optometrists supply approximately one half of the eyeglasses now being sold in the United States. As individuals, they do not always confine themselves to simple refraction and to the fitting and dispensing of glasses. Some of their more venturesome members instill drops in the course of refraction, despite the danger of catastrophic results in cases of unsuspected glaucoma. Some instill local anesthetic agents and use corneal tonometers, obviously in an effort to make the diagnosis of glaucoma. Optometrists have secured licensure in all states, but in some they have sought, through legislation, to secure the legal right to diagnose and treat ocular disease, and to eliminate the dispensing optician, who fills prescriptions, or to bring him under the control of optometry.

Podiatry, formerly known as chiropody, is an independent profession, licensed in all of the states. A few of the 7,000 podiatrists of this country work in hospitals, but most are engaged in private office practice. A 4-year professional training is based on a minimum prerequisite of 1 year of college training. In earlier times, podiatrists restricted themselves to minor aspects of the care of the foot. In recent years, some of them have shown a desire to extend their area of jurisdiction, by legislation if necessary, especially in regard to surgery of the foot and leg.

The nurse anesthetists of the United States, thought to be approximately 15,000 in number, administer roughly 50% of the anesthetics given in surgical operations. The rest are given almost exclusively by physicians, partly by Board-certified anesthesiologists, partly by other physicians. The Board-certified anesthesiologists received their training in the 200-odd residency programs approved by the Council on Medical Education and Hospitals of AMA.

Recruits for the 152 schools for nurse anesthetists approved by the American Association of Nurse Anesthetists must be graduate nurses. Their training in anesthesia formerly covered a 12-month period. It has recently been increased to 18 months. Virtually all graduates of these schools take an examination in order to become members of the American Association of Nurse Anesthetists. This is regarded as constituting a form of certification.

Several states have enacted legislation for licensure of nurse anesthetists. In most jurisdictions, however, the surgeon who performs the operation must assume responsibility for the medical acts of the nurse anesthetist.

Medical assistants have been organized and trained in recent years to assist physicians in many aspects of office practice. They serve, among other things, as receptionists, secretaries and record clerks. Sometimes they perform simple laboratory procedures under direct supervision of the physician who employs them. The medical assistants are represented by the American Association of Medical Assistants.

Some of the remaining paramedical fields are related rather closely to one another; frequently, these related fields are practiced under supervision of one or another of the physician specialties. This simplifies matters from an administrative point of view and it eliminates some of the complexity and confusion which might result if 40 or 50 technological specialties were to report directly to each of the many segments of medical practice.

Of the related groups, one might note that the subspecialties of clinical chemistry, mycology, virology, parasitology, histologic technique and blood banking are of interest to the physician specialist in clinical pathology. The ophthalmologists have close ties with the opticians, the contact lens technicians and with certain specialized types of laboratory technicians. They have no contact with optometrists, for the latter practice independently of the medical profession. The work of the audiologist is of interest to the otolaryngologist. Commonly, the psychiatrist is the senior member of a team which includes clinical psychologists, counseling psychologists and speech therapists. Additional examples might be cited to illustrate the practicability of bringing related types of technological workers into close administrative association with physicians who specialize in the corresponding fields of medical practice. This is a matter which will be discussed more fully in the following section.

THE COORDINATION OF HEALTH SERVICES

Specialization within the medical profession and the creation of numerous technological services create certain problems of coordination and teamwork. In offices of physicians, the administrative problems are relatively simple. Each physician uses the services of physician specialists through a system of consultation and referral. A variety of services are provided by his office staff and by nearby radiologists, clinical pathologists and physiatrists. The neighborhood pharmacist and the oculist are independent of medicine, but they provide materials and services on the basis of written prescriptions. Patients are referred back and forth between dentists and physicians.

Coordination of health services in a large hospital or clinic is more complex. The Administrator and his staff administer a wide variety of services of ever-growing importance and complexity. The Administrator's role with respect to nurses and technologists is variable, as will be noted later. Certain general policies of a professional nature are formulated by the Medical Board. The latter also makes recommendations to the Administrator concerning service functions of the type already mentioned. However, the medical profession itself is essentially autonomous in the performance of its professional duties.

The system of consultation and referral, as employed in office practice, has proved to be an effective means of coordinating the professional activities of physicians holding staff positions in hospitals and clinics. It has the necessary flexibility to meet the needs of the individual patient. Responsibility for decisions may shift at times from one physician to another; nevertheless, there is no uncertainty at any given moment as to who has that responsibility.

In large hospitals or clinics, patients are commonly brought together in groups, as in wards or in the various divisions of a clinic. Usually each ward or unit serves the patients of a particular specialty of medical practice. The chief of each ward or unit has full responsibility; the interns and residents are answerable to him. Thus it is that the organizational principles which control the relationships of physicians with one another are relatively simple, even though the institution be a large one with many subdivisions. Each unit can be tightly organized, but relations between units are based on consultation and referral, not on centralized hospital-wide control of medical practice.

The departmental organizations of physician specialists are well adapted to supervise technical workers who specialize in their own fields. Radiologists of the Department of Radiology are well qualified to guide the work of x-ray technicians. Clinical pathologists are in a position to supervise the work of medical laboratory technicians. Physiatrists can provide integrated supervision of the work of physical and occupational therapists. These physician specialists have knowledge of the art and science of medical practice; they have detailed knowledge of the technical procedures, and they have a personal interest in the recruitment and training of adequate numbers of competent technical assistants. The technical assistants welcome leadership and guidance based on a sympathetic understanding of subject matter and working conditions.

Technical workers who serve the needs of several departments, or of all departments, present special problems. In some hospitals, members of the various clinical departments operate special segments of radiology, physical therapy or clinical pathology. It is hardly to be expected that they, as busy clinicians, will spend any great amount of time teaching technicians or directing their activities; nor do many of them have sufficient familiarity with the techniques to do so. Under such conditions, the technical workers have a minimum of guidance and support on professional matters. The Administrator looks after matters of space assignment and budget needed by such technical workers, but without being able to direct their professional activities. A somewhat similar situation prevails in most small hospitals. Very few of them are fully departmentalized, and as a result the technicians in question must serve all members of the clinical staff, with little or no guidance of physician specialists who have intimate familiarity with the technical and professional problems involved.

The administrative problems are sometimes rather complex whenever the tasks within a given field are assigned to workers of several different degrees of skill. In the field of nursing, for example, professional nurses may serve as specialists in pediatrics, obstetrics, in the operating room or in the department of public health. The professional field is thus subdivided into separate fields by virtue of vertical lines of cleavage. We may refer to the groups thus created as vertical strata. On the other hand, the division of nursing personnel into professional nurses, practical nurses and nursing aides is a horizontal type of stratification, resulting from horizontal lines of cleavage.

As noted already, the various technological specialties exhibit vertical and horizontal stratification to a varying degree.

The horizontal stratification within the nursing service of a large hospital or clinic creates administrative problems of a rather complex type. Nurses and sociologists have conducted some very interesting surveys (16, 17) which show, through continuous observation and through interviews, that the informal structure of a nursing service often differs considerably from the formal structure depicted in tables of organization. Each of the horizontal strata tends to develop group loyalties. Each group seeks to defend its status, and to improve its status if possible. Any reassignment in roles, made for economic reasons or because of temporary shortage in personnel, disturbs harmonious working relationships between strata.

The factor which brings about horizontal stratification is fundamentally one of subdividing a task into simple routines which are easily mastered, and into complex operations requiring greater skill based on more extensive education. In early days, all hospital routines were simple, and were largely custodial in nature. The bacterial concept of disease eventually provided a foundation for antiseptic surgery, for the modern operating room and for a more complex type of nursing service. The professional nurses, the practical nurses and the nursing aides now form a nursing team of growing complexity. As indicated already, conditions are in a state of transition, but it may well be that recruitment for the various tasks will be adequate if a well-balanced pattern of vertical and horizontal stratification can be evolved.

Recruitment of professional nurses, practical nurses and nursing aides in adequate number does not automatically guarantee smooth operations in daily activities, even if each group were properly trained. The medical staff of a hospital, organized into specialty departments, is in a position to provide leadership and friendly guidance for specialized types of nursing needed in such fields as psychiatry and pediatrics.

Since the medical staff is departmentalized, however, it is not designed to participate in administrative functions on a hospital-wide basis. For this reason, it has a limited role in providing leadership and guidance for general-duty nursing or for other types of non-specialized nursing service designed to meet the basic needs of all clinical departments. The Medical Board has legislative functions, and it has a role at the conference table, but it has virtually no administrative functions at the operating level. It can outline the needs of the patients, but does not have a role in implementing them. The Administrator and his Board of Directors can and do sponsor conferences and workshops. They control the nursing budget, but not the professional activities of the nurses. Thus it is that the nursing service has become semi-autonomous, but authority over budget and professional policies is diffused.

Tables of organization specify, as a rule, that professional nurses shall be responsible for teamwork and shall direct the activities of practical nurses and nurses' aides who work with them. However, by the very nature of things they cannot control the number of professional nurses to be employed, or the number of practical nurses, nurses' aides or student nurses. For these reasons, they cannot enforce predetermined concepts concerning the roles of each. This is clearly indicated by the sociological studies already mentioned. It is even more evident from the fact that leaders of the nursing profession in the United States have promoted state licensure in an effort to define the roles of professional nurses, and to draw a line between them and other segments of the nursing team. They succeeded during the first two decades of the present century in securing legislation in the various states, designed to draw a line between the professional and the "untrained" nurse. Recently, they have promoted legislation designed to license the practical nurse as well as the professional nurse, and to define the roles of each. This newer type of legislation has now been enacted in all of the states.

It is evident in retrospect that the nursing profession is using governmental agencies as referees, in an attempt to solve jurisdictional problems which it was unable to solve at grass-roots levels. Obviously, the licensure of practical nurses introduces new complexities. The practical nurses have become well organized at state and national levels and are displaying great vitality. It may well be that present roles will change. Unless nurses, physicians and administrators collaborate in solving these problems by voluntary means, one can assume that political decisions will tend more and more to dominate the picture.

Stratification, both vertical and horizontal, also exists among technological workers in the fields of radiology, clinical pathology, physical therapy and occupational therapy. In most of these fields, a rather simple type of horizontal stratification exists, with assistants or aides in addition to the professional technological groups. A certain amount of vertical stratification also exists to provide subspecialties in these various technological fields. In none of these cases does stratification or licensure create serious administrative problems as long as the technical groups are closely associated with physician specialists in their respective fields. These specialists understand the technical problems and are able to provide guidance and to enlist loyal cooperation toward common objectives. Under some circumstances, however, physician leadership is not at hand, as in some of the small hospitals and in some of the large ones with divided laboratories under weak supervision. Like nurses, the technicians in such cases are prone to look to licensure as a means of defining roles and jurisdictions, in a rather futile effort to minimize the confusion and frustration which exists at grass-roots levels.

The demand for licensure is even more insistent on the part of technicians who own and operate private laboratories designed to provide service in radiology, clinical pathology or physical therapy. It cannot be said that these commercial laboratories are an element in horizontal stratification. Nevertheless, they do create fragmentation, and confusion in roles, and this leads to efforts at licensure. Indeed, the owners and operators of commercial laboratories usually make the initial appeal to the legislatures. It is they who provide the most effective lobbies. This has been especially true of commercial laboratories in the fields of clinical pathology and physical therapy. Six states have licensing laws in the former, 37 in the latter. The physical therapists, for many years, have waged a defensive campaign against certain masseurs, chiropractors and others who have sought licensure of a type which would limit or preclude the activities of well-trained physical therapists, even when working in well-recognized hospitals and clinics. They have found it expedient to sponsor licensure for themselves, and to oppose restrictive legislation on the part of others. In the meantime, some of the physical therapists have taken advantage of the situation and have established private laboratories. Some work only on prescription of physicians, others solicit patients of their own. In neither case do they have adequate medical advice on matters which require it.

The foregoing comments on coordination have dealt almost exclusively with technological fields in which medical judgment enters intimately and more or less continuously into daily operations. The tasks can be classified and routinized to some extent, but modifications and adjustments must be made each day in order to meet the needs of the individual patient. Frequently, unforeseen developments arise in the course of an x-ray examination or in the course of treatment by physical therapists. In either case, a decision must be made by the physician specialist who directs the activities of the technical worker in question. In like manner, the clinical pathologist can recognize anomalous situations and can consult with clinical colleagues, if necessary, and can guide the investigation into more fruitful channels. This type of leadership can be highly effective in the hands of a physician specialist who is intimately familiar with medical practice and with procedures carried out by technicians. It is the basis of coordinated effort in the fields in question. This close coordination is lacking if the technical worker acts independently in a private laboratory. It is defective in a hospital if laboratories are fragmented and if guidance comes only from busy practitioners who are unfamiliar with the details of technique. Defective leadership, for whatever reason, leads to frustration and to agitation for licensure. The latter creates rigidity, but does not provide coordination or elevation of standards.

In contrast to the foregoing examples, one can identify many fields in which medical requirements can be formalized sufficiently to eliminate much or all of the need for continuing medical guidance. This is true, for example, of dietitians. Medical record librarians play an important role, but they proceed in accord with standard specifications. Moreover, their work is subject to leisurely inspection and to correction. Opticians supply glasses on prescription of physicians. The physician can inspect the glasses and make certain that they have been properly designed to meet the needs of his patient. The pharmacist also dispenses materials on prescription. He also dispenses non-prescription drugs, a rather obvious adaptation to practical realities.

The needs of medical practice are served by large numbers of professional administrators. They play a most important role in hospitals, clinics and foundations, and in the operation of prepaid health care plans. They, too, are a part of the health team. They do not enter directly into the practice of medicine, but their influence on medical practice is growing constantly.

In conclusion, those who are involved in providing medical service will do well to give careful consideration to stratification, to the temptations of independent practice and to other factors on which teamwork stands or falls. In some fields, physician leadership should be continuous, with due regard to detail and to the dignity and prestige of the allied professions. Such leadership is personal, and often by precept; it cannot be provided by remote control, or by lengthy discussions at the conference table. But not all of the allied groups need a continuous personalized type of physician leadership. In some cases, the service can be formalized and responsibilities placed, on the basis of well-drafted plans. It is important that a distinction be made between those that can and those that cannot.

RECRUITMENT AND RELATED MATTERS

The unskilled workers in hospitals, trained on the job, are recruited by their employers. Ordinarily, the workers take no part in recruitment. However, labor unions are making progress in organizing such groups; this affects recruitment to some extent. The nurses and technologists have formed training programs and professional associations, as already noted. They reject unionism and the right to strike as being inconsistent with professionalism, but some of them—the nurses particularly—sometimes bargain collectively at state and local levels. They make no effort, however, to limit membership in their profession except on the basis of reasonably well-defined standards of education and licensure. Indeed, organizations which represent the professional nurses and technologists wage energetic campaigns of recruitment. Obviously, they have little fear of competition from their own kind in this age of expanding technology.

Training programs of the very highest type are always in short supply, but there is rarely any dearth of technological training programs of average quality. Recruitment is the bottleneck in most of the paramedical fields.

Campaigns of recruitment, conducted by the paramedical groups, help to eliminate shortages in personnel, and are obviously in the public interest. The elevation of educational standards makes it possible for the members to play new roles and for the leaders to recruit candidates of higher caliber. The only question which remains is whether they can recruit adequate numbers of individuals willing to work for salaries which prospective employers are willing and able to pay. In stressing their collegiate programs, the leaders of the nursing profession seem to have chosen future roles as teachers, as supervisors and as skilled assistants in diagnosis and therapy. They appear to be reconciled to the prospect that practical nurses and nursing aides will have ever greater responsibilities over large segments of bedside nursing.

Other paramedical groups are likewise divided more or less into professional and subsidiary categories. If and when the professional categories raise their educational standards, they can look forward to the possibility of becoming small elite groups, but they cannot hope to compete in numbers with the subsidiary groups which move in behind them. This is not a matter of logic or of planning; it is essentially a matter of ability to recruit. Scholarships and subsidies for vocational training can shift the balance somewhat, but experience shows that human motivation, in a context of supply and demand, determines recruitment. A long-continued failure in recruitment usually means that educational standards and professional roles have been drafted in an unrealistic manner.

Source Materials

For most of the paramedical fields, the official journals of national societies are the best single source of information on problems of education and professional policy. In many cases they include minutes of annual meetings of the societies in question. Newsletters, if published, are valuable; however, back issues may not be readily available. The journals of physician groups are sometimes informative, but usually the coverage of technological problems is limited. One finds many articles of interest in several of the leading hospital journals of the United States, i.e., in *Hospitals, Hospital Progress, Hospital Management, Modern Hospital* and *Hospital Topics.*

The literature of the paramedical fields subsequent to 1945 is rather well indexed in *Hospital Literature Index,* published by the American Hospital Association, and somewhat less exhaustively in *Index Medicus* and in earlier issues of *Current List of Medical Literature.* A new index, the *Cumulative Index to Nursing Literature,* promises to be quite valuable. It should be noted, however, that much of the significant information on matters of policy is to be found in news items and editorials, as well as in the official minutes of societies. Even if available, this material is difficult to index, for the main headings may not provide the necessary information. In the final analysis, the student of such matters must peruse journals and minutes, page by page, often covering a period of many years.

Books, monographs and pamphlets are of considerable interest, and this is particularly true of the voluminous publications in the field of nursing.

Items of General Interest

1. *Encyclopedia of Associations.* Volume I: National Organizations of the U. S. (3d ed.; Detroit: Gale Research Company, 1961). (Includes brief statements concerning most of the national organizations of medical and paramedical personnel. Gives membership, objectives, headquarters address and serials published.)

2. *Occupational Outlook Handbook:* Employment Information on Major Occupations for Use in Guidance, Bulletin No. 1300 of the U.S. Department of Labor, 1961 ed. For sale by Govt. Printing Office. (Gives descriptions of various occupational fields, including those related to medicine.)

3. AMA Council on Medical Education and Hospitals: Areas Allied to Medicine. J.A.M.A. 182:780-781, Nov. 17, 1962. (Recent information on number of schools and of graduates in various paramedical fields.) See also, J.A.M.A. 174:1477-1526, Nov. 12, 1960, for educational programs. (Similar material of later date can be secured from the AMA Council on Education and Hospitals.)

4. *Hospitals,* Journal of the American Hospital Association, Guide Issue, August 1, 1959, Part 2. (See tables 1-12 on personnel.)

5. McGlothlin, William J.: *Pattern of Professional Education* (New York: G. P. Putnam's Sons, 1960).

6. Goode, William J.: Encroachment, Charlatanism, and the Emerging Profession: Psychology, Sociology and Medicine, American Sociological Review 25:902, Dec. 1960. (Excellent discussion of professionalism by a sociologist.)

Nursing

Limitations on space do not permit a review of the numerous articles and books which deal with changing policies regarding the diploma and collegiate schools. References to this important literature are given in the historical treatise of Mary M. Roberts (9). Particular attention should be given to the Cleveland Survey (1920), the Goldmark Report (1923), the Committee on the Grading of Schools of Nursing (1928, 1934), the Lucille Brown reports (1936, 1948), the Eli Ginsberg report (1948), and the treatise of Margaret Bridgman (1953). These are a few of what have been termed the milestones of American nursing.

The writer regrets being unable to comment on the outstanding work of the Red Cross, both in relation to wartime service and to disaster relief. The recent activities in blood procurement can only be mentioned in passing.

The following references will direct attention of the reader to other references which may be of particular interest. The *American Journal of Nursing* (1900+) is the most important single source of information concerning American nursing. Other official journals include *Public Health Nurse* (1909-52), *Nursing Outlook* (1953+) and *Nursing Research* (1952+). *RN: A Journal for Nurses,* an independent publication, contains much material of interest. *The Canadian Nurse* (1905+) is an excellent source.

7. *Facts About Nursing: A Statistical Summary* (New York: American Nurses' Association, 1961). (A very valuable source of well-tabulated information. Earlier editions extend back to 1935.)

8. *Publication Lists of the American Nurses' Association and of the National League for Nursing* are available on request at Headquarters, 10 Columbus Circle, New York, N.Y. (Pamphlets, reprints, etc., available for distribution.)

9. Roberts, Mary M.: *American Nursing: History and Interpretation* (New York: The Macmillan Company, 1955). (An authoritative treatise by a former Editor of the *American Journal of Nursing*. Good references.)

10. Nutting, M. Adelaid, and Dock, Lavinia L.: *A History of Nursing*. 4 vols. (New York: G. P. Putnam's Sons, 1907-12). (An exhaustive survey of the older literature by two of the early leaders of American nursing.)

11. Cook, Sir Edward: *The Life of Florence Nightingale*. 2 vols. (London: Macmillan & Company, 1914).

12. American Nurses' Association Board of Directors: Principles of Legislation, American Journal of Nursing 53:1476, December, 1953.

13. American Nurses' Association Board of Directors: ANA Board Approves a Definition of Nursing Practice, American Journal of Nursing 55:1474, December, 1955.

14. National League for Nursing: Analysis of State Board Test Scores, 1957, Nursing Outlook 7:298-301, May, 1959.

15. Lesser, Marion S., and Keane, Vera R.: *Nurse-Patient Relationships in a Hospital Maternity Service* (St. Louis: C. V. Mosby Company, 1956). (An interesting portrayal of some of the current concepts of new roles for professional nurses.)

16. Hughes, Everett C., Hughes, Helen MacGill, and Deutscher, Irwin: *Twenty Thousand Nurses Tell Their Story* (Philadelphia & Montreal: J. B. Lippincott Company, 1958). (A review of recent sociological studies in nursing.)

17. Reissman, Leonard, and Rohrer, John H.: *Change and Dilemma in the Nursing Profession* (New York: G. P. Putnam's Sons, 1957). (Roles, stresses and strains, as viewed by sociologists.)

18. Deming, Dorothy: *The Practical Nurse* (New York: Commonwealth Fund, 1947).

18a. Bridgman, Margaret: *Collegiate Education for Nursing* (New York: Russell Sage Foundation, 1953).

19. Merton, Robert K.: Relations Between Registered Nurses and Licensed Practical Nurses, American Journal of Nursing 62:70, October, 1962. (Written by a sociologist.)

20. Spohn, Roberta R.: *The Future of Education for Professional Practice:* A Guide for the Study of the ANA's Proposed Goal on Nursing Education and Principles of Nursing Education (New York: American Nurses' Association, 1962).

X-ray Technology

The X-ray Technician (1929+) is the official journal of the American Society of X-ray Technicians. It is a rich source of information.

21. Greene, Alfred B.: The Registry Comes of Age: Twenty Years of Progress of the American Registry of X-ray Technicians, The X-ray Technician 15:149, January, 1944; 15:192, March, 1944; 15:237, May, 1944; 16:25, July, 1944. See also: Quo Fata Vocant. Ibid. 26:76-88, September, 1954. (These articles include much interesting material in addition to that connected with the Registry.)

22. S. Elizabeth D. Doser: The X-ray Technician and a College Education, The X-ray Technician 30:491-496, May, 1959.

23. Roster of Physicists Certified by the American Board of Radiology, American College of Radiology Bulletin, 170-174, April, 1962.

Medical Technology

The American Society of Medical Technologists, composed of graduates of AMA-approved schools of medical technology, publishes the *American Journal of Medical Technology* (1934+), a journal which contains abundant material on matters of educational and professional policy, as well as on the purely scientific aspects of the field.

A physician group, the American Society of Clinical Pathologists, published in the *Journal of Laboratory and Clinical Medicine* during the period 1922-29. Subsequently, it published in its own journal, the *American Journal of Clinical Pathology*. The two journals contain numerous articles concerning medical technology, especially in the earlier years.

Various independent technological groups in the United States have published newsletters over the past two decades, but unfortunately these newsletters are rarely to be found in medical libraries. In recent years, however, one of the specialty groups, the American Association of Clinical Chemists, has published a journal, *Clinical Chemistry* (1955+). It contains occasional articles on matters of policy.

24. Ikeda, Kano: Specialization in Medical Technology, American Journal of Medical Technology 10:159-164, September, 1944.

25. Ikeda, Kano: The Future of Medical Technology, American Journal of Medical Technology 12:146-155, July, 1946. (Historical analysis by a clinical pathologist who had an important role in guiding the development of medical technology.)

26. Hillkowitz, Philip: The Dawn of Medical Technology, American Journal of Medical Technology 12:221-225, September, 1946. (Written by a clinical pathologist who served as Chairman of the Board of Registry during the first 13 years of its existence.)

27. Smith, Harry P.: Clinical Pathology: Its Creators and Its Practitioners, American Journal of Clinical Pathology 31:283-292, April, 1959. (Includes comments on history of medical technology.)

28. Clemmer, John J.: Value Received, American Journal of Clinical Pathology 35:3, January, 1961. (History of American Society of Clinical Pathologists and its relation to training and certification of medical technologists.)

Physical and Occupational Therapy

Early American efforts in physical therapy are recorded in *Physical Therapeutics* and its predecessors (1891-1932), a journal sponsored by a physician group, the American Electro-Therapeutic Association. The leading technological group in the United States, the American Physical Therapy Association, has published a journal since 1921 (*P. T. Review,* 1921-26; *Physiotherapy Review,* 1926-48; *Physical Therapy Review,* 1948-61; *Journal of the American Physical Therapy Association,* 1962+).

The American Occupational Therapy Association is the leading representative of the technological workers in occupational therapy. The Association has published a journal since 1922 (*Archives of Occupational Therapy,* 1922-24; *Occupational Therapy and Rehabilitation,* 1925-51; *American Journal of Occupational Therapy,* 1947+).

Additional source material on professional and educational policy is to be found in the *American Journal of Physical Medicine* (1952+). The *American Archives of Rehabilitation Therapy* (1953+) and the *Rehabilitation Therapy Bulletin*

(1951+) are official journals of the American Association for Rehabilitation Therapy. The Association has over 10 sections for subspecialties (blind orienters, corrective therapists, industrial therapists, mental hygienists, music therapists, physical therapists, recreation therapists, speech therapists, vocational counselors, etc.). The National Rehabilitation Association has sponsored a journal, *National Rehabilitation News* (1935-47); also *Journal of Rehabilitation* (1947+).

The *Archives of Physical Medicine and Rehabilitation* is the official organ of the American Congress of Physical Medicine and Rehabilitation and of the American Academy of Physical Medicine and Rehabilitation. The latter is exclusively a physician group. The *A.M.A. Archives of Environmental Health* (begun in 1950 under another name) serves as official journal of the American Academy of Occupational Medicine.

29. Dunton, William Rush, Jr.: History of Occupational Therapy, Modern Hospital 8:380-382, June, 1917.

30. Dunton, William Rush, Jr.: Occupational Therapy, Occupational Therapy and Rehabilitation 9:343-350, December, 1930.

31. Hull, Harmon H.: A Survey of Occupational Therapy, Occupational Therapy and Rehabilitation 10:217-233, August, 1931.

32. Hazenhyer, Ida May: Physical Therapy as a Vocation, Physiotherapy Review 19:119-125, May-June, 1939; 22:76-82, March-April, 1942.

33. Hazenhyer, Ida May: A History of the American Physiotherapy Association, Physiotherapy Review 26:3-14, January-February, 1946; 26:66-74, March-April, 1946; 26:122-129, May-June, 1946; 26:174-184, July-August, 1946.

Clinical Psychology

Developments subsequent to 1945 are well portrayed in the *American Psychologist,* official journal of the American Psychological Association.

34. Hunt, William A.: *The Clinical Psychologist* (Springfield, Ill.: Charles C Thomas, Publisher, 1956).

SIDNEY J. SHIPMAN, M.D.

*Specializing in diseases of the chest,
Dr. Shipman is Clinical Professor of
Medicine at the University of California
Medical School. He received his medical
degree at the University of Michigan
Medical School in 1919. He has served
several organizations as president: the
California Medical Association (1955),
the National Tuberculosis Association
(1953), the San Francisco Medical Society
(1943) and the Tuberculosis and Health
Association of California (1939).
Dr. Shipman is currently Chairman of
the AMA Committee on Voluntary
Health Agencies.*

8. Voluntary Health Agencies

VOLUNTARY HEALTH AGENCIES are peculiarly American institutions. While similar agencies have been formed in various
countries abroad, particularly in the English-speaking countries, the great voluntary health agency movement which developed during the first half of this century has been predomi-
nantly an American idea. Health and welfare efforts abroad
have been largely governmental in nature.

By definition, voluntary health agencies may be said to be
associations of lay and medical people in varying proportions,
organized to combat a disease or diseases by voluntary efforts.
Their purposes have been stated to be: (1) aid to the unfortunate, (2) dissemination of knowledge, both medical and lay,
concerning the disease or diseases in question, (3) promotion
of research, (4) initiation of legislation required to combat the

disease or diseases effectively and, (5) service as watchdogs of official agencies at all levels.

One might suppose that philanthropic voluntary organizations devoted to human welfare and with such high ideals would have had smooth sailing, but such was not the case. Organizational and personality difficulties loomed large in their affairs from their inception. Only their lofty purposes, supported by the unswerving devotion of many dedicated laymen and doctors and the widespread desire of the American public to support worthy philanthropy, insured the continuance and growth of the voluntary health agencies.

An additional source of difficulty for these agencies in recent years has been the concept that all giving could be compressed into one package, an idea fostered by Community Chests or United Funds and supported by big industry and organized labor, largely to avoid the annoyance of multiple fund drives. There was a certain amount of logic in the objections to individual fund drives put forward by these groups, and the voluntary health agencies were forced to defend themselves by every means in their power.

The American Medical Association was not unaware of the problems confronting the agencies, both the United Funds on the one hand and the voluntary health agencies on the other. In 1952 the Board of Trustees officially recognized the problem by appointing a committee, the purpose of which was

A study to secure comprehensive financial, scientific and sociological data on fund raising groups in order to acquaint the profession and public with the monetary efficiency of fund procurement, and disposition of such funds obtained by these groups.

The methods to be employed were outlined as follows:

1. Secure and review standards and guides used by national groups and associations organized to supply this information to their members: National Information Bureau; National Social Welfare Assembly; National Health Council; Better Business Bureau; and some state bureaus.

2. Hold conferences with representatives of national voluntary health agencies and united funds and representatives of national groups mentioned in item 1.

3. Review fund-raising mechanisms utilized by voluntary health agencies and review federal research and activities pertaining to the diseases covered by voluntary fund-raising agencies.

In addition, the American Medical Association published a handbook for medical societies and individual physicians on the national voluntary health agencies, with the aim of making readily available unbiased data furnished by the voluntary health agencies themselves regarding their structure, financing and program. The 1962 edition of this handbook (3) lists thirty voluntary health agencies. In addition it discusses briefly sixteen more agencies of medical interest.

These data are useful in determining the present status of the agencies listed and their relative importance in the field. The handbook is not intended to be an expression of opinion, nor does it attempt to portray the historical difficulties encountered by the agencies in their growth and development. To give an idea of these aspects of the voluntary health organizations it is necessary to consider the histories of at least four of the major agencies in some detail.

NATIONAL TUBERCULOSIS ASSOCIATION

Reason for Formation

Before the formation of the National Tuberculosis Association, tuberculosis was the chief cause of disease and death in mankind, although Robert Koch had discovered the tubercle bacillus in 1882. The discovery was hailed as opening the way to a solution of the tuberculosis problem; however, actual progress in controlling the disease proceeded at such a slow pace that physicians and laymen alike who were particularly interested were moved to organize in associations in order to secure more rapid progress. Edward Livingston Trudeau, himself a victim of the disease, formed the first semi-charitable sanatorium in the United States in 1884 at Saranac Lake, New York, and worked steadily in an effort to interest both medical men and laymen to support his institution and to organize to combat the disease. Trudeau recognized that tuberculosis was transmitted from one person to another and that the way to combat it was to isolate those who were sick and prevent the transmission of the disease to those who were well.

Lawrence F. Flick of Philadelphia, who had also had tuberculosis and who specialized in the treatment of the disease, attempted to organize a crusade in the 1880's with little success. By 1882, however, he had founded the Pennsylvania Society for the Prevention of Tuberculosis, apparently the first voluntary health agency in the United States composed of lay and medical persons. Although it was difficult for him to obtain adequate funds, he did get money from the Henry Phipps Institute of Philadelphia and began a research program which was to continue at the Henry Phipps Institute with productive results for many years.

The National Association for the Study of Prevention of Tuberculosis, later to be known as the National Tuberculosis Association, or NTA, was formed in 1904. At that time the death rate from tuberculosis was approximately 200 per 100,000. One can only speculate as to how much effect the formation of the National Tuberculosis Association had in reducing the death rate to approximately 6 per 100,000 at the present time, but it was certainly a major influence in bringing about modern control measures throughout this country, and the debt owed to the early pioneers in tuberculosis control is hardly measurable. Pioneers were Edward Trudeau, Lawrence Flick, Herman Biggs, S. Adolphus Knopf, William Osler and many others.

Formation and conduct of the organization did not proceed without bickering or acrimony; this was partly due to the fact

that Flick, one of the chief organizers, apparently had a difficult personality and aroused intense antagonisms as readily as
he did warm support. Indeed, he was such a maverick that by
1912 he had abandoned the association (or the association had
abandoned him) and the future of the voluntary health movement lay in other hands, fortunately less controversial ones.

Trudeau, in his isolation at Saranac Lake, through his influence and his warm friends Biggs and Knopf, was a powerful
instrument in developing the early vigor of the association. He
was elected president at the first annual meeting, where he said
prophetically:

> The first and greatest need is education, an education of the
> people and through them education of the state. It is evident that
> if every man and woman in the United States were familiar with
> the main facts related to the manner in which tuberculosis is com-
> municated and the simple measures for their protection, the
> people would soon demand and easily obtain effective legislation
> for its control.

In saying this, Trudeau was advocating what was to become
one of the chief efforts of the National Tuberculosis Association, namely, health education, which later was to prove a difficult stumbling block in the proper determination of fund-
raising costs.

Fund-Raising

Indeed, fund-raising was a serious matter for the young
association. Fortunately the group stumbled upon a veritable
gold mine. This was suggested by Emily P. Bissell, who
adopted the Danish idea of a Christmas stamp, later to be
known as the Christmas seal, which she proposed should be
sold before Christmas for the purpose of raising funds to combat tuberculosis. Originally, Emily Bissell raised funds by this
means for the support of the Delaware Tuberculosis Society,
then in dire financial straits, but influential friends, including

publishers and writers, were instrumental in demonstrating the success of fund-raising by this simple means. Somehow it caught the imagination of the American public, coming as it did near Christmas. It was too good a method of fund-raising to remain local. In 1908, thirty-three state branches of the Red Cross sold the seals, raising $135,000, which was turned over to tuberculosis institutions. By 1910 the directors of the National Tuberculosis Association realized that here was a method which would solve the financial problems of the association. In 1920 the Red Cross, which had pioneered the sale, abandoned the seal sale altogether to the National Tuberculosis Association. Since then the National Tuberculosis Association and all its affiliates have depended on the sale of Christmas seals for the major part of their financing. Minor efforts, such as the sale of health bonds or the stimulation of bequests, have been made, but these campaigns have been minor and subordinate to the Christmas seal sale.

The Framingham Demonstration

As noted before, it is difficult to say how much the efforts of the association have contributed to the decline of the tuberculosis death rate. During the first fifteen years of the association's existence, the death rate declined to 125 per 100,000. Living standards in the United States were rising; diets were improving, and it seemed reasonable to expect the tuberculosis death rate to decrease, but even so it seemed likely that the association's program was having some effect. Fortunately the Metropolitan Life Insurance Company became interested in a demonstration, later to be known as the Framingham Demonstration because of its location in Framingham, Massachusetts. It showed what could be done in a typical American community of approximately 17,000 people when all available knowledge and technics were applied to the discovery and control of tuberculosis. The purposes were to examine everyone in the community periodically and to isolate and care for all tuberculous patients as soon as possible. When the demonstration began, the death rate was apparently 121 per 100,000, according to official records. After the project was underway, it was discovered that the death rate was really much higher. Inadequate reporting had failed to show that there were many more active cases of tuberculosis in the community than had been known to physicians and public health authorities. In six years of the demonstration the tuberculosis death rate dropped 68 per cent in contrast to 32 per cent in neighboring communities where laissez faire still ruled. This was proof that the National Tuberculosis Association's efforts were sound and that its program could be fruitful if support were forthcoming. It seemed that at length physicians and public health authorities had in their grasp sufficient knowledge to really begin an adequate tuberculosis control program.

After the Framingham Demonstration, the sanatorium movement, both public and private, developed rapidly in this country. As an offshoot of the National Tuberculosis Association, the American Sanatorium Association was formed, a suborganization which later became known as the American Trudeau Society—since 1960, known as the American Thoracic Society. This comprises over 5,000 of the leading chest specialists of the United States. It directs the research activities of the National Tuberculosis Association and publishes a well-known journal, originally called the *American Review of Tuberculosis,* a title later changed to the *American Review of Respiratory Diseases* as the association broadened its field of interest to include all respiratory diseases.

Another suborganization of the National Tuberculosis Association is the National Conference of Tuberculosis Workers composed of full-time employees of the various affiliates and locals. Thus the National Tuberculosis Association now consists of the parent organization and two subsidiary organizations, with more than 2,400 tuberculosis associations throughout the country, all of which rely on the Christmas seal sale for financial support. About 95 per cent of the total support of tuberculosis associations now comes from this source. At present, the total amount is approximately $26,250,000 per annum; 94 per cent of this sum is retained by state and local associations, and 6 per cent is sent to the headquarters of the National Association in New York. Recent expenditures for one year were as follows:

On the national level:

Research	$ 495,548
Education	591,535
Service (including program con- sultation and nursing service)	427,766
Administration	128,739
Fund-raising	154,396

On the constituents and local level:

Research	$ 926,459
Education	10,259,207
Service	8,815,775
Administration	2,562,945
Fund-raising	4,767,083

Organizational Structure

Voluntary health agencies vary in their organizational structure. The purpose of lay and medical representation on boards of directors varies. The present organizational structure of the National Tuberculosis Association has been developed throughout the years in an effort to preserve the balance between medical and lay influence. The present Board of Directors is composed of 112 members and is the true policy-making body of the association. Of these members, 57 represent constituent associations, 50 are elected at large, 3 are elected officers, and 2 (the president and president-elect of the American Thoracic Society) are ex-officio members of the board. Of the board members, 58 are physicians.

As in most organizations of this type, much of the work is carried out by committees, and an effort is made in committee formation to include representation from the American Thoracic Society and the National Conference of Tuberculosis Workers. Medical guidance is obtained through the American Thoracic Society particularly through its governing council and its own committees which include committees on medical research, medical education and therapy.

The Full-Time Staff

In addition to the National Tuberculosis Association staff at 1790 Broadway, New York, the fifty-seven constituent tuberculosis associations, which include the fifty states, five large cities in Puerto Rico, and Guam, are staffed by varying numbers of full-time people, depending on their needs. The voluntary workers, organized for the most part along the lines adopted by the National Tuberculosis Association, with approximately equal medical and lay representation, constitute the policy-making body on a constituent level, while the full-time staff supplies administrative personnel.

Each of the constituent associations enters into a seal sale contract with the parent body, and the local associations, largely on county levels, enter into contracts with the constituent associations. Committees known as qualifications and contract committees check the activities and standards of the constituent and local associations to see that the requirements of the contracts are properly met.

Present Programs

Tuberculosis associations throughout the country work closely with other voluntary health agencies. The association assumes responsibility for the sound development of all parts of the community tuberculosis control program, a program that permits great flexibility in the utilization of local community efforts in dealing with health departments and other related health associations. The following principles have been approved for the programs of voluntary tuberculosis associations:

1. Investigation and analysis of the facts.

2. Education of the individual and the community in the significance of the fact for needed action.

3. Demonstration of the support of activities to prove their value, or to provide solutions where services do not exist or other funds to support them are not available.

4. Encouragement and support of legislative proposals and appropriations to make permanent those services necessary to the community's tuberculosis and related health needs.

5. Study and review to determine the effectiveness of, and the needs for, each activity.

6. Christmas seal sale funds also may be used to finance a program in the field of other respiratory disease, to promote the development of official health departments and school health programs in accordance with the principles governing the use of such funds for tuberculosis control.

Program Expansion

The question is sometimes asked, Why is it that an organization which has accomplished so much in one field should not arrive at the point where it can close its doors, disband and admit that the goal it set for itself has been accomplished? The answer is that tuberculosis in the United States is not really eliminated, although it can be said to be under control. Tuberculosis is an infectious disease, and as long as foci exist, it is conceivable that under conditions of stress, or widespread disaster, as after atomic bombing, a recrudescence of the disease might be expected. Also, under modern conditions of intercourse with foreign countries, the importation of tuberculosis is a danger which cannot be ignored so that tuberculosis anywhere is a menace everywhere.

An unfortunate accompaniment in the decline of tuberculosis has been a lessened interest on the part of medical men, particularly an increasing problem in stimulating the interest of young doctors in the control of the disease. The old-fashioned tuberculosis specialist who devoted most of his time to patients with this disease is now a rarity. The American Thoracic Society has attempted to stimulate renewed interest in tuberculosis by furthering the training of young men in all phases of thoracic disease, hoping by this means to develop enough trained physicians in the field of thoracic diseases whose knowledge of tuberculosis would be adequate and whose interest, though broader, would be sufficiently detailed to meet the requirements of gradual tuberculosis elimination. They have succeeded in stimulating the National Tuberculosis Association, through its Board of Directors, to adopt this viewpoint. Thus, the association believes it has sound reasons for continued existence, even though the tuberculosis problem has diminished so much in importance and the death rate has fallen to such a low figure.

American Cancer Society

The second major voluntary health organization in the United States may be said to be the American Cancer Society. Like the National Tuberculosis Association, it developed as a result of the combined interest of a host of physicians in various specialties who met cancer in their daily life and innumerable laymen who had suffered from cancer or who had lost members of their families through the disease. Among the general public, hopelessness and fatalism militated against worthwhile progress. Gynecologists, however, early recognized that many women could be saved from cervical cancer by even casual routine examinations.

It was this background that caused the American Gynecological Society in 1914 to propose an organization "for the study and prevention of cancer primarily for the purpose of educating the public at large in the absolute necessity of operative treatment at the earliest indications of cancerous growth." Educating the public had long been a prime factor in the activities of the tuberculosis association, and it was obvious to the Gynecological Society that much could be accomplished in the field of cancer through use of the same technic. Surgeons in other fields were quick to see the advantage of widespread educational efforts aimed at the early diagnosis of cancer, and the idea spread to influential laymen. Thus the new American Society for the Control of Cancer was formed, with Thomas M. Debevoise, Secretary and George C. Clark, President. Because of the early interest of the gynecologists, it was easy to interest the General Federation of Women's Clubs in the problems of female cancer. This organization has continued its warm support to the present time.

However, the early years were difficult ones for the new organization, partly due to the fact that, like tuberculosis, the word "cancer" carried unpleasant connotations and was scarcely respectable. Thus, in its efforts to educate, the society was handicapped by a taboo which was illogical but none the less present. Doctors were well aware of this widespread fear on the part of the public and naturally were reluctant to trespass upon forbidden ground. Fortunately, through careful efforts the society was able to overcome a great deal of public aversion to learning the facts about cancer and, about the time of World War I was able to publicize pamphlets pointing out early symptoms and the necessity for medical examinations whenever they appeared. In 1921 it was possible to hold the first National Cancer Week. The society estimated that over one million people heard lectures, and many more saw the exhibits, pamphlets and other educational material.

Up to this time the Cancer Society feared fear itself. It was afraid to arouse unwarranted fears on the part of the public without more to offer, and in this attitude it was joined by the great majority of those in the medical profession. George A. Soper, Ph.D., who became Managing Director in 1923, thought otherwise. He urged that fear be used as a tool since it was already present in society at large. Nevertheless, he failed to win over a large segment of the medical profession, which refused to adopt his viewpoint. In 1927 the society accepted an offer of a $50,000 prize offered by William Lawrence Saunders, Chairman of the Board of Ingersoll-Rand and Director of the Federal Reserve Bank of New York, to anyone who could produce a cure and an additional $50,000 for a preventative of cancer; the offer was to expire in January of the following year. As a result, a wide variety of alleged cures reached the society, alerting its governing body to the fact that cancer quackery was a major stumbling block in the public approach to the problem. It became obvious that the society not only had an obligation to further research into the true nature of cancer and its eventual cure, but to combat the hideous wealth of nostrums through which the public was being victimized.

As in the case of tuberculosis, the Cancer Society was not alone. The Massachusetts Department of Health passed a law aimed at the control of cancer in 1926, and other state health departments followed. Soper was replaced by Clarence Cook Little, D.Sc., in 1929. Whereas Soper had been undiplomatic, although rather effective, in early Cancer Society activities, just as Lawrence Flick was in early affairs of the National Tuberculosis Association, Little brought an aura of prestige, having been President of the Universities of Michigan and of Maine and former Assistant Director of the Harvard Medical School. Little was a suave administrator, an excellent public speaker, and an accomplished researcher in his own right. He set out to increase the stature of the society by winning friends and influencing people. In doing this, he wisely foresaw, as the National Tuberculosis Association had before him, that it would be necessary to secure the solid backing of the organized medical profession first of all. He therefore attended medical meetings, arranged lectures at medical schools, spoke or provided speakers at various medical meetings, and saw to it that Cancer Society literature was widely disseminated at medical conventions and in doctors' offices. This campaign met with rather marked success so that Little was able to advocate in a few years the gradual adoption of a renewed public campaign, which had been kept in the background up to this point in his directorship. As the society had found earlier, Little now found that his chief ally in the lay approach was the General Federation of Women's Clubs.

Thus the Women's Field Army of the American Cancer Society came into being in 1936. It was agreed that the program should be primarily in the hands of lay women and that it required intimate family contacts. It is now agreed that these and allied efforts probably were a major factor in the 50 per cent reduction in uterine cancer between 1936 and 1959.

The Field Army was self-supporting. Not only this, but it sent 30 per cent of the money it raised to the American Cancer Society. The women wore uniforms, distributed pamphlets, helped unfortunate victims of cancer, were instrumental in influencing legislative bodies, and formed the basis of a strong field movement for the society, a feature which it had lacked since its inception. In short, the women had not only taken active interest but had become the solid foundation of the society. One woman, Mary Lasker, became extremely interested and active. Through her efforts Emerson Foote, whose parents had died of cancer, was placed on the board and brought the fresh outlook of a successful business man and promoter to that body. The number of laymen on the governing board was rapidly increased; many of the nation's outstanding business men were enlisted. The interest of *Reader's Digest* was aroused, and articles appeared in 1944 giving the pertinent facts about cancer to the public. As a result, the 1945 fund drives were the best on record. Radio, which had hitherto observed the taboo concerning the word "cancer," was persuaded to mention it on the air. As a result of this, the 1945 fund drive brought in $4,292,000. This was enough to convince the doctors that the 50-50 arrangement for board members, previously adopted by the Tuberculosis Association, was a sound one and the idea was adopted by the Cancer Society.

To imagine that all of the problems of the Cancer Society would be settled by this means proved to be an unwarranted assumption. It required several years for the lay and medical people to understand each other. As may be imagined, Little was placed in an ambiguous position between the two groups and chose to resign after having contributed greatly to the development of the organization. Finally, the issue of control, which proved to be the chief stumbling block to effective rapport, was resolved by agreement that the Board of Directors would be composed equally of physicians and laymen and the Executive Committee would be composed mostly of laymen.

At present the society's purpose may be said to be a total nationwide attack on cancer. In this battle it proposes to utilize present knowledge to save lives, to aid in educating the profession and the public and to devote at least 30 per cent of its funds to research.

Organizational Structure

The Board of Directors is now composed of 74 members, 37 of whom are physicians or other scientists. The House of Delegates comprises a body of 120, of whom 60 are physicians and other scientists. There are 60 divisions, corresponding roughly to constituent associations of the Tuberculosis Association; each elects one medical, or scientific, and one lay delegate. In addition, the 37 medical and scientific members of the board constitute a medical and scientific committee. The chairman appoints all committees dealing with medical and scientific affairs except research. These committees are as follows: (1) Professional Education Committee, (2) Service Committee, (3) Clinical Fellowships Committee, (4) Committee on New or Unproved Methods of Treatment, (5) Statistics Committee and (6) special advisory and ad hoc committees as needed.

The national society issues charters to divisions which meet charter standards, receives standardized division orders, sets general policy. Each division is organized in a manner similar to the national society and appoints two representatives to the national society as mentioned above. There are over 3,000 local county units and a membership of over 11,000 physicians as board members.

Fund-raising

Personal contributions are solicited and trusts, legacies and memorials welcomed. In 1938 Congress authorized Cancer Control Month to be determined by Presidential Proclamation. In 1961 the total income from cancer societies was $38,494,171. Of this 60 per cent was allocated to Divisions and Unit programs. Expenditures were as follows:

Research	$11,061,317
Education	9,827,202
Service	7,350,626
Fund-raising	3,730,890
Administration	2,775,826

Program

Thus, approximately 29 per cent of the society's funds is devoted to public education, the present best method of saving lives from cancer. The Public Education program features intense public programs of information about cancer and its early symptoms; this is attained by efforts devoted to: (1) secondary school and college students, (2) club and organization members, (3) employees of business and industry, (4) neighborhood groups and (5) the general public. The public is urged to seek medical consultation and advice whenever any of the early symptoms of cancer occur. Also, regular cancer-detection examinations by qualified physicians are stressed.

The Professional Education program aims to enlighten the medical profession as far as the early detection, early diagnosis and treatment of cancer is concerned. Fellowships and training grants are given, not only to doctors but to nurses and medical technicians. Excellent teaching films have been produced.

Cytological examinations for cancer have been furthered by the American Cancer Society, and a certain amount of individual care of cancer patients has been undertaken.

AMERICAN HEART ASSOCIATION

Perhaps it is logical that the American Heart Association should have emerged from efforts by the National Tuberculosis Association and its constituents to develop an organization devoted to the chief cause of American death. The heart is contiguous to the lungs and pumps blood through them; it is visible on every chest x-ray. It has been looked at with more or less curiosity and understanding by every so-called chest specialist.

Heart specialists had been organizing to a certain extent since early in the century; some say that the Heart Association was actually formed in the early twenties, but the fact is that tuberculosis associations were in existence and they had begun heart divisions which carried the early load and actually led to the formation of the American Heart Association, modeled partly along the lines of the National Tuberculosis Association. In 1948 the Executive Secretary of the Heart Association had his office in the headquarters of the National Tuberculosis Association, which donated the space and contributed $10,000 a year to its support. Some proposed out-right marriage of the heart and tuberculosis agencies and even went so far as to include cancer, but nothing happened. It soon became obvious that the Heart Association was about to stand on its own feet. Dr. David B. Rutestein was appointed Medical Director in 1946 and was influential in securing lay member-ship with all its benefits. By 1948 the society had become truly a voluntary health organization with well-recognized lay and medical membership. Early fund-raising activities were ham-pered by internal dissension, but Ralph Edwards really started the ball rolling by a contest on his radio program, "Truth or Consequences"; most of us remember the "Walking Man." Edwards raised $1,570,000. This, combined with an addi-tional million raised by eighteen state affiliates, made a total of two and a half million dollars, almost one third of which went into research. The Heart Association had grown up.

Major Purpose

At present the Heart Association states that its chief efforts are directed toward the integration of research, professional and public education, and community services for control and ultimate conquest of diseases of the heart and blood vessels.

National Structure

A Board of Directors of 120 members, 65 of whom are physicians, are elected by the Assembly from nominations of state affiliates. The Assembly is a body of 440 delegates elected by the state affiliates, local chapters and scientific coun-cils. Its membership is half medical and half lay. There is a voting membership of over 20,000 medical and 15,000 lay people. There are 55 affiliated state and territorial associations, 296 local chapters and more than 3,000 heart councils and committees.

Fund-Raising

The American Heart Association carries on a February Heart Fund campaign. In addition, about 11 per cent of the income is contributed by bequests and other contributions. Altogether this raises approximately $26,000,000 a year. Expenditures were as follows in 1961:

Research	$4,067,406
Medical programs	721,766
Public education	516,523
Community services	405,599
Administration	413,100
Organization and Development	303,174
Fund-raising	371,665

Approximately 60 per cent of prorated funds are allocated through the Research Committee for projects and research fellows and established investigators. Thirty per cent of the funds remain with local chapters and, prorated to states, are also allocated to research. Approximately 10 per cent is allocated to professional education. The American Heart Association publishes four excellent scientific journals: *Circulation, Circulation Research, Modern Concepts of Cardiovascular Disease,* and *The Heart Bulletin,* as well as much additional material, both medical and lay. Of the money, 7.5 per cent is allocated to public education.

THE NATIONAL FOUNDATION

The first steps toward organizing a systematic voluntary battle against poliomyelitis were taken in 1933. Franklin D. Roosevelt, newly elected President of the United States and partially crippled as a result of polio, believed that swimming at Warm Springs, Georgia, was beneficial for him and should benefit others. To obtain additional support for the Warm Springs Foundation, a National Committee for the Birthday Ball for the President was formed and funds raised by the annual balls. The first one was held January 30, 1934, and the National Committee collected over one million dollars. The second and third raised much less.

At this point Basil O'Connor, who became and was to remain the chief moving spirit of the National Foundation, reached the conclusion that a permanent independent polio foundation would be necessary and that too much identification with the President was unwise. Nevertheless, in 1937 the President himself was chosen to announce the formation of a new foundation to combat polio, and in 1938 the National Foundation for Infantile Paralysis was born. Basil O'Connor was elected president.

Apparently every major voluntary health agency has had its stormy petrel; dapper Basil O'Conner was no exception for the National Foundation. Surrounded by tycoons of American business and flanked by stars of the screen and stage, he set in motion the March of Dimes that proved to be one of the greatest fund-raising ventures of recent times—and it is still marching. What followed is history. The development of the Salk vaccine and later the live-virus vaccine were projects undertaken and supported by the National Foundation.

The major purpose of the Foundation as outlined in the American Medical Association handbook (1962 edition) is as follows:

The National Foundation for Infantile Paralysis was organized in 1938, to lead, direct, and unify the fight against poliomyelitis by promoting study and research into the cause, nature and prevention of poliomyelitis and prevention of its harmful sequelae as well as to provide medical care for patients afflicted with the disease. In 1958 the National Foundation shortened its name and expanded its objectives to become an organized force for medical research, patient care and professional education (with specific goals initially), flexible enough to meet new health problems as they arise. Its initial program covers arthritis, birth defects (congenital malformations), virus diseases, disorders of the central nervous system, as well as poliomyelitis.

Organizational Structure

A Board of Trustees forms the 30-man membership of the National Foundation. This board grants charters to local groups for the formation of chapters. There are medical committees that advise the board in medical matters. These consist of a Committee on Research, both for the basic sciences and for the medical sciences, a Committee on Professional Education which includes research and a Committee on Research and Medical Care. Members of these committees are appointed by the President at the recommendation of the Vice-President for Medical Affairs.

There are 3,100 local chapters in the United States and administered areas. These local chapters in general subscribe to the over-all policy of the National Foundation and submit financial audits directly to the National Foundation. The 3,100 local chapters receive medical advice from approximately 8,000 members of county medical societies, who constitute the chapters' medical advisory committees.

Finance

Financing is now carried on by the new March of Dimes. This is one of the most effective fund-raising mechanisms in the United States. In 1961 it grossed over $26,900,000. In addition to the March of Dimes, there are certain other sources of income, including donations and interest. The funds are divided 25 per cent to a National Medical Research Fund and on a 50-50 basis between the local chapters and national headquarters to be expended for research, medical care projects, and health education, both medical and lay. The latest audited figures, as given in the American Medical Association handbook, are:

Research	$ 5,220,000
Education	4,081,000
Medical care program	11,993,000
Community services	2,505,000
Administration	2,296,000
Fund-raising	4,900,000

Program

Until recently the program of the National Foundation was devoted almost entirely to polio research. With the development of the Salk vaccine, research has been supported to increase the effectiveness of this vaccine and to promote development of live polio virus vaccine. Research has been undertaken in the effort to find a drug effective against polio virus and to improve general methods of treatment of severely involved polio patients. Recent research into the nature of other enteric viruses that apparently cause diseases similar to the milder forms of poliomyelitis has been undertaken, and since virology has been such a fundamental aspect of the program up to the present time, the Foundation has supported basic research on virus genetics. Also, owing to the nature of poliomyelitis the Foundation has encouraged further research on congenital disorders of the nervous system and disorders of this system supposedly caused by viruses.

Research into the cause and prevention of birth defects has been supported, and recently the Foundation has supported research into the nature of rheumatoid arthritis, hoping to find a cure for this disease as well. Along these lines early detection and better treatment technics have received attention.

In the field of education, grants have been made to medical schools to improve their teaching programs and to professional associations to improve standards of education and practice. Fellowships and scholarships on basic and clinical education at the graduate and postdoctorate levels have been supported.

THE NATIONAL COUNCIL ON ALCOHOLISM

The National Council on Alcoholism, Inc., of 2 East 103rd Street, New York 29, New York, was organized in 1944 and is a voluntary agency devoted to the control and prevention of alcoholism through education, research and community services. It is the only agency in the field that provides inclusive services for a broader public health program on a national and international level. It is governed by 350 contributing and participating voting members who elect the Board of Directors. The Board, which actually constitutes the policy-making body of the Council, is composed of 58 members, 10 of whom are physicians.

As in most other national voluntary health agencies, local councils on alcoholism must meet stated qualifications before acceptance by the national organization. They must provide regular audits and reports and must have shown themselves to be a representative community organization with established progress. There are, at present, 68 affiliated local councils on alcoholism.

In 1961, the total receipts of national and local organizations were $8,808,746; $28,496 were spent on fund raising and $45,201 were used in administration. The program involved rather extended expenditures for research, education and services. The research program included a grant for biochemical research on alcoholism made to the University of Tennessee Medical School and various cooperative grants made in conjunction with the federal government. Mrs. Marty Mann, the Executive Director, is a dynamic, able executive and an accomplished public speaker.

THE NATIONAL ASSOCIATION FOR MENTAL HEALTH

The National Association for Mental Health, 10 Columbus Circle, New York 19, New York, was incorporated in 1950 as a consolidation of the three principal national voluntary health agencies at that time working in the field of mental health. Its purposes were to develop a coordinated citizens' voluntary movement to work toward the improved care and treatment of the mentally ill and handicapped; for improved methods and services in research, prevention, detection, diagnosing and treatment of mental illness and handicaps; and for the promotion of mental health.

Voting membership consists of five delegates from each affiliated state association plus members at large of the Board of Directors. The Board of Directors consists of 83 members, of whom 8 are physicians elected by the voting membership. There is also a professional advisory council appointed by the President which determines medical policy. There are 47 affiliated state associations with 700 local chapters. Fund raising is by means of local mental health campaigns and by participation in United Fund and Community Chest activities. The national office solicits grants from foundations, corporations and individuals and also receives income from the sale of literature and from unsolicited contributions and legacies. The total receipts on the national, state and local levels for 1961 were given as approximately $6,000,000. Sixty per cent of these funds remain in the local chapter, 20% in the state office and 20% in the national office.

Mr. Phillip E. Ryan, the present Executive Director, has had extensive experience in voluntary health service work and in the past was an able executive with the National Health Council. He will undoubtedly prove to be a very valuable addition to the staff of this dynamic and capable organization. In 1961 approximately 60% of funds were allocated to research and 33% to national education.

In view of the importance of mental health in modern society, this organization probably has a major opportunity for future development.

There are many other worthy voluntary health agencies,

large and small, young and old, which are impossible to list here. The essential facts regarding these agencies may be found in the *Handbook of Medical Societies and Individual Physicians on National Voluntary Health Agencies,* 1962 edition, published by the American Medical Association. The data given in this handbook will furnish the reader with the information necessary to judge whether the programs of the organizations are good or not. The handbook is recommended as a reference volume for all who are interested.

NATIONAL HEALTH COUNCIL

This organization is composed of the various health agencies in the United States. It arose as a result of efforts of the late Dr. Livingston Farrand, the first Managing Director of the National Tuberculosis Association, and George G. Vinson, President of the Rockefeller Foundation, who believed that the time had come in 1920 for some joint planning and coordination of the various agencies interested in health problems. Dr. Farrand commissioned Dr. Donald Armstrong, who had headed the Framingham Demonstration of the National Tuberculosis Association, to study the matter, and in 1921 the organization known as the National Health Council opened its office. Charter members were:

American Medical Association's Council on Health and Public Instruction
American Public Health Association
American National Red Cross
American Social Hygiene Association
Conference of State and Provincial Health Officers of North America
National Child Health Council
National Committee for Mental Hygiene
National Tuberculosis Association
National Organization for Public Health Nursing
United States Public Health Service's Council on Advisory Members

This list has gradually expanded to take in most of the active national health agencies in the United States.

As in the case of most of the voluntary health agencies, the early years of the National Health Council were marked by storm and stress. Financing was a difficult problem. After many lean years, in 1948 the Rockefeller Foundation generously offered $75,000 per year for three years, during which the member agencies were urged to take over active support to insure the continuance of the Council. It was believed that a minimum of $15,000 per annum from the agencies was required. The National Tuberculosis Association, always a prime mover in the affairs of the National Health Council, offered $5,000, and matching sums were provided by the American Cancer Society and the American National Red Cross. By 1952 there were 39 member agencies, and the annual contributions from the agencies had increased to over $100,000.

Growing Criticisms

What about the voluntary health agencies? Are they good or bad or both? If they have faults, should or can these be corrected? How?

For several years groups of private citizens and, indeed, the voluntary health agencies themselves had been asking these questions. The National Health Council had interested itself in the problem and had been studying the feasibility of recommending uniform accounting procedures to various agencies in order to eliminate the complaint that it was impossible to estimate the true cost of fund-raising or overhead.

Finally in 1958, in response to growing public pressure, the Rockefeller Foundation formed a committee to survey the voluntary health and welfare agencies in the United States and to make suitable recommendations. Robert H. Hamlin, M.D. was appointed study director, and the result of the study, entitled "Voluntary Health and Welfare Agencies in the United States; an Exploratory Study by an Ad Hoc Citizens Committee," was published in 1961 (2). There were three principal recommendations:

1. The Committee is very earnest in recommending that a new National Commission on Voluntary Health and Welfare Agencies be created to continue the Committee's unfinished task. Full details will be found in the text of this report. Such a Commission could stand as a court of appeal for the agencies themselves. It could develop criteria for a better appraisal of the work of voluntary agencies. It could develop methods to assist in strengthening coordinated planning by the agencies. And, finally, it could give continuing thought to the changing role of voluntary agencies in our dynamic society.

2. It is the firm belief of the Committee that every agency supported by contributions from the public is under an obligation of public accountability. It owes the public a full and frank disclosure of its programs and their financing. No agency should claim to be in exclusive possession of a patented method of social salvation.

3. The obligation of full disclosure and accountability leads to a second recommendation of this Committee, namely, that a system of uniform accounting be developed by the American Institute of Certified Public Accountants. This would greatly facilitate the work of budget reviewing bodies, potential contributors, and voluntary agencies themselves.

Whether Dr. Hamlin was surprised at the storm the Committee report aroused can only be surmised. He undoubtedly contributed to the uproar by mentioning the report at a meeting of the National Tuberculosis Association held in Cincinnati in May, 1961, and discussing the report with newspaper representatives afterward. Headlines blazed. Here was material of interest to every citizen of charitable intent.

Not the least interested were officials of the health agencies themselves. In an address entitled "Government by Elite Vigilantes," presented at the 1962 New March of Dimes Pre-Campaign Meetings September 1961, Basil O'Connor commented:

National voluntary health organizations do not in fact vary in their organizational structure or their methods of conducting their activities from the well-known units of activity in American life, such as industrial corporations or universities or the so-called private foundations which have the responsibility of administering twelve billion tax-exempt dollars, which are public funds belonging to the American people.

National voluntary health agencies have a successful record of achievement based upon courageous pioneering in general and special cases.

Before there were any National Institutes of Health in the federal government, and for at least ten years after the first one was created, the national voluntary health organizations were one of the few sources for support of research in the field of life sciences. There can be no question that the activity of these organizations was an important factor in bringing to the attention of the federal government its responsibility for the health of the people of this country and its increasing activity in that area.

In the area of medical scientific research the national voluntary health agencies have caused the American people to become "research minded"; they have demonstrated the necessity and value of basic research in the life sciences . . . and are responsible for intensive and extensive programs of scientific research on specific diseases.

In the area of professional education, they have promoted interest in medical careers at all levels through the offering of scholarships, fellowships and support of professional associations.

Despite the similarity of structure and general activity which the national voluntary health agencies bear to the other types of organizations I mentioned, they have been the object of continued vicious and unwarranted attack in all media of communication for a period of fifteen years, beginning with the publication of the Gunn-Platt Report on voluntary health agencies sponsored and financed by the Rockefeller Foundation. This report recommended and caused the creation by others of a national organization to compel all public fund-raising in the field of health or welfare to be done through one organization . . . In 1960 alone at least fourteen vicious and unwarranted attacks were made in the press and magazines on the national voluntary health agencies.

In May, 1960, in response to numerous requests the Rockefeller Foundation invited a group of knowledgeable citizens to reassess the role and responsibility of the voluntary health and welfare agencies in the United States.

As a result of the invitation of the Rockefeller Foundation, an Ad Hoc Committee of distinguished citizens was organized to explore eight so-called "complex issues," which were in no sense "complex" to the national voluntary health agencies that had fully explored them on more than one occasion in the ordinary course of their activities. . . . A Study Director was appointed. . . . I think it would not be claimed that the Study Director had any special qualifications for the task imposed upon him and I think examination of the facts would show clearly that he did not spend an amount of time with the voluntary health agencies that would enable him to make intelligent recommendations to the Rockefeller Committee . . . In Cincinnati, Ohio, on May 22, 1961, this Study Director publicly made the charge, which was carried by the press, that "national voluntary health agencies are wasting the American people's money and misleading them on how it is spent.

Commented tall, scholarly, and usually mild-tempered Dr. James E. Perkins, Executive Director of the National Tuberculosis Association:

The National Tuberculosis Association welcomes the report by Dr. Robert H. Hamlin on his exploratory study of voluntary health and welfare agencies in the United States to the extent that it presents interesting and important data and constructive recommendations, although I do not completely agree with all of the recommendations contained in the report.

I would like to stress that the study was necessarily superficial and represented, for the most part, Dr. Hamlin's own personal observations and opinions. In support of this, I would like to point out that the names of the ad hoc committee were attached only to the Foreword of the report, and that the Foreword itself stressed that the members of the committee would not subscribe without reservation to every particular in the report, nor would they give equal emphasis to each point.

One disadvantage of the report is that Dr. Hamlin has lumped together all of the various welfare agencies with the health agencies, although they are necessarily quite different. There is, of course, some welfare aspect to almost every health problem and some health aspect to almost every welfare problem, but many of the comments in the report obviously refer much more to welfare agencies than to health agencies. This makes it seem as if many of the criticisms and recommendations were directed as much at the health agencies as at the welfare agencies, which in many instances is simply not true.

I am particularly critical of the report because it gives short shrift to the current activities and program of the National Health Council, which is and has been doing precisely many of the things recommended by Dr. Hamlin. The National Health Council has grown steadily in recent years until it has in its membership every major health agency, both governmental and voluntary, in the United States. It has an important ongoing program of coordination, joint planning, and the conducting of certain projects which can best be done by a centralized organization like itself, yet are of extreme importance to the programs of its member agencies. Indeed, several Health Council projects were underway long before the Hamlin study was undertaken.

I refer to the *Uniform Accounting Principles Project* of the National Health Council, which has been conducted during the past year, supported entirely by contributions from Council members concerned. A report on this project will be published later this year. There is also the NHC *Study of the Current Role of the Voluntary Health Agency* begun in 1959. A statement on the results of this study will also be available in the near future.

Also, the *Health Careers Project* of the National Health Council, supported largely by the member agencies, has made significant advances in getting young people interested in some health career to help meet the current personnel shortage referred to by Dr. Hamlin in his report.

Large sums would no doubt be required for the National Commission on Voluntary Health and Welfare Agencies proposed in the Hamlin report. Such funds, insofar as health agencies are concerned, could be used far more effectively by the National Health Council to implement the projects which it would like to embark upon but cannot because of a lack of funds.

The Rockefeller Foundation, incidentally, was largely responsible for the development of the current National Health Council through substantial financial support for a three-year period after World War II. However, I must criticize the foundations for their lack of substantial support of the National Health Council and its projects. I want to point out that the Health Careers Project is nowhere as effective as it might be because decreased support by the foundations could not be offset by the substantial increased support by the voluntary health agencies themselves. A recent attempt to get some additional money for the Health Careers Project from foundations was completely unsuccessful. As a result, this very important project has had to be curtailed.

Additional funds from foundations for the National Health Council would enable it to assist immediately in the implementation of the Uniform Accounting Principles Project as soon as the final report is available within a few months.

Another important project which antedates the Hamlin report is the proposed National Commission on Community Health Services, a joint project of the National Health Council and the American Public Health Association. Here again, recent attempts to obtain funds from foundations have been unsuccessful. Yet, with Congress about to pass the new Community Services Bill (HR 49981), an intensive study of the best utilization of such funds through adequate community health service programs would seem to be imperative if these many millions of dollars, about to be made available by Congress, are to be spent most wisely.

I seriously question whether any further intensive study of the voluntary national health agencies would identify any additional problems or suggest any solutions beyond these contained in the current report of Dr. Hamlin's group. Various national voluntary health agencies, NTA among them, were glad to cooperate with Dr. Hamlin in his study and spent many hours with him or in preparing reports which he requested for his study. Further expenditure of precious time, money, and energy along these lines by the voluntary health agencies would not be fruitful, in my opinion, and could better be devoted to the important activities of the health agencies themselves.

In spite of these criticisms Dr. Hamlin believes the recommendations of the Committee should be carried out and that, if they are not, the national voluntary health agencies may find themselves in serious trouble. Whether the forthcoming report of the National Health Council on uniform accounting practices will answer some of the questions remains to be seen.

Undoubtedly further "Hamlin reports" will appear. The current areas of disagreement between the voluntary health agencies and United Funds must be straightened out at all levels, both as regards fund-raising and program. There is need for both bodies.

The American Medical Association has attempted to view with sympathetic understanding the problems that have plagued the philanthropic organizations devoted to the betterment of health and welfare in the United States and to offer its aid and council whenever requested. Its publications have been impartial and factual with the aim of giving the reader the data which would enable him to arrive at his own conclusions regarding the worth and stature of the organizations involved. Most of the facts needed may be found in the AMA handbook on voluntary health agencies (3), published in 1962.

REFERENCES

1. Gunn-Platt Report on Voluntary Health Agencies (New York: The Rockefeller Foundation, 1945).
2. Hamlin, R. H.: Voluntary Health and Welfare Agencies: an exploratory study by an ad hoc citizens committee (New York: The Rockefeller Foundation, 1961).
3. *AMA Handbook for Medical Societies and Individual Physicians on National Voluntary Health Agencies* (Chicago: The American Medical Association, 1962).
4. Carter, R.: The Gentle Legions (Garden City, N.Y.: Doubleday & Company, 1961).

JOHN D. PORTERFIELD, M.D.

Dr. Porterfield is Coordinator, Medical and Health Sciences, University of California, having served for 5 years as Deputy Surgeon General of the U.S. Public Health Service. Upon graduation from Rush Medical College, Chicago, he interned at the Public Health Service Hospital, San Francisco, receiving his commission in USPHS in 1939. His various Service assignments have been in the program on mental health, hospital facilities, venereal disease control, and research grants. He has a degree in Public Health from Johns Hopkins University. He is a past-president of the American College of Preventive Medicine and is President-Elect of the American Public Health Association.

9. Government In Health

A NATION'S HEALTH is the product of many factors: the inheritance and experience of each of its members; the state of its economic, social, and cultural development; environment; and the stage of scientific knowledge and development, among others. In recent years health has been increasingly described as a "right," commensurate with the other basic rights of mankind. People everywhere have a rising expectation about health. And they are looking to the organized efforts of society to meet those expectations.

Yet neither government, nor private organizations, nor the health professions can present health to mankind as a right or gift. In the final analysis, the most they can do is increase the possibilities for health. Governments can act to increase man's health potential by fostering the advance of scientific knowledge and by assuring that the means for health are available to all the people. A large proportion of the health protection and services afforded the people stem from the activities of government—at all levels. The quality and scope of health activities undertaken by the central government reflect the concern of the nation's leaders for the health of the people.

The United States government administers a wide variety of programs directly affecting the health of mankind. Its actions in this field, as in others, are founded upon laws enacted by the people's elected representatives under the terms of the United States Constitution.

CONSTITUTIONAL BASES OF HEALTH ACTIVITY

By the time they reach high school, most American school children have memorized the Preamble to the Constitution and have some rudimentary knowledge of what the entire document contains. Unfortunately, only a small percentage of the educated adult population has gone beyond that point to acquire a mature comprehension of the federal system of government under which the nation lives and operates.

In a brief survey like this, of course, it is not possible to dwell on the details or implications of that system. To understand the constitutional bases of health activities, however, the following salient facts must be kept in mind:

1. The Constitution establishes the United States government in three branches with separate powers: (a) the Congress, a bicameral legislature, to make the national laws; (b) an executive branch, headed by the President, to administer the national laws; and (c) a judicial branch to interpret the laws.

2. The United States government has no powers except those which are granted to it by the Constitution. Those powers are substantial, however, and the government has the

authority to exercise them over both the states and the individual citizens.

3. The Constitution and national laws are superior to state constitutions and laws. Article VI makes this fact clear:

This Constitution, and the laws of the United States which shall be made in pursuance thereof; and all Treaties made, or which shall be made, under the authority of the United States, shall be the supreme law of the land; and the Judges in every State shall be bound thereby, any Thing in the Constitution or Laws of any State to the Contrary notwithstanding.

All elected and appointed officials of all three branches of the federal government and of every state government are bound by "Oath or Affirmation, to support this Constitution."

4. The states are inseparable units of one nation; they are not independent governments. The Constitution delegates certain powers to the federal government; it prohibits certain other powers to the states; and it reserves all powers not so delegated or prohibited to the states or to the people. Around these provisions the so-called states' rights issue has arisen frequently from the earliest years of the nation to the present time.

The "reserved" powers of the states are not clearly defined. From time to time, controversy arises as to whether a power asserted by the federal government or by a state is valid under the Constitution. No state may determine such issues. The Supreme Court determines the line between federal and state powers, and its decisions have the force of national law.

5. The states have broad powers within their own borders. Each state organizes its own government and raises revenue to support it. It has the power to set up local governments and to authorize these governments to levy local taxes. No two states have precisely the same system of local government; and no state applies one system throughout its jurisdiction.

State governments exercise most of the inspectional, licensing, and regulatory powers which are designed to protect the natural resources, the safety, health, and morals of their citizens. The power of the states to legislate for these purposes is known as "the police power." The exercise of this power has given rise to the states' fifty sanitary codes, their different requirements for marriage and divorce, legal adoption, education and employment of children, licensure of practitioners of the healing arts, safety of buildings, eligibility for public assistance and public medical care, commitment of the mentally ill and mentally retarded, and a host of other matters directly affecting the lives of people.

The federal government exercises no authority in any of these matters, except in territory under its jurisdiction and in instances involving two or more states. The federal laws affecting foods, drugs, cosmetics, and biologic products sold in interstate commerce, for example, are regulatory in character; but they do not cover the production and sale of these items within a state. State laws and regulations apply in such circumstances.

FEDERAL AND STATE POWERS IN HEALTH

The division of federal and state powers in health matters creates some inconsistencies which are difficult to explain. As one example, an annual federal grant for cancer-control activities has been allotted to each state for the past twelve years. But there is no unified approach to the problem of cancer control. One state may provide cancer diagnosis and treatment for any citizen requesting those services; another may conduct research in cancer and provide comprehensive services for medically indigent patients; still another may provide laboratory diagnostic services to any physician requiring it. And many states conduct surveys and educational programs or require the routine reporting of cancer cases, but do not provide any specific services for the control of cancer.

The fact that the federal government has not acted to correct such inconsistencies does not mean that it is without the power to act. Other considerations enter the picture. Aside from the fact that there may be advantages in pursuing a variety of approaches to any given problem, professional leadership is best exercised through precept and mutual endeavor rather than through coercion.

The development of a national program to control water pollution illustrates how the potential and active powers of the federal government operate. Early in this century it began to be known that the nation's great river systems would become sources of pollution as the cities and industries along the waterways grew. At that time, the purification of public water supplies was believed to be the answer to a major public health problem, i.e., the spread of water-borne enteric diseases. The federal government took no action except to conduct investigations on the pollution of inland waters.

By the time of World War II, the need for federal action to control the interstate pollution of water resources was widely recognized, although some states and industrial groups opposed any assertion of federal authority in this field. In 1948, Congress enacted legislation which instructed the U.S. Public Health Service to "develop a comprehensive water pollution control program." It authorized grants to the states for this purpose and the conduct of research and investigations. There were no provisions for federal action to require the elimination of sources of pollution within any state.

This law was amended and its provisions expanded in 1956 and again in 1961. Authority was added to award research grants and to make grants to municipalities for the construction of waste treatment plants. Enforcement authority was included in the 1956 legislation; the federal government was empowered to conduct hearings on interstate pollution, to issue cease and desist orders and to prosecute offenders in the federal courts. The 1961 law strengthened these enforcement powers, principally by extending the federal enforcement jurisdiction to intrastate as well as interstate waters under suitable safeguards. This law also established water quality as a criterion in planning and building federal reservoirs.

In this instance, therefore, the federal government has asserted an increasing degree of active power to control a national health problem.

The Constitution does not delegate specific powers to the government for health purposes. Nor are many of the state constitutions specific in this respect. This omission is not surprising when it is recalled that the words health and welfare did not mean the same things in the eighteenth century as they do in the twentieth century. By and large, health was considered a personal affair, a matter to be solved by each individual as best he could. The concept that society has a stake in health and can intervene to improve human health is of comparatively recent origin. On the other hand, the general terms in which the framers of the Constitution expressed the powers of the government to act in the national interest have proved adequate for the changing health needs and aims of the American people.

The federal government exercises its powers for health activities under the Preamble and the following provisions of the United States Constitution:

1. The power to regulate commerce with foreign nations, and among the several states, and with the Indian tribes (Article I, Sec. 8, Par. 1).
2. The powers of taxation . . . " to provide for the common defense and general welfare" (Article I, Sec. 8, Par. 3).
3. The powers to raise and support armies, to provide and maintain a navy, and to make rules for the government and regulation of the land and naval forces (Article III, Sec. 8, Pars. 12-14).
4. The power to exercise exclusive legislation in federal territory, such as the District of Columbia, military bases, national parks, Indian reservations, and so on (Article I, Sec. 8, Par. 17).
5. The power to make treaties (Article II, Sec. 2, Par. 2).
6. The power "to make all laws which shall be necessary and proper for carrying into Execution the foregoing Powers, and all

other Powers vested by this Constitution in the Government of the United States, or in any Department or Officer thereof" (Article III, Sec. 8, Par. 18).

Governmental activities, of course, rest on the authority of the Congress to appropriate tax monies for their support.

FEDERAL HEALTH FUNCTIONS

The health activities of the government are authorized by specific laws designed to achieve specific purposes. Financed by appropriations passed by the Congress each year, the programs are administered by various departments, agencies and commissions of the federal government. In general, the programs deal with the health of the general population, with the health of special groups in the population and with international health matters. The following lists show areas of federal concern in the three categories.

General Population

1. Protection against health hazards affecting the entire population.

2. Identification of national health problems and development of plans to meet those problems.

3. Advancement of the health sciences through research and training.

4. Development of health facilities and resources.

5. Support of public health services provided by state and local bodies.

6. Collection and dissemination of national vital and health statistics and related data.

7. Protection against the importation of communicable diseases from abroad.

8. Organization and support of disaster and emergency health services.

Special Population Groups

1. Protection of certain groups in the population against hazardous occupations and adverse working conditions.

2. Support of health services provided by state and local agencies for children, the blind, the handicapped.

3. Payment for medical care programs administered by state and local agencies for the indigent and other financially dependent groups.

4. Provision of special services for farm families.

5. Provision of hospital and medical care to members of the armed services and their dependents, veterans, merchant seamen, American Indians and Alaska natives, federal prisoners, narcotic addicts, patients with leprosy and civil service employees of the government injured as a result of their employment.

6. Provision of hospital and medical expense insurance for civil service employees of the federal government.

International Health

1. Membership in the United Nations and participation in its specialized agencies, such as the World Health Organization.

2. Membership in the Pan American Union, the Organization of American States, the Southeast Asia Treaty Organization and participation in the health activities of these organizations.

3. Cooperation, under treaties with the governments of Canada and Mexico, in the solution of health problems on the northern and southern borders of the United States.

4. Participation in cooperative health programs under treaties with countries in Central and South America, Africa, the Eastern Mediterranean, Southeast Asia and the Southwest Pacific.

5. Support of health research in foreign countries and training of health personnel from foreign countries.

Distribution of Federal Health Functions

The functions listed above are widely dispersed in the structure of the federal government, as are counterpart activities in state and local governments. In the past two decades, however, there have been continuing efforts to coordinate related activities.

The federal government has, for the most part, grouped its health and medical activities for the general population with related programs in the fields of social insurance, public assistance and education. The Department of Health, Education, and Welfare is the unit principally responsible for these general functions.

Many other federal agencies have health functions which are secondary or supplementary to their main mission. Thus, the Departments of the Army, Navy, and Air Force, the Veterans Administration, and the Department of Justice administer medical services for military personnel and their dependents, veterans, and federal prisoners, respectively. The Department of State operates a medical program for Foreign Service personnel on duty outside the United States.

The Department of Labor administers federal laws relating to conditions of work, including industrial health and safety standards. The Bureau of Mines of the Department of the Interior has responsibility for safety and healthful working conditions in mineral industries.

Some industries have a direct bearing on the public safety. The federal government exercises regulatory powers over these industries, and establishes standards of health and conditions of work for those employees on whom public safety may depend. Among the federal agencies concerned with these matters are: The Atomic Energy Commission, the Federal Aviation Agency, the Coast Guard and the Interstate Commerce Commission.

The Department of Agriculture administers several programs which are related to human health. It has a program, for example, to develop new knowledge of nutrition and better use of food. It regulates livestock in order to eradicate animal diseases and, in so doing, contributes substantially to the control of such human diseases as tuberculosis, brucellosis and trichinosis. This Department is also responsible for inspecting domestic and imported meats and meat products.

The international affairs of the government are administered by the Department of State. The Department has adopted the policy of designating appropriate federal agencies to represent this nation in the specialized agencies of the United Nations. Thus, the Public Health Service participates, on behalf of the United States, in the World Health Organization and the Pan American Health Organization. In bilateral programs administered by the Agency for International Development, the Department of State also calls upon other federal agencies for technical assistance in education, health, agriculture and other fields.

Research

Since early in the nineteenth century, research and the systematic collection of data have been important activities of government. For more than a hundred years, the emphasis was on the sciences important in an agricultural economy and on the exploration of vast uncharted territories. Until World War I, medical research concentrated on the control of infectious diseases.

In the past three decades, however, with the great growth of population, cities and industries, the needs changed radically. During World War II, federal research and development increased sharply; but it was not until the postwar period that the government played a significant role in the support of science. The annual expenditures of the federal government for research and development increased from $624 million in 1947 to $7 billion in 1959. Most of these funds (about 75 per cent) support the research work of scientists outside the federal government, who receive federal grants or work under federal contracts. Science training is also aided through scholarships, aid to educational institutions and student loans.

Public Health Service research programs in health and related fields constitute the major scientific effort of the federal government. About half of the nation's total health research is supported by Public Health Service grants. In some fields, such as research in hospital administration and in air and water pollution, the proportion is higher. Several other federal agencies conduct or support research in biology, medicine, engineering and other disciplines related to health. Among these are:

Departments of the Army, Navy, and Air Force: Laboratory and clinical research on problems related to military, naval, and aviation medicine.

Department of Agriculture: Basic and applied research on soil and water conservation, animal and plant diseases, entomology, human nutrition, and farm and home economics.

Atomic Energy Commission: Basic and applied research in biology and medicine with respect to the effects of nuclear energy, radiation, and fissionable materials.

National Aeronautics and Space Administration: Research and development in space medicine and related fields, including biological, physiological, and neuropsychiatric studies.

National Science Foundation: Support of basic research and education in the sciences through contracts, scholarships, and graduate fellowships; clearinghouse for scientific and technical information.

National Academy of Sciences–National Research Council: The Academy, a quasi-official agency under Congressional charter, receives funds only for research projects undertaken at the request of the government. Its members are distinguished scientists elected annually by the current membership. Its Council is composed of the elected officers of the Academy, six other elected members, and about 225 individuals appointed by the President from academic, industrial, and governmental organizations. The Council plans and stimulates research on scientific problems which require the cooperation of scientists in a variety of fields.

Statistical Services

The socio-economic trends which contributed to an expanded governmental effort in research also led to an increase in the types of numerical data gathered by the government. Every major agency of the Federal Government collects, analyzes and disseminates data in its field. Statistics and auditing are, in fact, among the principal means by which these agencies render an account of their stewardship. The sole purpose of some agencies, however, is to provide reliable data on various aspects of the nation's resources. The following are of particular interest in the health field:

The Bureau of the Census, the nation's comprehensive statistical center, gathers continuous, up-to-date demographic data. Besides the enumeration of population, it conducts periodic censuses on housing, agriculture, manufacture, mineral industries and other subjects. Upon request, special surveys are conducted for other Federal agencies and for state and local governments.

The Bureau of Labor Statistics collects and analyzes data on employment, productivity, wages, housing construction, industrial relations, accidents, price trends and cost standards of living. Many of these studies provide basic information related to industrial health. In addition, the Consumers Price Index reports trends in drug prices and costs of hospital, medical, dental and nursing services.

The statistics and data-gathering activities of the Department of Health, Education, and Welfare will be described in the next section.

THE DEPARTMENT OF HEALTH, EDUCATION, AND WELFARE

The establishment of the Department of Health, Education, and Welfare in 1953 marked the culmination of nearly a century of effort by many leading citizens to create a national health agency with "cabinet status," that is, in the highest councils of government.

As health, education, and welfare services developed and as their interrelationship became increasingly apparent, various presidents, dating back to President Harding in 1923, sought to bring them together in one federal administrative agency. They were seen as a natural family of related services and their coordination was deemed highly desirable. In 1939, the Federal Security Agency, embodying most of the operating units of the present Department, was established.

In the following decade, several proposals were made to bring together all the medical services of the Federal Government in one administrative agency or to establish separate units for health, for education and for social welfare. None of these plans found acceptance, however, and Reorganization Plan No. 1 of 1953, authorized by the Congress earlier that year, created the Department of Health, Education, and Welfare. All of the functions of the former Federal Security Agency were transferred to the new Department. The principle underlying the organization also remained the same; namely, the grouping in one executive unit of those interrelated federal functions which have as their main purpose the advancement of *national* health, education and social welfare.

Figure 1 shows the organization of the Department. The Office of the Secretary is composed of policy level aides in program-planning and coordination and of a group of staff and administrative services. The Special Assistant to the Secretary for Health and Medical Affairs advises the Secretary on national health policy and legislation and reviews the programs of the Department in these fields.

The five major operating units of the Department are the Public Health Service, the Office of Education, the Social Security Administration, the Food and Drug Administration, and the Office of Vocational Rehabilitation. The Department also administers Saint Elizabeth's Hospital for the mentally

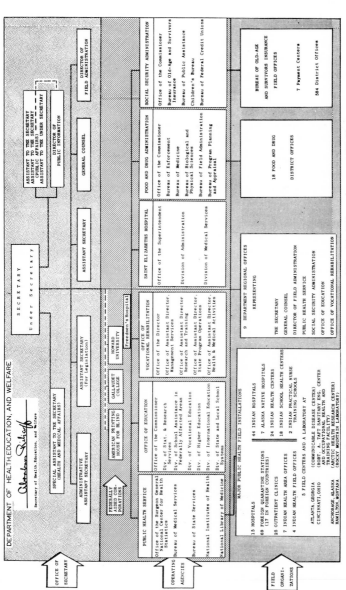

FIG. 1.—Organizational chart, Department of Health, Education, and Welfare.

ill (in Washington, D.C.) and supervises three federally aided corporations—Gallaudet College, the world's only college for the deaf, Howard University, and the American Printing House for the Blind.

The Department maintains nine regional offices, each headed by a regional director appointed by the Secretary, to administer its field activities. In addition to their personnel in the Regional Offices, the operating agencies of the Department maintain field offices necessary to their operations. These include the district offices of the Social Security Administration and the Food and Drug Administration; and the hospitals, quarantine stations, field laboratories, and Indian area offices of the Public Health Service.

In fiscal year 1961, the Department had a staff of more than 70,000 people and operated with a budget of almost $4 billion. The great bulk of this amount—almost 90 per cent of all the funds appropriated to the Department—was allocated to groups and agencies outside the federal government. These funds took the form of grants-in-aid to match and supplement state and local expenditures for health, education and welfare programs, and grants to colleges, universities, hospitals and scientific institutions for research and training programs.

Each of the operating agencies, of course, has a number of specific missions. The agencies also vary in size, method of operation and external relationships. Their programs and functions are described in the sections which follow.

Social Security Administration

The Social Security Administration is headed by the Commissioner of Social Security, who is appointed by the Secretary with the consent of the Senate. It is organized in four bureaus: the Bureau of Old Age and Survivors Insurance, the Bureau of Family Services, the Children's Bureau and the Bureau of Federal Credit Unions.

The Bureau of Old Age and Survivors Insurance (BOASI) administers the nation's social insurance system which is financed entirely by the Federal Old Age and Survivors Insurance Trust Fund. The Fund, which totaled approximately $21 billion in 1960, has been built up by tax contributions of employees and employers under the Social Security Act of 1935 and its amendments. About 75 million people are contributing to the fund, and about 13.7 million beneficiaries (individuals and families) are receiving OASI payments.

This program helps the people of the United States seek to maintain dignity and independence in their declining years, or when severe disability or death strikes the breadwinner. Over 90 per cent of the population are now covered by the Old Age and Survivors Insurance Program. Supplementary pension plans inaugurated by many employers or purchased by individual citizens substantially increase the benefits to millions of OASI beneficiaries.

In a quarter of a century, these combined efforts toward independent status have substantially reduced the need for public assistance to elderly people and to orphaned children. Despite the fact that there has been a great increase of people who are 65 years and over, it is anticipated that the number of disabled persons requiring public assistance will be reduced over the years.

A major problem in the administration of disability benefits to OASI beneficiaries is the medical determination of disability. This task is assigned to state vocational rehabilitation agencies which, in turn, purchase the medical examination of claimants for disability benefits from private practitioners. The expense is borne by the Trust Fund. There is considerable variation in the standards applied for the determination of disability, as well as in the fees charged for the examinations.

Only about 5 per cent of the 13.7 million OASI beneficiaries were receiving supplementary public assistance in 1959. Nevertheless, the Old Age and Survivors Insurance Program is frequently confused with the federal-state programs of public assistance. The latter refers to the payment by state and local governments of funds from general taxes (including federal grants) to individuals and families dependent upon society for the means of subsistence and medical care. Federal funds are used to aid the aged, dependent children, the blind and the totally and permanently disabled. The Bureau of Public Assistance administers this program.

The Social Security Act of 1935 did not provide for medical care of recipients of public assistance. The 1950 amendments to the Act, however, permitted the use of federal funds to purchase medical services on behalf of recipients of the four federally-aided categories of public assistance. Since then, there has been a continuous rise in federal, state and local expenditures for this purpose. In 1959, approximately $342 million in tax funds was paid by state public welfare agencies to individual physicians, hospitals, nursing homes and other sources of care. In addition, about $100 million was paid to needy individuals so that they could purchase medical services.

This annual expenditure of nearly half-a-billion dollars for the purchase of medical services for approximately 7 million individuals may seem excessive. Yet it provides only a very small proportion of the dependent population with the full range of preventive, curative and restorative medical services which could substantially reduce the costs of dependency.

In 1959, 38 of the 50 states had medical care programs. Most of these programs were administered by state welfare departments, but 13 were under the direction of physicians.

There is a very varied pattern in the administration of these programs. The services provided range from comprehensive preventive, curative, and restorative services to programs that merely purchase drugs. Many of the programs have no effective working arrangements with other public agencies which conduct medical programs, such as the state health department or vocational rehabilitation service. As a rule, physicians employed in state welfare departments have no responsibility other than to determine whether a blind person is blind or a disabled person is totally and permanently disabled. With or without medical administration, most state welfare departments purchase only palliative services, rarely preventive or restorative medical care.

The Chief of the Children's Bureau is appointed by the President with the advice and consent of the Senate. The Bureau administers grants to the states for three programs: maternal and child health services; crippled children's services; and child welfare services.

In 1960 Congress appropriated $46.5 million for these purposes. An additional sum of $1.5 million was appropriated to assist the states in providing surgical treatment for children with congenital heart defects. One half of the federal grants for maternal and child health and crippled children's services must be matched, dollar for dollar, with state funds. The remainder of the federal funds are distributed without matching, on the basis of financial need of each state. Federal grants for child welfare services must be matched by the states in full. State plans for each of these programs, which are administered by state health and welfare departments, are reviewed and approved by the Children's Bureau.

The Children's Bureau conducts surveys and studies of child life and allocates funds for special project grants for mentally retarded children. In recent years, emphasis has also been placed on juvenile delinquency and neurological disorders. The Bureau is cooperating with the National Institutes of Health of the Public Health Service in studies of cystic fibrosis, mental retardation and juvenile delinquency.

Office of Education

The Office of Education is headed by the Commissioner of Education, who is appointed by the President. The original function of the Office was the collection of statistics and information to show the conditions and progress of education in the United States. It still carries on this work and makes reports and studies available to state and local authorities.

Over the years, other responsibilities have been added to the work of the Office. These include making grants to land-grant colleges and administering the programs of federal aid for vocational education (including the training of practical nurses) and for schools in areas affected by federal activities. It also administers a program for the training of teachers of mentally retarded children.

The National Defense Education Act of 1958 established a number of programs designed to improve education in the United States, especially in the fields of science, mathematics and foreign languages. The Act authorized student loans, graduate fellowships, grants to the states and other measures to assist institutions of higher learning.

Office of Vocational Rehabilitation

The Office of Vocational Rehabilitation is administered by a Director appointed by the Secretary of Health, Education, and Welfare. The Office administers a comprehensive program designed to prepare for and restore disabled persons to useful work. It provides grants to state vocational rehabilitation agencies to help support and improve their services and to nonprofit institutions for research and demonstrations in physical medicine and rehabilitation and for the training of professional personnel in these fields.

Federal grants for rehabilitation services are allotted according to a formula based on population and per capita income of each state. Most of the state programs are organized in state departments of public instruction, under the direction of the state board of vocational education.

A National Advisory Council on Vocational Rehabilitation,

composed of outstanding specialists in the field and leaders in public affairs, assists the Office of Vocational Rehabilitation in the formulation of policies and plans. It reviews applications and recommends research and training grants for approval.

The number of disabled people who have been rehabilitated and returned to active work has increased from about 56,000 in 1954 to 80,700 in 1959. In its research and demonstrations, the Office of Vocational Rehabilitation is currently giving special attention to the rehabilitation of such severely disabled groups as the mentally retarded, the mentally ill, persons with severe hearing and speech defects, and patients with multiple sclerosis and epilepsy. The Office works closely with the Public Health Service on research, demonstration and training programs in fields of common interest.

Food and Drug Administration

The Food and Drug Administration is under the administration of a commissioner appointed by the Secretary. It enforces the federal laws designed to insure the purity, safety, quality and truthful labeling of foods, drugs and cosmetics. It is the only agency of the Department whose major mission involves regulatory control and enforcement activities. It is organized in five bureaus: the Bureau of Biological and Physical Sciences, the Bureau of Enforcement, the Bureau of Field Administration, the Bureau of Medicine and the Bureau of Planning and Appraisal.

The Bureau of Biological and Physical Sciences conducts scientific investigations in the FDA laboratories in Washington, D.C. These include a wide range of analytic studies in the fields of bacteriology, pharmacology and toxicology, as well as the development of methods to detect adulteration. The Bureau of Medicine is primarily concerned with the development and use of new drugs and antibiotics. The Bureau of Enforcement is concerned with the regulatory and legal procedures involved in the administration of the laws. It develops and recommends regulations for promulgation by the Secretary of Health, Education, and Welfare. Its actions are based on the work of the Bureau of Field Administration which is organized in 17 districts. Each district office has a testing laboratory and is staffed by inspectors and chemists.

The district offices exercise surveillance over products prepared for interstate shipment or imported from abroad. The Food and Drug Administration estimates that more than 100,000 establishments in the United States engaged in producing, processing, marketing or storing food, drug and cosmetic products come within its purview. The possible over-the-counter sale of drugs requiring a physician's prescription also brings about 56,000 retail drug stores under FDA regulations. The products subject to federal regulations are constantly increasing in number and volume. Moreover, the numbers of potentially toxic chemical and hormonal substances used in the production, marketing and storage of foods, drugs and cosmetics are increasing even more rapidly.

State laws for the regulation of foods, drugs and cosmetics vary widely in scope. In 24 states and the District of Columbia, the health department is responsible for administering the laws pertaining to food, drug and cosmetic control, and in 24 other states the department of agriculture has that responsibility. The Food and Drug Administration works in close cooperation with the state agencies, as well as with the Public Health Service in the latter's biologics control and environmental health activities.

Public Health Service

The Public Health Service is the principal health agency of the federal government. In the broadest terms, its mission is to protect and advance the health of the American people.

As the principal instrument of the government in this field, the Public Health Service has a wide variety of specific statutory responsibilities. To a considerable extent, however, its programs have been developed in cooperation with the states, universities and hospitals, professional organizations and other agencies and groups having an interest in health.

Within this partnership, the Public Health Service has responsibilities in the broad fields of health research and training, medical care for legally designated beneficiaries, and public health practice, including the development of resources, facilities and technics. It is also responsible for certain direct services, such as interstate and foreign quarantine and working with other countries on international health matters.

The Public Health Service began as the Marine Hospital Service in 1798—making it one of the oldest federal agencies. It was charged with the responsibility for direct medical services to sick and injured merchant seamen, a group important to the nation's economic and defense lifeline whose needs were not being met adequately by other means. This, in a sense, is a keynote to all future governmental activities in health. The Public Health Service has gradually acquired responsibilities where needs were not being fulfilled by other means.

During the nineteenth century, with the great population influx from abroad and westward migration and with occasional explosive disease epidemics, the functions of the Service grew. The states retained primary responsibilities within their own borders, but the Public Health Service became increasingly concerned with interstate problems and assisted the states through consultation, technical services and the detailing of personnel.

The Social Security Act of 1935 gave great impetus to programs of grants-in-aid for general health purposes and for specific problems, such as venereal disease and tuberculosis.

All these lines of activity have continued and broadened since World War II. A number of new problems began to press heavily against the nation during and since that time.

The aging of the population and the continuously rising death rates from chronic diseases reflected the growing burden of those diseases and other causes of long-term disability. A serious shortage of hospital facilities was a corollary problem of the first magnitude. These needs also stimulated attention to the limited medical research in the chronic diseases.

Social and technologic changes also had a great impact on health. The population continued to grow, as did cities and industries. More than two thirds of the population now lives in huge metropolitan centers. American industry has expanded and diversified at a phenomenal rate. All these factors combined to bring such problems as water and air pollution, accidents, and radiological health hazards to the fore.

The response to these problems has been insistent and steady. Beginning in 1946 and continuing up to the present time, a series of laws has been passed and executive actions have been taken which significantly affected the nation's medical research and training effort, increased health services to the states, and expanded the work and responsibilities of the Public Health Service. The following are illustrative.

Begun in 1946, the program of grants for the construction of hospitals and other medical facilities has had a major impact on the nation's health resources. It has not only made hospital care available to millions of people but has resulted in better planning of facilities and better distribution of personnel.

In the area of environmental health, new programs have grown to maturity rapidly in air and water pollution, accident prevention and radiological health.

The addition of the National Office of Vital Statistics in 1946 and the establishment of the National Health Survey in 1956 have enabled the Service to provide a continuing picture of the state of the nation's health.

The medical research effort in the Service has grown tremendously. In addition to its own substantial research investment at the National Institutes of Health, it now supports half of the health and medical research undertaken in all American colleges and universities.

Appropriations to the Service increased from about $142 million in 1946 to $1,034 million in 1961. Over 70 per cent of this amount is allocated to others in the form of grants to the states, private institutions and individuals outside the federal government. The remaining 30 per cent is for the direct operations of the Service, i.e., administration of its hospitals and clinics, enforcement of foreign quarantine, collection and reporting of vital statistics and technical assistance to the states and localities.

The number of full-time personnel employed by the Service rose from about 11,000 to more than 28,000 people in something like 300 occupational categories. Included are physicians, dentists, nurses, engineers, pharmacists, research scientists, veterinarians, social workers, statisticians and a host of other specialists.

ORGANIZATION OF THE SERVICE.—The Public Health Service is administered by the Surgeon General, who is appointed by the President, with the advice and consent of the Senate, from the Service's Regular Commissioned Corps. The Commissioned Corps is a quasi-military career organization in which all officers are drawn from the medical, scientific and related professions.

Decentralization of authority to the bureaus and larger field offices of the Service help the Surgeon General carry out his responsibility. External advisory bodies, some established by law and others through administrative action, provide invaluable aid and advice to the Public Health Service. Outstanding experts from all parts of the country advise the Surgeon General and his associates on policy, programs, and relations with the professions and the public. At the present time, there are some 140 public advisory groups assisting the Service.

The functions of the Service are administered through four main bureaus—the Office of the Surgeon General, the Bureau of State Services, the Bureau of Medical Services, and the

National Institutes of Health—plus two units with equivalent bureau status—the National Library of Medicine and the National Center for Health Statistics. The present bureau structure is defined in the Public Health Service Act of 1944. This Act codified all previous laws pertaining to the Service; most legislation affecting the Service since that time has been in the form of amendments to the Act.

The rapid growth of the Service in the last two decades prompted a thoroughgoing review of its mission and organization early in 1960. The Surgeon General appointed a study group to review needs and trends and to recommend organizational changes which could accommodate the Service's expanding role in the decade ahead. Some of the major changes recommended by the study group, such as the creation of new bureaus, cannot be put into effect without legislative approval. Certain organizational moves can be made within the limits of existing law, however, and the Surgeon General, with the approval of the Secretary, has been effecting changes which are within his authority. Figure 2 shows the organizational structure of the Service as of July, 1961.

Office of the Surgeon General.—The Office of the Surgeon General, a bureau under the immediate supervision of the Deputy Surgeon General, provides staff facilities for central management and program coordination. This bureau consists of an Office of Personnel and five divisions. Two of these—the Divisions of Finance and of Administrative Services—are staff units. The other three—the Divisions of Public Health Methods, International Health, and Health Mobilization—conduct studies on health resources and trends and administer the Service's international and emergency health programs, respectively.

National Center for Health Statistics.—The National Center for Health Statistics is the principal source of health data in the United States. It is composed of the National Vital Statistics Division, which collects and analyzes data on births,

PUBLIC HEALTH SERVICE - 1961

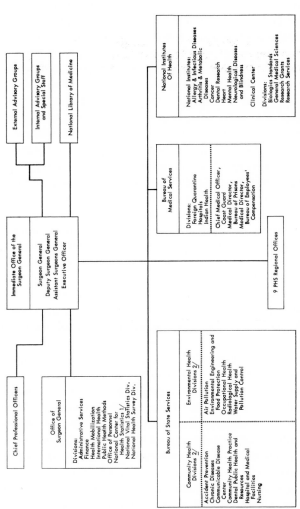

FIG. 2.—Organizational chart, Public Health Service.

1/ Separate organizational status similar to the National Library of Medicine is proposed under the reorganization plan.

2/ These groupings would become bureaus under the reorganization plan.

deaths, marriages, divorces and communicable diseases reported by the states; and the National Health Survey Division, which administers a continuous fact-finding program to gather reliable data on the extent of illness and disability in the United States. At present, this Center is located in the Office of the Surgeon General, but the reorganization plan would give it separate organizational status.

National Library of Medicine.—The National Library of Medicine is a national resource devoted to the collection of medical books, journals, pamphlets, prints, films and recordings. It is one of the largest libraries in a special subject discipline in the world. The Library publishes the monthly Index Medicus which is collated by the American Medical Association for annual publication. It also translates and issues abstracts of modern foreign language literature and maintains bibliographic and reference services. A new building at Bethesda, Maryland, was completed late in 1961 to house the Library's collections adequately and to increase its services to other medical libraries and scholars.

The National Institutes of Health.—The National Institutes of Health is the center of research activities in the Service. Its functions are to conduct and support research into the causes, prevention and treatment of the diseases and disabilities of man. It is located on a 300-acre tract in Bethesda, a suburb of Washington, D.C.

The National Institutes of Health is composed of nine research institutes—Cancer, Heart, Dental Research, Mental Health, Neurological Diseases and Blindness, Arthritis and Metabolic Diseases, Allergy and Infectious Diseases, Child Health and Human Development, and General Medical Sciences—three Divisions, and the Clinical Center. The Division of Research Services provides central research and administrative services. The Division of Research Grants processes and coordinates grants and fellowships to non-federal scientists. The Division of Biologics Standards is responsible for the safety and potency of vaccines, serums and other biological products produced for sale in interstate commerce. The Clinical Center is a 500-bed facility, a combination laboratory and hospital to permit the clinical study of disease problems.

Research financed by appropriations to the National Institutes of Health is carried on in two ways: in its own laboratories and through grants to scientists working in the nation's medical schools, universities and other non-federal research centers. Through this means, the talents of thousands of scientists and the resources of hundreds of institutions are brought to bear on the problems of health and disease. The NIH also administers a program of fellowships, traineeships and training grants, which helps provide the training of urgently needed scientists and research workers.

Bureau of Medical Services.—Medical and hospital care for statutory beneficiaries of the Public Health Service and the conduct of foreign quarantine activities are major responsibilities of the Bureau of Medical Services. It is composed of the Divisions of Hospitals, Indian Health, and Foreign Quarantine.

The Division of Hospitals provides medical and dental care and hospitalization to merchant seamen, Coast Guard and Coast and Geodetic Survey personnel, federal employees injured in line of duty, and other smaller groups of beneficiaries. It operates 12 general hospitals at port and coastal cities; two neuropsychiatric hospitals, which also specialize in the treatment of narcotic drug addiction, at Lexington, Kentucky, and Fort Worth, Texas; and a hospital for patients with leprosy (the National Leprosarium) at Carville, Louisiana. It also operates 25 full-time clinics and provides part-time services through 150 private physicians who furnish emergency care in communities inaccessible to PHS facilities.

In July, 1955, responsibility for providing health and medical services to 350,000 Indians and Alaska natives was trans-

ferred from the Bureau of Indian Affairs to the Public Health
Service. Facilities in the Indian health program number 54
hospitals and 34 other installations located in 18 states. These
now comprise the Division of Indian Health. The aim of this
program is to raise the level of Indian health, which resembles
that of the general population a generation or more ago, to
standards which now prevail generally in the United States.

In addition to the programs which it administered directly,
this bureau provides professional personnel who are detailed
to medical programs administered by other federal agencies.
For example, the Service details all of the professional staff
required for medical programs of the Coast Guard, the Bureau
of Prisons and the Bureau of Employees Compensation of the
Department of Labor.

Bureau of State Services.—The Bureau of State Services,
as its name implies, deals principally with the states and localities in the development and improvement of public health
services. It administers a wide variety of grants to states, communities, universities and other groups. In addition to a grant
for general public health services, there are separate grants to
the states for mental health services and for the control of
tuberculosis, venereal disease, cancer, heart disease and water
pollution. Grants are also made for the construction of hospitals and other health facilities and of waste-treatment facilities.
The Bureau also provides traineeship awards for graduate
nurses and for professional public health personnel. In addition, it conducts studies of community health practices to evaluate traditional methods and devise new ones.

The development of new methods and technics is only the
first step leading to their practical application in community
health programs. The technics must be verified and subjected
to intensive tests under actual field conditions. Once this is
done, they are introduced and recommended to state and local
agencies through demonstrations and pilot programs.

The Bureau of State Services encompasses two major

groupings of activities. The Surgeon General's study group has recommended bureau status for each of these groupings.

Through the Environmental Health group, the Service proposes to undertake and encourage a comprehensive approach to all aspects of the physical environment which affect human health. The aim is to focus a wide spectrum of scientific and technical specialties on present and emerging problems in this field. This grouping includes the Divisions of Air Pollution, Water Supply and Pollution Control, Occupational Health, Radiological Health and Environmental Engineering and Food Protection.

The Community Health grouping includes the programs which relate to health manpower, hospital and medical facilities and community health services. Here too the intent is to foster a coordinated approach in providing comprehensive health care and to aid state and local efforts in this field. Comprehensive health care envisions a continuum of preventive, curative and restorative services to individuals and families in which personnel with varied technical skills participate under both private and public auspices. The units in this group are the Divisions of Chronic Disease, Hospital and Medical Facilities, Community Health Practice, Accident Prevention, Dental Public Health and Resources, Nursing and the Communicable Disease Center. The latter, located in Atlanta, is a nation-wide resource for investigation and training in the control of infectious diseases.

STATE AND LOCAL HEALTH SERVICES

At this point of discussion, a pertinent observation might be made about the frequent references to the health functions of state and local governments that are necessarily included in the preceding description, or in any description, of the role of the federal government in public health. It is evident that, although the three levels of government represent distinct and separate entities, their interrelationship is such that they constitute a partnership for the promotion of human health. This stems, of course, from our democratic and decentralized system of government. However, other factors have also contributed to this health partnership.

One of the strongest links, for example, has been the progressive interest of health officials, at all governmental levels, in the development of effective working relationships. The trend is by no means new, as witnessed by the initiation in 1903 of the annual conferences of the Surgeon General of the Public Health Service with state and territorial health officers. Congressional legislation in 1902 authorized such meetings and made them mandatory. For several years they were more in the nature of scientific meetings than "working" conferences. Gradually, however, discussions of administrative problems and relationships were stressed as well as advances in the prevention and control of disease. By the 1930's these regular conferences and the related committee structure had become a highly valued coordination medium for federal and state health officers.

In 1935, in anticipation of the enactment of the Social Security Act, the entire time of the annual conference was given over to discussion of the proposed programs to be carried out under the provisions of that and related legislation. Recommendations were made on the proposed allocation of funds and the regulations governing the expenditure of federal funds. In 1942, the Association of State and Territorial Health Officers was formed to provide responsible representation on matters concerning federal health grants. In its relationship with the Public Health Service and as an independent organization, the Association reflects the kind of practical coordination and communication that modern public health demands. This does not imply perfect agreement on all points. It does mean mutual willingness to consider all viewpoints, to adjust and to realize that coordination is essential in a complex society.

The past two decades have seen many new and aggravated complexities, as well as remarkable advances in the health and medical sciences. After World War II, for example, health and medical research produced new findings and technics at a pace unmatched in history; the population increased sharply; the nation's economy and technology advanced and changed rapidly; and the trend toward urban and suburban living continued unabatedly.

All these can be viewed as evidence of national vitality— a vitality based in part on the earlier concentrated efforts to control communicable diseases and improve sanitation practices in this country. Exciting as the changes might be from this viewpoint, they nevertheless brought a multitude of new problems for health workers at all levels of government.

It is true that the potential capacity for meeting these problems has been vastly increased through research and improved technics. These gains, however, impose a further obligation— to apply the new knowledge as quickly and as widely as possible. If this can be done, the rewards in terms of humanitarian and economic benefits promise to be far beyond anything accomplished in the past. How soon it can be done, however, depends on when certain transitional handicaps can be overcome. Health workers believe the most pressing handicaps are (1) serious shortages in funds, facilities and personnel trained in the new public health skills and specialties, and (2) the obsolescent patterns for health protection remaining in too many communities.

State Health Activities

All state governments rank public health protection among their major responsibilities, and every state has an agency, usually called the department of health, which is charged with the over-all health program. More and more state health departments are initiating activities geared to current needs. Organizational changes are being made to accommodate new services and shifts in emphases and to provide better liaison and sharing of responsibility with other state agencies that participate in health activities. Such agencies might be, for example, state departments of education, welfare, labor, agriculture, public safety, highway patrol and separate licensing boards. Health-related activities are also conducted in many states by industrial accident commissions, boards of control, commissions for the blind or for mental disease among others.

The pattern varies widely among the states in regard to the functions, scope and relationships of these agencies. Even among state health departments, activities are dispersed and varied. In 1950, the Public Health Service did a comprehensive study of the distribution of health services within state governments. For the country as a whole, the number of separate state agencies with some significant health responsibility stood at 60. The number of such agencies in any single state ranged from 10 to 32.

Although no comparable study has been done since then, there can be no doubt that the dispersion of health activities among state agencies today would at least equal, and probably surpass, that shown in 1950.

State efforts for the improvement of health are broad in scope. They range from solely regulatory or advisory functions to the operation of complex programs of direct services and include a variety of patterns in between. Most states also provide financial aid to their political subdivisions for approved health projects.

State governments usually perform the following health functions directly:

1. Study and appraise state health problems and formulate plans for their solution.
2. Maintain and operate diagnostic laboratories.

3. Maintain and operate institutions for the treatment of tuberculosis and mental illness.

4. Collect and interpret vital and health statistics.

5. Provide academic, field and in-service training for professional health personnel.

6. Disseminate health information for the general public.

7. Administer state-wide hospital construction programs.

8. Demonstrate new health programs or new methods and technics.

9. License for health reasons individuals, agencies and enterprises serving the public.

10. Supervise utilities of public health importance, such as water and sewage treatment works.

11. Provide financial assistance to local units of government for health purposes.

In addition, states usually reserve for themselves regulatory powers over most health matters and promulgate rules and regulations which are applicable throughout the state. Some regulatory authority, however, such as responsibility for protection of food, water, and milk supplies, may be delegated to political subdivisions. Some of the larger counties or municipalities may also be authorized to operate tuberculosis and mental hospitals. State agencies furnish guidance to local health workers, and this tends to establish some stability of service throughout the state.

Figure 3 is taken from a recent analysis of the organizational charts of 50 state health departments. By combining characteristics into a composite model chart, a theoretical representation of the typical organizational structure was developed. The study on which the chart is based also revealed the following:

1. A total of 103 clearly defined activities appeared on the 50 organizational charts.

2. The five organizational units that stood out on the basis of frequency and in a position directly responsible to the health commissioner were: administration, preventive medi-

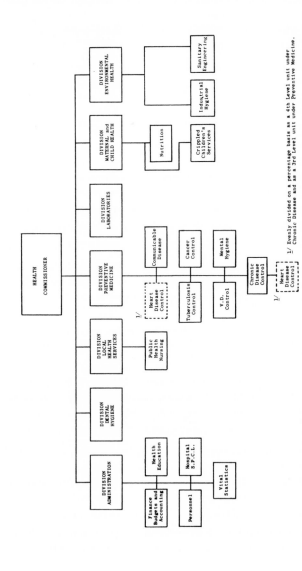

FIG. 3.—Disposition of activities which occurred in 50% or more of 50 state health department organization charts.

1/ Evenly divided on a percentage basis as a 4th Level unit under Chronic Disease and as a 3rd Level unit under Preventive Medicine.

cine, environmental health, local health services and laboratories.

3. A tabulation of health officer span of direct supervision showed a range of from 4 to 22 units.

Local Health Activities

The structure of local governmental jurisdictions is even more complex and diverse than that of the states. The continental United States contains approximately 37,000 units of local government—counties, municipalities, townships and other minor civil divisions. These units have a substantial degree of autonomy. For example, they have power to raise at least a part of their own revenue and to issue local ordinances and regulations. In terms of size, the county is a state's major subdivision. There are more than 3,000 counties in the United States.

The accompanying table shows the coverage of the country by local health organizations, as of January 1, 1960. Four types of local health units are shown in the table:

1. *Single county units* which serve a single county. They may or may not serve the cities within the county, depending upon the existence of separate city health units.

2. *City health departments* which serve a single city. In three instances—New York (which serves five counties), Philadelphia and New Orleans—these departments serve a total of seven complete counties because of coterminous boundaries.

3. *Local health districts* which serve two or more counties or other types of local governmental units. In such districts contiguous areas combine their resources and are formally organized in a single operating health unit under unified direction.

4. *State health districts* which provide either direct or advisory and supervisory services to local units of government. In such districts, control is vested in the state.

As the table shows, 58 per cent of the local units are of the single-county type, and 20 per cent are city units. These two

EXTENT OF COVERAGE OF THE COUNTRY BY HEALTH ORGANIZATIONS OF DESIGNATED TYPES
REPORTING LOCAL HEALTH SERVICES
JANUARY 1, 1960

TYPE OF HEALTH ORGANIZATION	HEALTH ORGANIZATIONS[1]		COUNTIES		POPULATION[2]	
	No.	%	No.	%	No.	%
Total number of counties and population in U. S.	—	—	3,072	100.0	177,021,000	100.0
Total number of health organizations reporting, counties and population included:	1,557	100.0	2,425	78.9	167,150,351	94.4
Single county	902	58.0	(902)	(29.4)	(69,702,064)	(39.4)
City health department	307	19.7	(7)[3]	(0.2)	(49,913,173)	(28.2)
Local health district	237	15.2	(665)	(21.6)	(15,648,281)	(8.8)
State health district (actual service and supervisory)	111	7.1	(851)	(27.7)	(31,886,833)	(18.0)
Total number of counties and population in unreported areas	—	—	647	21.1	9,870,649	5.6

[1] Includes all reporting units considered by the respective state health departments to be organized health departments.

[2] Estimated as of July 1, 1959. Based on estimated populations of local areas as reported by the states to the Bureau of the Census, with adjustments made on the basis of state totals as estimated by the Bureau of the Census as of that date.

[3] These seven counties are served by city health departments, the county and city being conterminous. The cities involved are: New Orleans, New York (5 counties), and Philadelphia.

types of units serve more than two thirds of the population.

The 647 counties that lack organized local health services contain only 5.6 per cent of the population. Most of these counties are located in the mountain and Great Plains areas where large areas and sparse population present problems in the organization of local health units.

There are far more important yardsticks than geographic coverage, however, in assessing the effectiveness of community health services. One of the most significant is the number of trained full-time health workers the community can afford or is willing to employ. Mustard stated this aptly:

> The vast majority of routine health services received by the people of the United States is delivered by local agencies. The Federal Government may subsidize and indirectly shape local health departments, the state health department may determine major policies for local agencies, set standards, promulgate regulations, and even directly supervise them, but the final determining factor in the effectiveness of a public health program rests with the workers in the locality where the problems are occurring.

There were 44,007 full-time public health workers on the staffs of the reporting local health units. Even with the addition of part-time workers, the personnel ratio was extremely low. The ratios of physicians and nurses, in particular, were low in most of the units.

City health departments usually employ a higher proportion of health workers in relation to population than do other types of units. Although relatively few in number, health organizations serving communities of 500,000 and over, employed approximately 40 per cent of the professional and technical personnel. In almost 70 per cent of the reporting local units, there were less than 20 professional and technical workers for every 100,000 people.

Shortages of personnel of all types seriously hamper the delivery of modern public health services. In 1925, for example, physical therapists, occupational therapists and psychiatric social workers were almost unknown; there was only a handful of dietitians, medical technicians, x-ray technicians, and medical social workers throughout the country. Today each of these groups are numbered in the substantial thousands—and still there are not enough. The new technologies and the growing burden of chronic diseases continue to keep demand well ahead of supply.

Public health agencies are well aware of the problem. The proportion of funds from state and local sources spent for training has climbed steadily since 1957. Between 1958 and 1960 there was an over-all increase of 24 per cent for training functions.

A total of $238 million was spent by the reporting local health units in 1959. Of this amount, 70 per cent was derived from local sources, 24 per cent from state-appropriated funds,

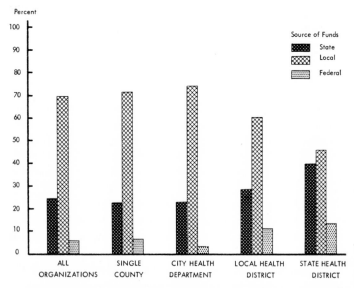

FIG. 4.—Percentage of funds expended from different sources in each type of health organization.

and 6 per cent from Federal funds. Of the four types of health organizations, city health departments depend on federal funds the least and state health districts the most (Fig. 4).

On a national basis, expenditures for local health purposes averaged $1.56 per person. Only 31 per cent of the local health units, however, spent more than $1.50 per capita, and 37 per cent spent less than $1.00 per person.

The amount of local funds devoted to health services in 1959 had more than doubled since 1950, and state funds had increased 154 per cent. These are impressive increases. When analyzed against the decline in purchasing power of the health dollar, however, it becomes apparent that there has been no real upward trend in local health expenditures. There has, in fact, been a slight decline. The decline takes on special significance because it occurred during a period of prosperity and when the groups which can benefit the most from organized health efforts—the very young and the old—were increasing greatly.

Another important index of community health services is the way in which they are organized to meet current health needs. For the most part, the local health organizations in existence today were designed for an earlier day. Health problems were relatively simple; major attention was given to the control of infectious diseases and environmental sanitation. Although still vital, these activities no longer constitute the *total* health program. A wide array of services, only part of which are usually offered by official health agencies, are needed to solve the complex health problems of the 1960's.

This calls for two things: (1) broadening the scope and skills of official health agencies, and (2) extending the health partnership to a great many new groups, agencies and individuals. Comprehensive care for long-term illness, for example, requires many kinds of professional and technical services, backed up by active community support. To make inroads against problems such as these, there must be joint planning and joint action on a sustained basis among health officials, private practitioners, voluntary agencies, hospitals and civic groups, to name only a few. There must be speedier application of research discoveries to the health needs of human beings. There must be experiments in new technics and new and better ways of delivering health services to the people.

These are among the challenges of public health work in the future. In September, 1961, federal legislation was enacted to strengthen and expand community health services and facilities, and make them more generally available. Under this legislation, a variety of new approaches to care for the long-term patient will be pursued. More nursing homes will be built and the quality of care in these homes will be improved. Fresh attention will be given to home care, home nursing, rehabilitation and a host of other services designed to prevent disability and reverse its course. New health technics will be developed and tested in communities throughout the land.

The health problems ahead are complex and insistent. All levels of government in the United States seem destined to play a very strong role in the solution of these problems. But the role will continue to be cooperative and complementary, supporting and stimulatory. It will add up to a role of leadership, but in the tradition of shared leadership that has brought American health to its present high levels and that will reach for even higher goals in the future.

EDWIN J. FAULKNER

*President of the Woodmen Accident and
Life Company of Lincoln, Nebraska,
Mr. Faulkner was the first President of
the Health Insurance Association of
America, 1956-57. His vital interest in the
current topic is reflected in his service on
committees of the federal government
and the American Medical Association
to study medical care plans. He has also
written two books on health insurance.*

10. The Story of Voluntary Health Insurance

THE GENIUS OF private enterprise for responsiveness to the needs, wants and desires of the public, for flexibility to meet changing conditions, and for progress stimulated by competition is nowhere better exemplified than by voluntary, or private, health insurance. Although not a new type of insurance, health insurance has become a significant factor in the American economy only since 1933. Its quantitative expansion and qualitative improvement in the past three decades are modern business phenomena without parallel. Today 134 million Americans are protected by some type of private health insurance, more than are insured under any other type of insurance. In 1960 they paid premiums exceeding $7 billion for their health insurance and received benefits amounting to $5.7 billion. A reflection of the importance of health insurance to Americans is the increased attention paid to it by political parties, public officeholders, and candidates for office at both national and state levels. Whether the federal government should assume greater responsibilities for the provision of health insurance was one of the major issues of the 1960 presidential campaign.

DEFINITIONS

Health insurance is such a "many-splendored" thing, developed by so many and heterogeneous insurers, that it lacks uniformity of policy contract, operating procedure and even terminology. In these circumstances, in order to assist the reader to an understanding of the material set forth in this chapter, it seems desirable to define some of the terms peculiar to health insurance as they will be used herein.

Health insurance is insurance against loss by sickness or accidental bodily injury. This type of insurance has also been called "accident and health insurance," "sickness and accident insurance," and "disability insurance." There are two principal divisions of health insurance: disability income insurance and medical expense insurance. *Disability income insurance* is that form of health insurance which provides a benefit payable periodically during the continuance of the insured's disability. *Medical expense insurance* is that form of health insurance which provides a benefit intended generally to reimburse the insured for certain or all expenses he incurs for health care, including hospital, medical, surgical and ancillary health care costs.

THE DIMENSIONS OF HEALTH INSURANCE

Like the octagon, health insurance has at least eight different "dimensions" in terms of which it may be viewed or defined.

1. *Perils* (causes of a probable loss).—Health insurance

insures against financial loss resulting from two perils, accident and sickness.

2. *Contractual arrangement.*—Health insurance is provided under a variety of contractual arrangements between the insurer and the insured. The three principal kinds of contractual arrangement are: individual including family, group, and blanket. *Individual and family contracts* are arranged between the named insured for himself or for himself and the named members of his family on the basis of an individual application which presents evidence of the proposed insured's insurability. An individual contract is issued to the insured who pays the separately-billed premium directly to the insurer or its representative. *Group contracts* cover a group of persons, the employees of a common employer, members of a labor union, or other association of people, organized for purposes other than securing insurance, and their dependents. The group contract is issued to the employer, the association, or a trustee in behalf of those to be insured. Certificates of coverage under the group contract are issued to the persons so covered. Individual evidence of insurability is usually not required of members of the insured group. Premiums are billed to the contract holder (the employer, association, or trustee) who may collect a "contribution" from each of the persons insured or may pay the entire premium for them. The minimum size of groups eligible for group insurance is governed by state statute and may be as few as five or as many as 25 persons. *Blanket contracts* are issued to insure a group of persons subject to a common peril who are not individually identified, for example, the members of an athletic team, the students enrolled in a school or the passengers on a common carrier.

3. *Types of loss.*—Health insurance may be viewed in terms of the types of loss it insures. These correspond to the two principal divisions of health insurance, *disability income insurance* and *medical expense insurance.* Health insurance

companies generally insure both types of loss; service plan insurers restrict themselves to medical expense insurance, sometimes just one phase of this division. For instance, Blue Cross plans concentrate on hospital insurance, Blue Shield plans on medical and surgical insurance, while miscellaneous plans like Health Insurance Plan of New York, Kaiser-Permanente, Ross-Loos and others may comprehend all medical expense insurance benefits or be limited to one or more of them.

4. *Basis of payment.*—Health insurance varies in terms of the basis on which payment of benefits is made. *Valued payments* are those made in cash in an agreed-upon amount upon occurrence of the event insured against, irrespective of the actual amount of the loss. For example, an insurer could agree to pay a valued benefit of $20 per day for each day of the insured's confinement to a hospital, irrespective of the cost incurred for such hospitalization. *Reimbursement benefits* provide that the insurer will pay the insured or his assignee the actual amount of the covered expense incurred, up to the limit stated in the contract. *Service benefits* are an entitlement to receive specified hospital or medical services enumerated in the insurance contract in lieu of cash and, in certain instances, without payment of an additional charge. For example, a Blue Cross insured may be entitled to receive hospital care in semi-private accommodations up to 120 or 180 days per year. It is usual for the so-called "full service" benefit to be restricted to individuals or families whose income is less than a certain amount per annum. If the insured's income exceeds this amount, $3,600 per year for an individual or $6,000 per year for a family, for example, the provider of service may make a charge to the patient above the amount received from the service plan. Service plan insurers pay the hospital or doctor who renders service to an insured member according to a previously-negotiated schedule of charges and fees.

5. *Kind of insurer.*—Health insurance is provided by a

variety of kinds of insurer. *Insurance companies* predominate both in number and variety. Such insurance companies may write only health insurance or, in addition, may write life or casualty insurance. They may be organized on the stock, mutual, assessment, fraternal or reciprocal plan. They may operate in only one state or in all of the states of the Union. *Service plans* (best exemplified by Blue Cross and Blue Shield) are often organized under nonprofit corporation statutes, generally operate in only one state or a portion of a state, and are subject only in varying degrees to the insurance laws of the state. *Miscellaneous plans,* such as Health Insurance Plan of New York and Kaiser-Permanente in California, have various corporate structures. They are primarily local in the scope of their operation. A usual characteristic of their service benefit approach is the maintenance of clinical facilities for the use of a closed-panel, salaried medical staff in treatment of their members. They may or may not own hospital facilities.

6. *Continuance provisions.*—Health insurance contracts offer a number of different provisions for the continuance of the insurance from term to term (premium-paying date to premium-paying date). Among individual forms, *noncancelable contracts* give to the insured the right to maintain the insurance in force to a specified age without change in its provisions by the timely periodic payment of the premium, an amount stated in the contract. *Guaranteed renewable contracts* vest in the insured the right to renew the contract from term to term to a specified age but reserve to the insurer the privilege to change the table of premium rates applicable to all members of different classes of risk. *Limited or restricted renewal contracts* are renewable by the insured with the consent of the insurer, but the insurer specifically eschews the right to refuse renewal for enumerated reasons, such as deterioration in the health of the insured after issue. *Optionally renewable contracts* may be renewed at the unfettered joint option of insured and insurer. *Cancelable contracts* can be ter-

minated by either party at any time but without prejudice to the payment of benefits for any loss sustained before the date of termination. If the insurer terminates, the unearned portion of the premium must be returned to the insured. Some health insurance contracts are written for a single definite term and are not intended to be renewed.

Group insurance contracts likewise vary as to the provision for continuance of coverage. The contract may be guaranteed renewable, optionally renewable, guaranteed renewable for the persons protected during their continued eligibility for insurance, or cancelable as to all members of a class within the insured group.

The pronounced trend in health insurance is toward provisions that assure a high degree of continuity of coverage.

7. *Methods of distribution.*—No kind of insurance is distributed to the public in so many different ways as is health insurance. It is sold by mail, by agents or brokers working for a commission, by salaried representatives, by lodge deputies, through vending machines, and over the counter in insurance agencies. An insurer may employ one or several methods of distribution.

8. *Freedom to insure.*—Finally, health insurance may be either voluntary or compulsory. Compulsory health insurance is imposed by law, state or federal. It may take the form of compulsory, cash sickness-benefits, which employers are required to procure for their workers in the states of Rhode Island, California, New Jersey and New York, or it may consist of the total and permanent disability benefits, for which those who are subject to the Federal Social Security law and their employers are taxed. Compulsory health insurance benefits are delineated as to type, amount and duration in the statute establishing the system. Such benefits are paid without reference to individual need. Voluntary health insurance, on the other hand, is purchased only if the insured wishes to secure it. Voluntary health insurance benefits are selected as

to kind and amount by the purchaser in terms of his own needs and wants.

THE FUNCTIONS OF HEALTH INSURANCE

Health insurance is a facet of the complex character of modern society. It reflects the interdependence of men. As our former, relatively simple, pastoral kind of life, in which people enjoyed a high degree of personal and family independence, gave way to an urban, industrial way of life, society had to contrive a whole series of socio-economic mechanisms to provide people with a measure of security. Health insurance is one of these.

Aside from death, mankind has no greater or more innate fear than that of disability. Disease and injury are always with us, perils from which none is exempt. Though great progress has been made in abating disease and safeguarding against injury, disability still takes a tremendous toll. Health insurance is primarily concerned with helping people bear the burdens of lost earnings and the costs of care involved in sickness and injury.

Disability can be relative or absolute. It can vary with a person's age, occupation, financial status, location, physical structure and temperament. The subjective factors influencing the extent and duration of disability pose problems for health insurance underwriters and are the reasons for some of the requirements insurers must impose for initial evidence of insurability, limits of coverage, and proof of loss, substantiated by a physician. Though disability is not a fixed, precise and immutable state, its significance to society is that condition of ill health arising from sickness or injury that prevents the individual from pursuing his normal routine of living. The all-pervasive nature of the peril of disability and its highly uncertain incidence as to the individual explain society's intense concern with human disability.

Earning Ability as a Capital Asset

The human life has a capital value that can be expressed as a function of the income-producing capabilities of the individual. Three hazards can destroy the capital value of the human life. They are premature physical death (dying too soon), economic death due to superannuation (living too long) and disability (loss of earning capacity because of sickness or injury). Only through insurance can the economic value of the human life be capitalized and its realization guaranteed to the individual, his family, his business and his creditors. The function of life insurance is to protect against the financial consequences of premature death and superannuation, while health insurance safeguards against losses due to disability. Only when adequate amounts of both life insurance and health insurance are in force is the individual's life-value guaranteed.

The Extent and Cost of Disability

Doctors, other persons engaged in the health care professions, and insurers know from their daily experience the vast extent and tremendous cost of disability. Not all who are engaged in the healing arts, however, realize that each year it is more costly to be ill. In 1960 private health care expenditures in the United States exceeded $18 billion. The cost to a general hospital of providing a patient day of care has been rising at an annual rate in excess of 5 per cent per year since the conclusion of World War II, and there is little prospect that this rate of increase will abate in the foreseeable future. In July, 1961, the *Consumers Price Index,* prepared by the Bureau of Labor Statistics, stood at 128.1 (the average of costs in the years 1947–1949 is taken as 100). In the same month the medical care element of the *Consumers Price Index* stood at 161.2, reflecting a greater rise in the past decade than any other element in the *Index* except public transportation.

Despite the enormous scientific progress of medicine, disability is a constant threat to every American. A recent United States Public Health survey found that, during the course of a year, 85 per cent of all people complained of some illness, 68 per cent consulted a doctor, 52 per cent were absent from work for one day or more and 44 per cent were bed-confined because of illness. As significant as these data are, trifling illness is of little real concern either to the individual or society. But serious, prolonged and expensive disability confronts both the individual and society with significant problems. If serious disability is defined as one of four weeks or more duration, on the average, in America today there are 26 such prolonged illnesses per 1,000 man-years; and the average wage loss attributable to such illnesses is equivalent to 30 per cent of the workers' annual income. The chance that a person will have a long-term illness (one of four weeks or more duration) at age 30 is 2.7 times the risk of dying; at age 40, 2.3 times the risk of dying; at age 50, 1.8 times the risk of dying. The chance that a person will experience such a long-term disability sometime between ages 35 and 65 are 33 in 100.

Though America is the world's healthiest nation, the incidence and the high cost of disability are such that for most people the financial impact of serious illness or injury cannot be borne without prior preparation. It is characteristic of the majority of Americans that they live from paycheck to paycheck. High taxes and the cost of high living have inhibited for most families the accumulation of substantial savings. Our national penchant for mortgaging the future paycheck by installment purchases usually precludes the ability to pay the costs of disability out of current income. Under these circumstances, prior provision against the loss of income and the costs of disability through adequate health insurance is a necessity for nearly all of our people.

The Services of Health Insurance

It has been stated above that health insurance performs an essential function in capitalizing the human life value by replacing income for the individual and the family when disability destroys earning capacity. This is regarded by most people as the primary function of health insurance. However, the service of health insurance goes beyond that of income replacement and includes indemnification of medical expenses, as credit insurance in connection with both installment purchases and such long-term obligations as home mortgages, and as a limited form of life insurance through the benefit paid for accidental health. Health insurance has many important business uses. It may reimburse an employer for the loss of the services of a disabled employee. Professional men procure health insurance to help pay their business overhead expenses while they are disabled. Health insurance is needed along with life insurance to provide funds with which to implement buy-and-sell agreements between business partners and among the owners of closely held corporations.

It is well to remember that it is neither practical nor desirable for health insurance to attempt to pay the entire loss suffered because of disability. If, through insurance, the insured's entire loss of income and all expenses were to be reimbursed, there would be for some a temptation to malinger and to secure unnecessary and extravagant treatment. Because of the subjective nature of much illness, the moral hazard involved in health insurance must be borne in mind constantly by the insurer. Insurers often utilize two safeguards in their contracts to discourage malingering and abuse of coverage. The first of these is the "deductible." The deductible, with which most people are familiar in automobile collision insurance, is the provision of the contract that requires the insured to pay the first few dollars of any loss before the insurer becomes liable. This tends to eliminate from coverage the trifling claim for insignificant loss which is relatively expensive to administer. Routine, recurrent and piddling health care costs are more economically borne as a regular item of the family budget than insured. The second safeguard health insurers utilize to abate malingering and overutilization is the "coinsurance" provision. Service plans sometimes refer to it as the "co-pay provision." By this provision the insured bears some small part, usually 20 per cent, of every element of loss, with the insurer paying the balance of the loss. Thus, for example, if under a major medical expense policy the insured incurred eligible medical expenses of $1,000, the insurer would pay $800 of the total and the insured $200. Health insurance underwriters know that any benefit, the enjoyment of which is not necessarily inconsistent with the desires of the insured, is foredoomed to underwriting failure.

FACTORS STIMULATING THE GROWTH OF HEALTH INSURANCE

The spectacular growth of health insurance in the United States is the happy result of the coincidence of many influences, all working in the same direction. The stage was set for the explosive growth of health insurance by America's transition from a rural economy to an urban, industrial nation. In this transition the simple family and community arrangements that sufficed three generations ago for the health care of the individual became inadequate. With the change in our mode of living, small homes and city apartments replaced the commodious farmhouse. In most urban dwelling units there is not room for the sick person. Nor do working wives and mothers have the time to tend the ill members of the family. Concurrent with this transition in our way of life, the science of medicine was making enormous progress. The old family doctor has been largely outmoded by the necessities of modern medicine, the expanded use of hospital facilities and the increased employment of specialists—all at considerably greater cost than was characteristic of health care in the past. Other factors that provided health insurance with its opportunity for enormous and rapid expansion included a heightened security-consciousness on the part of most Americans, stemming from the distress of the depression years of 1931–40. The economic problems of the hospitals in this period led directly to promotion of Blue Cross and the later development of Blue Shield. Attention was directed to insurance of costs of disability by the establishment of the Social Security system in 1935. At that time and in the years that followed, proponents of government action argued for the inclusion of health insurance benefits among those for which the Old Age and Survivors Insurance program has responsibility. When, during the wage freeze of World War II, organized labor was estopped from bargaining for higher wages, it turned its attention to "fringe benefits," among which health insurance was prominent. Government gave recognition to the social desirability of adequate health insurance by providing that health insurance premiums paid by employers for their employees under an organized plan could be counted as tax-deductible business expenses. In addition to all of these social, economic and political influences tending to encourage the expansion of health insurance, the activity of the insurers themselves to this end should not be overlooked. In the 20 years following World War II, the number of insurers offering health insurance doubled. Keen competition stimulated insurers to improve the benefits offered. Because of this competition and public pressure for continuing improvement, health insurance facilities have been expanded to adequate levels. The impact of all of these diverse influences has been a record of growth unequaled in the annals of business. In the 25 years following the low point of 1933, health insurance premium volume increased 3,500 per cent, and by 1961, private health insurance in America had become an $8 billion-a-year business.

QUALITATIVE IMPROVEMENT OF
HEALTH INSURANCE

Quantitative expansion of health insurance has been paced
—even stimulated—by qualitative improvement in health insurance benefits and operating technics. Contracts have been
simplified and now are written in clear, nontechnical language.
Onerous restrictions and eliminations have become largely a
thing of the past. For instance, the modern health insurance
contract no longer requires confinement indoors as a qualification for income-replacement benefits. Benefits have been
liberalized in amount and duration. It is now possible for the
insurable individual to secure income benefits payable during
disability up to five years, ten years, or even the entire duration
of disability. Conditions excluded from coverage are now
largely confined to suicide or attempts thereat, disability sustained while in military service or as the result of war or act
of war, aviation injuries other than those sustained as a pas-
senger on a commercial airline, or disease or injury suffered
when the insurance is not in force. The concept of broad,
blanket coverage of medical expense has gained great head-
way. Contracts providing such benefits are variously called
major medical, catastrophic, or comprehensive medical expense coverage. These contracts usually are written without
specific limits on the benefits payable for the various kinds of
medical expense, such as hospital confinement, surgical cost,
drug cost, etc. Some major medical expense contracts do limit
the amount of reimbursement for hospital room occupancy to
$20 or $25 per day. Subject to a deductible adjusted to the
insured's earned income and a coinsurance provision, such
contracts cover nearly all medical expense costs up to the
maximum amount selected by the insured, usually $5,000,
$10,000, or $15,000 per injury or illness.

Improvement in health insurance has not been limited to
the modernization of the policy contract. Administrative tech-

nics have been refined as the business has grown. To serve the mass market, group and blanket forms of contract have been devised to simplify the distribution process. To reach the rural or remote risk, insurers now employ farmers' co-operatives and Rural Electrification Administration Districts as collection devices. Preauthorized check plans and combined billing technics have been introduced to simplify premium payments for individual insurance. Substandard risk selection has been perfected to provide coverage for the impaired or substandard risk at an appropriate premium. Greater equity and adequacy have been injected into the premium rate structure as experience has permitted insurers to grade the premiums (as in life insurance) according to the age and sex of the insured, as well as the amount and duration of benefit and the occupational hazard presented. The payment of benefits has been streamlined through the introduction of simplified uniform claim forms that have been developed by the Health Insurance Council with the cooperation of the American Medical Association and the American Hospital Association. Frequently, these forms provide for the assignment of benefits to the doctor or hospital that provides the insured with care.

RELATIONSHIPS WITH MEDICINE

Health insurers are dependent on physicians for much of the information they need to underwrite their risks and pay the benefits owed their insureds. Some health insurance contracts are issued only when the applicant can pass a satisfactory examination given by a doctor of medicine. In other cases, issued on a nonmedical basis, the insurer may request information about the applicant's medical history from his attending physician. Waiver of privileged communication signed by the applicant is customarily furnished with the request for information.

When the insured files claim for benefits under a health insurance contract, his physician's statement is an important part of the proof of loss on which the insurer computes the amounts payable. The physician's statement includes diagnosis, description of any surgery or radiology, dates of treatment and amount of charges made. To be entitled to health insurance benefits, the insured must be under the care of a licensed doctor of medicine. Uniform claim forms, standard in wording and format, have been designed by the Health Insurance Council in cooperation with the Council on Medical Service of the American Medical Association and are in general use. Prompt completion of the physician's statement is essential to timely and satisfactory payment of benefits to the physician's patient.

During the continuance of disability, the insurer has the right to have the insured examined periodically by its medical representative and in the event of death to secure an autopsy.

In the past many physicians have been concerned that the development of private health insurance would have a disruptive influence on the traditional patient-physician relationship. Assurance is given on this score, however, by the findings of the American Medical Association Commission on Medical Care Plans whose study was completed in 1959. The Commission reported:

> If all arrangements for the insurance are limited to the subscriber and insurer, and if all medical relationships remain exclusively between the patient and his physician, then the insurance program has no effect on the traditional patient-physician relationship.
>
> On the other hand, if a benefit is payable only in the event a subscriber receives care from specified physicians, or if a benefit otherwise payable would be reduced if health care were not sought from a specified list or group of physicians, then the insurance program might have a very definite effect on the traditional patient-physician relationship.
>
> In other words, the extent to which any insurance program influences the traditional patient-physician relationship can be gauged primarily by the extent to which the insurance agreement

limits methods of treatment or absolute free choice of physician at the time of seeking health care. If no arbitrary provisions are contained in an insurance program, then it can be assumed that the program will not affect the traditional relationships.

Health insurance provided by insurance companies and service plans is an arrangement between the insured and insurer and places no restriction on freedom of choice of physician. In point of fact, critics of private health insurance have complained that private health insurers do nothing to assure the quality of the care that their insureds receive. This complaint is only partly true. Insurers do have a concern that their insureds receive the best possible care. The insurer is eager to abate disability and reduce health care costs. However, the private insurance business recognizes that no lay group, whether government, labor union or insurance, is competent to interfere in the professional aspects of medical treatment. Insurers believe that the best assurance that their insureds will receive good quality medical care lies in the high ethical standards and insistence on proper qualification to practice which are characteristic of the American medical profession. Rather than seeking to interfere in professional matters, insurers prefer to rely on the effective self-disciplinary measures that are implemented by organized medicine. Commenting on the proper relationship between the medical profession and insurers, the Commission on Medical Care plans stated:

The relationship between the medical profession and insurers should be one of free and sympathetic cooperation without prejudice or bias. It is recognized that component medical organizations may sponsor or operate health insurance mechanisms. However, individual physicians should assume the responsibility of cooperating with all recognized and proper methods of insuring health care costs, should assume the responsibility of being informed, and should advise and encourage their patients and the public in the proper evaluation and utilization of such methods.

The partnership of the private practice of medicine and private health insurance has been recognized by the leaders both of the profession and of the business. The continuing responsibility of the individual doctor for the success of this partnership was summarized in the report of the Commission on Medical Care Plans, as follows:

Preservation of the fee-for-service principle and of freedom from third-party interference depends upon a universal recognition by the individual providers of health service of their moral responsibility to charge fees based upon the intrinsic value of service rendered and not influenced by the existence of any mechanism for the financing of health care costs.

The development of the unallocated-expense types of health insurance re-emphasizes the responsibility of the providers of service to safeguard against abuse, extravagant utilization, and unnecessary procedures that would raise the total burden of health care. Inflation of health care costs, particularly when attributable to such practices, could well lead to imposition of third-party controls.

These points have been recognized by the American Medical Association on previous occasions and were well stated in a report of the Council on Medical Service adopted by the House of Delegates during the 1954 Clinical Session, when this Commission was created. It seems appropriate to include the following excerpt from the 1954 statement:

"It should be remembered that insurance does not create any new wealth. It merely assists in conservation. Insurance may conserve the ability of an insured person to fulfill his normal financial obligations. It does not enhance his ability to discharge added responsibilities if they are in the form of increased fees. To use insurance as an excuse to revise professional fees upward is but to contribute to the defeat of its purpose."

COMPETITION IN HEALTH INSURANCE

Although there is a large body of state statute law that governs both the health insurance contract and the operation of health insurers, the best regulator of both price and practice in health insurance is the open, free and keen competition that exists among the very large number of insurers. This competition is in the public interest, because it engenders experimentation, looking toward improvement in coverage, cost and availability. It stimulates widespread adoption of such improvements.

The two principal types of health insurer, the insurance company and the service plan, approach the task of underwriting the costs of health care from somewhat different points of view. Service plans emphasize their "nonprofit" character (a characteristic shared with mutual insurance companies), while many insurance companies are proprietary in nature. However, whether a plan is organized for profit or not seems to have little effect on the plan's ability to provide sound and adequate insurance. Nor does the profit or nonprofit nature of the insurer exert discernible influence on the proper practice of medicine.

Proponents of both service benefits and cash benefits claim superiority for their approach. Each type of plan has advantages that appeal to different prospective insureds. Both types are based on insurance principles and neither actually provides medical care. The service plans contract with the providers of care (doctors and hospitals) on a fee-for-service basis, while the insurance companies simply pay the benefits called for in their contracts directly to the insured or on his assignment to the doctor or hospital. The insured makes his own arrangements for care. The line between service benefits and cash benefits is no longer as clearly drawn as once was the case. Some insurance companies now issue contracts providing service benefits, while service plans offer some arrangements in which benefits are paid in cash rather than in service.

Another broad area of difference between health insurance companies and service plans is in the method of calculating the premium charge for insurance coverage. Service plans generally use the so-called "community-wide flat rate." Insurance premiums are based on a "merit rating" approach. Service plans apply the same basic rate for all groups within a given area. In other words, all groups pay the same premium for the same benefits, irrespective of differences in age, sex, or occupational hazard. Insurance companies, on the other hand, assign a premium rate to the groups that they insure which recognizes differences in the risk, depending upon the complexion of the group. The preferential rate that insurance companies are able to offer groups whose average age is low, whose female ingredient is not predominant, and whose insured employees are engaged in nonhazardous occupations, has tended to encourage such groups to patronize insurance companies rather than service plans. Recognizing this tendency toward selection against them, on the basis of premium rate, some service plans are beginning to adopt the merit rating approach. It is a principle of insurance that premium rates must be equitable, adequate, and not unfairly discriminate against any group. Conversely, in the interests of equity, insurance charges must with reasonable accuracy discriminate among groups presenting diverse risk.

PROBLEMS OF HEALTH INSURANCE UNDERWRITING

Despite the enormous progress of the past 30 years, health insurance is not without its problems, both within and without the business. In part, these arise from the nature of the risk insured and, in part, from the great personal and social importance of the protection provided.

1. *Duplication of coverage and overinsurance.*—Moral hazard is regarded by many as the number one underwriting problem of health insurance. *Moral hazard* reflects the hazard that arises from the failure by individuals who are or have been affected by the contract of insurance to uphold the accepted moral qualities. The risk insured is one vastly affected by subjective influence. The insured often has it within his power to precipitate the event insured against or to aggravate a loss. Because of moral hazard, it is essential that insurers avoid overinsurance and duplication of coverage. To do this is

more difficult as the amount of health insurance in force expands. Present statutory provisions governing overinsurance are unsatisfactory and do not prevent the unscrupulous insured from securing coverage in excess of need. Health insurers are studying the problem with insurance supervisory authorities in an effort to develop statutory provisions that will prevent an insured from "profiting" from his disability, thus adversely affecting the cost of health insurance for all.

2. *Rising medical expense costs.*—The cost of most elements of medical expense have risen significantly. This is due far less to the disposition of hospitals and physicians to charge more, because they believe "the traffic will bear it," as alleged by some critics, than it is to the over-all inflation that has afflicted the economy and to the significant fact that the quality of medical care available today is vastly superior to that of just a few years ago. The magnificent scientific progress of medicine, which has meant so much to Americans in terms of longer life and generally better health, requires more frequent use of the hospital, the employment of a variety of highly-trained specialists and the use of expensive equipment and therapeutic agents. When the rising cost of health care is criticized by the lay public, the enormous improvement in the quality of care is usually overlooked. Nonetheless, as medical expense costs have risen, so necessarily have the costs of health insurance.

As year by year these costs edge up, the question is frequently asked, "Will health insurance eventually have to be priced out of the reach of the mass market?" The answer to this question probably lies beyond the competence of the insurers alone, although they can reduce the incentive to overuse of health insurance by strict adherence to deductible and coinsurance provisions, by developing a workable formula for avoiding overinsurance, and by vigorously merchandising benefits to pay a reasonable part of the costs of outpatient diagnosis and treatment and confinement in nursing homes, as a way of reducing use of more expensive general hospital care.

In large measure, however, containment of medical expense costs can be achieved only by patients, physicians, hospitals and ancillary health care personnel. Organized medicine has recognized that much progress can be made through the development and use of relative value studies as a guide to medical pricing. These schedules list and assign a weight or value to every known medical procedure. As such, they are not a "fee schedule" but do serve as a guide to physicians in making their charges and to patients and insurers in paying such charges. Were each physician to apply a conversion factor of his choice to the values in the relative value study approved by his state medical association, it would do much to establish needed stability in medical pricing practices. He would then have a complete list of his fees for every procedure. Adherence to it would answer the criticisms that "there is too much mystery in medical pricing" and that frequently, when the patient is insured, the physician increases his fee, thus vitiating the value of insurance. With a doctor no longer required to provide so much free service because of the wide spread of health insurance and the generally good times that have prevailed since World War II, there is no justification for the "Robin Hood" approach to medical pricing. Health insurers can predict with reasonable accuracy the incidence of illness and injury and the medical procedures they will necessitate. But if the charge for the procedure is altered from patient to patient and increased when an insurer pays the bill, the task of health insurance underwriters becomes difficult, if not impossible.

Physicians and hospitals are in a better position than any lay group, whether government, insurer, or labor union, to police their own practices and assure uniform adherence to the high ethical standards that are characteristic of the profession of medicine and of our voluntary general hospitals. Establishment of medical-insurance review committees by local medical societies and utilization committees by the medical staffs of hospitals has had a salutary effect on overcharging and overutilization. Those who provide health care can encourage the economies implicit in the system of progressive patient care in the hospitals, as well as by better scheduling of patients in and out of hospitals. Much could be gained were all insurers, doctors and hospital personnel to carry on a continuing program of public education on the importance of using but not abusing health insurance.

3. *Continuity of coverage.*—Frequently, in the past, the charge was flung at health insurers that "just when I needed the insurance most, you took it away from me." If at one time such criticism had justification, that day has long since passed. A recent survey by a number of state insurance departments indicated that less than one tenth of 1 per cent of health insurance exposed to renewal each year was terminated by the insurer. Pressure of public opinion and keen competition among insurers have been powerful influences toward a higher degree of continuity of coverage. Two thirds of the persons insured under health insurance contracts are covered by group insurance arrangements which preclude termination of the insurance of the individual unless the entire group is discontinued. Upon retirement from active employment by the covered employee, it is more and more the custom to provide the opportunity for the group coverage to be converted to individual insurance or to become paid up. In individual health insurance the trend is distinctly toward the noncancelable and guaranteed renewable types of contract.

4. *Government competition.*—Since 1911 when Wisconsin enacted the first state workmen's compensation law, the specter of government intrusion and ultimate pre-emption of the business of health insurers has harassed the underwriter. The threat of government competition has unquestionably energized the expansion and improvement of private health insurance. Despite the progress of private insurers, government

inroads have been considerable. All states now have work-men's compensation laws providing for the reimbursement of part of the wage loss and payment of most of the medical expenses for injuries and sickness sustained in and arising out of the course of covered employment. Four states, Rhode Island, California, New Jersey and New York, supplement workmen's compensation benefits by requiring employers to provide cash sickness-benefits for their employees who suffer from non-occupational disability.

At the national level, among the many insurance schemes of the federal government, the largest is the Social Security system. Total and permanent disability benefits for covered employees under Social Security were introduced in 1956 for those age 50 and over. In 1960 the age 50 limitation was dropped. Subject to a waiting period of six months, persons "covered" under Social Security who are totally and presumptively permanently disabled may commence receiving the old age pension that they would normally be entitled to receive at retirement. Currently, proposals are pending before Congress for the extension of Social Security benefits to "cover" hospital, nursing home and certain medical costs incurred by persons eligible to receive Social Security benefits. These proposals are being opposed because of their enormous and excessive cost, because they constitute a long step toward the socialization of medicine and the establishment of a national compulsory health plan, because they would result in a deterioration of the quality of health care, and are completely unnecessary, since the private practice of medicine and private health insurance have demonstrated their ability to provide and pay the costs of better-quality health care.

SUMMARY

Private health insurance in America has come of age. Its economic and social importance are established and undeniable. It has proved its competence to meet the need of the

American public for protection against the financial consequences of sickness and injury. It is an indispensable complement to life insurance in safeguarding the human life value. The private practice of medicine and private health insurance are natural partners in the American health care complex, the former to provide quality care, the latter to finance its insurable costs. Private health insurance is an important bulwark against the socialization of medicine. Its continued expansion and improvement will assist materially in the preservation of all private enterprise in America from socialistic envelopment.

REFERENCES

American Medical Association: *Disability Insurance* (Chicago: AMA, 1960).

Campbell, Rita R., and Campbell, W. Glenn: *Voluntary Health Insurance in the United States* (Washington, D.C.: American Enterprise Association, 1960).

Faulkner, Edwin J.: *Health Insurance* (New York: McGraw-Hill Book Co., 1960).

Follmann, J. F., Jr.: *Voluntary Health Insurance and Medical Care: Five Years of Progress, 1952–1957* (Health Insurance Association of America, 1958).

Gregg, Dr. Davis W. (Ed.): *Life and Health Insurance Handbook* (Richard D. Irwin, Inc., 1959).

McCahan, David (Ed.): *Accident and Sickness Insurance* (Richard D. Irwin, Inc., 1954).

Osler, Robert W.: *Guide to Accident and Sickness Insurance* (The Rough Notes Company, 1959).

Pickrell, Jesse F.: *Group Disability Insurance* (Richard D. Irwin, Inc., 1958).

Ungerleider, Harry E., and Gubner, Richard S. (Ed.): *Life Insurance and Medicine—The Prognosis and Underwriting of Disease* (Springfield, Ill.: Charles C Thomas, Publisher, 1958).

ARTHUR KEMP, Ph.D.

Currently Professor of Economics at Claremont Graduate School in California and Charles M. Stone Professor of Money and Banking at Claremont Men's College, Dr. Kemp received his Ph.D. in 1949 from New York University, where he taught economics for seven years. He has served numerous governmental and private organizations in an administrative and advisory capacity, including directorship of the AMA Economic Research Department, 1959–1960. Four books are included among his literary contributions on economics as related to political science and medicine.

11. Economics and the Practice of Medicine

Economics as a science is concerned with the social phenomena associated with the ways in which people satisfy or attempt to satisfy their wants or needs. Economics is concerned with the practice of medicine because the desire for medical care entails organizing human efforts so as to satisfy that desire. There are no special economic principles applicable only to the provision of medical care; the organizational form for providing medical services is not essentially different from other forms of economic activity, nor is the nature of medical needs or wants essentially different from other needs or wants.

In describing the facts of medical care in all its complexity, however, and in attempting to explain how medical needs or

261

wants are satisfied in the world today, it is probably inevitable that differences or dissimilarities, apparent or real, receive more attention than the similarities. This has had some unfortunate results, involving general attitudes on the part of the public toward the remuneration of the physician, the forms of financial mechanism adopted by different societies for the payment of medical care, and the political controversies over the organization of medical care. In an effort to redress the balance, this chapter will try to emphasize the general questions of economics and of political economy having the widest possible application and to use description merely as an illustrative device and not as an end in itself.

PAYING FOR MEDICAL SERVICES

Just as there are only two basic ways of coordinating the economic activities of large numbers of people, so there are only two basic ways of satisfying peoples' desires for medical care. This is true whether we are speaking of that form of medical care involving treating people who are ill, preventing illness or disease, or rehabilitating those who have been injured or ill. We can leave out of consideration the possibility of self-treatment for two reasons: first, because its extent is decidedly limited and, second, because the effective utilization of medical personnel and resources requires the coordination of large numbers of people if we are to take full advantage of modern medical science and the economic advantages of the principle of division of labor. Therefore, a system of medical care must, on the one hand, either compel or coerce some people to provide the medical care other people desire by means of centralized control and direction or, on the other hand, the system must permit and foster a way for some people to induce other people to provide that care voluntarily by offering them in exchange non-medical goods and services—usually in the form of money or generalized purchasing power.

The first method of providing medical care is the technique of the army and of the modern totalitarian state; the second is the technique of the marketplace, of a free society in which the activities of individuals rest upon the elementary proposition that, in an informed and voluntary exchange, both parties to the transaction gain benefits from it. The first method requires government intervention in medical care, in medical education, and in the insuring and financial methods for payment to an ever increasing extent. It requires coercion, to some degree, upon both the purchaser and seller of medical services in order to bring about a specific end—an end not necessarily desired by either the purchaser or the seller. Such a method of providing medical care is essentially paternalistic in outlook. It seeks to provide the individual with that quantity and quality of medical care that he *ought* to desire—as determined by some élite group of people who are not necessarily physicians —rather than what the individual himself wants. On the other hand, a medical care system organized through the market mechanism and voluntary exchange is a free, private enterprise, competitive, exchange system.

The existing medical care system in the United States and, indeed, in other countries as well, is not organized purely and simply along the lines of either method. There are almost an infinite number of possible combinations of voluntarism and coercion between the two extremes, and many of these either have been, or are being, tried out and experimented with— here and abroad. In their penetrating study of the British National Health Service, John and Sylvia Jewkes (5) have emphasized this point

Medical knowledge is the same in all the countries of the West; everywhere the same illness is likely to be treated by much the same procedures; good hospitals are run in much the same way and good medical practice follows similar lines. But when it comes to paying for medical services, to determining the respective roles of the State and the free market, to remunerating doctors and to defining the boundaries of their professional independence, then each country follows its own way and every possible combination of arrangements seems to have been tried somewhere.

At the risk of being accused of belaboring the obvious, it may be helpful to consider the possible ways in which individuals, acting separately or in groups, *can* pay for medical services and then to consider briefly the ways in which they *do,* in fact, pay for them with particular reference to the United States. The basic method of paying for medical services received is to utilize current income or past, accumulated income in the form of a savings fund. Such a savings fund may be a personal one, accumulated by the recipient of the medical service or his family, or it may be borrowed from a fund accumulated or saved by others, to be repaid by the user of the medical service or his family out of future incomes or revenues.

A second way to pay for medical services is to pay more or less regular and similar amounts, in advance of receiving the medical service, to some institution or to a group of purveyors of medical services or their agents who agree contractually to supply, in turn, specific medical service benefits at some future time. This method is essentially that of the service benefit plans, such as most but not all of the Blue Cross and Blue Shield plans, operated directly or indirectly by the purveyors of medical services. The objective is to sell, in advance of use and on a more or less prepaid basis, hospital or medical services expressed as services rather than as money remuneration. From the economic point of view, a decidedly restricted variation of the service benefit method of payment is what members of the medical profession refer to as "closed-panel" medical practice. Under this device, the purchaser buys, in advance of treatment, the right to receive services performed by a group of affiliated doctors or by hospitals or other facilities associated with the group. Medical services under such "closed-panel" group plans tend to be somewhat more "comprehensive"—a term abused almost as frequently as it is used —than under Blue Cross and Blue Shield plans but at the cost of greatly reduced choice in the selection of physician and facilities.

A third method of payment, in the economic sense, is medical care insurance proper although popular usage of the phrase and, indeed, physician usage as well, tends to be broader and to include service benefit plans. The purchaser buys from a "third party"—usually an insurance company or group—a form of cash indemnity contract under which the insuror agrees to pay to the insured, or to the purveyor of the service, in the event that he receives medical services, cash rather than service benefits. The cash received may be less than, more than, or equal to the price of the service.

A fourth method of paying for medical services involves a "fourth party" or even a "fifth party" to the complex. This consists of group-negotiated contracts, frequently combining some form of service benefit or medical care insurance and negotiated through some group device such as labor unions and/or management bargaining. The fifth method of financing medical care involves some sort of taxation, fee or assessment whether compulsory or voluntary but usually the former, and whether or not related to the medical service received. Proceeds from such taxes, fees or assessments are used to pay, in whole or in part, for the medical services provided.

Although it is possible for an individual to receive free, that is to say, gratuitous, medical care in the sense of voluntary charity care, given by a physician or a hospital without charge, it is not possible to have a *system* of free or gratuitous medical care. Most systems in which medical care is received by the individual patient without specific charge or with only a nominal charge constitute variations of the fifth method—payment in whole or in part by some degree of government coercion and taxation.

All of the methods described can be used in a medical care

system resting essentially on the voluntary cooperation of individuals. If government refrains from using its coercive powers either on the purveyors of medical care or on the users of medical care, and if it charges the recipients a fee or price equal to the cost of the service, so that government medicine simply competes in the market with alternative methods, this fifth type of payment could still be fitted within a system of voluntary cooperation. It is only accurate, however, to add that these conditions are seldom realized. Governments almost invariably use their coercive powers in one way or another, and, equally invariably, they tend to provide medical care services to some or to all at less than market prices or even at zero prices. In so doing, of course, one group of citizens is subsidized at the expense of another, or else the burden of the service is distributed in accordance with the incidence of the tax structure rather than in accordance with the medical services received.

What Is Socialized Medicine?

This suggests a question frequently encountered by members of the medical profession in their increasingly frequent conflicts with governments in political and economic affairs: What is socialized medicine? Definitions, it has been said, are neither right nor wrong, but are useful or not useful. They may also be said to be either objective or subjective. An objective and useful definition of socialized medicine or socialized electricity or anything else, from the economic viewpoint, is precisely the question of whether or not the service is rendered at less than market price. In this sense, socialized medicine exists if the fifth method of paying for medical care is employed and the recipients of that care pay less than the market price of the services they have received. It is not necessary that the price be zero—although the extent of socialization is certainly greater the greater is the difference between the market price (that either exists or would exist in a free market) and the price actually charged the recipient of the service. Subsidization of the purveyors of medical services always involves some degree of socialization of such services because the price of the service to the recipient will be less than market price, and the utilization pattern of the services will be different from that which would prevail in a free market. The only exception to such a generalization occurs if the quantities of all kinds of medical services desired are completely independent of price—in technical economic jargon, if the demand for medical services is infinitely inelastic. Such an exception to the general rule is, of course, only a theoretical and not a practical possibility.

Much dispute seems to take place over the extent to which "socialized medicine" involves restrictions on choice of physician, controls by government on physicians' fees or incomes, and on whether or not physicians are salaried employees of government. Interesting though these questions undoubtedly are, and although they have certain economic ramifications, they serve only to becloud the issue of economic socialization —the issue of providing medical services at less than market prices.

These then are the possible ways to pay for medical care, applicable to any economic system anywhere. They do not provide a description of the various ways and combinations of ways in which people *do* pay for that care.

Extent of Socialization in America

The systems employed in western, non-communist countries range from the British National Health Service, under which a very large proportion and variety of medical services are provided at zero price, to the United States where it is still true that the majority of people, in one way or another, pay for most of their medical services outside the tax structure.

Even in the United States, however, there is a substantial amount of socialization of medical services. There are, for example, more than 22 million veterans in the United States who have the legal right, under certain circumstances, to receive medical treatment for service-connected disabilities and, under certain other circumstances, for non-service-connected disabilities as well. Over 300,000 American Indians and probably more than 50,000 merchant seamen are eligible for medical services paid for by the national government. Servicemen and, under the recent extensions of the system of Medicare, wives and children of servicemen, have the legal right to medical services free of charge. Probably more than $7 billion is being spent annually on medical care goods and services by all levels of government in the United States—for the aged and non-aged needy, for veterans, for the construction of hospitals, for public health facilities and for medical research. Some 5.5 million civilian employees of the federal government and their dependents also have a part of their medical expenses paid out of government funds. It is also true that in this country, and others as well, the extent of socialization in the economic sense has been growing more rapidly in the area of medical services than in most other goods and services—despite the fact that the rationing of such things as liquor, tobacco, movies and television sets could be accomplished more easily, and more equitably than can the rationing of medical care.

Indeed, this has caused some curiosity among physicians as to why medical services should be singled out so frequently for socialization and political control. One doctor put the fundamental question both clearly and colorfully (10):

A curious paradox of some contemporary social philosophy is the idea that a man should spend what he earns for his pleasures rather than what he needs. It is appropriate, so this reasoning goes, that he should buy a television set, a vacation in Florida or an outboard motor boat, because these are cardinal rights. But for something that he really needs, such as his life or his health, or the life of his child, someone else should pay. This may be the

Government, his employer, his union, his great-aunt or anyone else who can be cajoled or coerced into paying the price for him. If no one else will pay for it, the doctor should serve him for nothing. This is the philosophy of the child, whose needs should be met by his parents but whose Christmas money or earnings for sweeping the front porch should be spent for his personal pleasures. This may be acceptable for the child of an indulgent parent, but it is not appropriate for a free man in a free society.

In the United States, but not to the same extent in other countries, the vast majority of people either pay directly for the medical services they receive or indirectly through the purchase of medical care insurance or service benefit contracts. Much work remains to be done in order to determine the extent to which part of the total costs are not met by the individual's payments but through the "cajoling or coercing" of employer or union into paying part of the costs. Nor is it clear to what extent individual employees are coerced into paying for their medical care in a way different from that which they might choose voluntarily as individuals, by virtue of the fact that they must participate as a condition of employment. We do not know how much involuntarism there is in voluntary health insurance.

Growth of Voluntary Mechanisms

If an average, or typical, American citizen can be said to exist at all, he is one who has purchased either a service benefit contract or a medical care insurance plan paying for a substantial part of the large and unexpected medical expenditures he is likely to be called upon to make. For the most part, however, he pays the smaller, budgetable medical expenses out of current income, out of a cash reserve, or by borrowing. Over 132,000,000 people—some 73 per cent of the total civilian population—had, at the end of 1960, hospital expense insurance or service benefit contracts; of these, 92 per cent also had surgical coverage and 66 per cent had regular medical expense coverage as reported in *Health Insurance News,* September, 1961. The extent of growth in coverage, and its rate of increase, were largely unforeseen and unpredicted. Indeed, the predictions and assertions made in 1938 and in 1948, that voluntary insurance devices could not be expected to be adopted by a major segment of the population, clearly have been proved incorrect by subsequent events (1, 2). Over half the total population has more than one type of coverage—hospital, surgical or regular medical. The most remarkable increase in recent years has been in major medical expense insurance, specifically designed to insure against the very large bills of very serious illnesses. This was scarcely available at all ten years ago, but is now held by some 28,000,000 persons.

Criticisms of Voluntary Insurance

The progress made in coverage, the extensive development of the voluntary mechanisms, is no longer debatable. What might have become a compulsory national health insurance program under the direct responsibility and control of the national government, or even a national health service scheme similar to that in Britain, still remains the responsibility of a private and voluntary insurance system. Yet the criticisms of medical care insurance and service benefit plans, and the issues of a political, economic and ideological nature are, if anything, more extensive and more violent than before—and they seem unlikely to become less so in the future. Moreover, it is difficult if not impossible to separate the economic issues from the ideological.

One criticism frequently expressed is that the medical care coverage by insurance or service benefit contracts is "inadequate" or "not comprehensive enough." Seldom do the critics supply objective definitions of such terms if, indeed, they are capable of being defined objectively. The implication seems to be that none of an individual's medical expenses ought to be paid by the first method of payment discussed above—that is to say, no part of medical expenditures ought to be paid out of current income or a savings fund. The fact that insurance payments of all kinds were "only" 25 per cent of total private expenditures on medical care in recent years is often cited as evidence that insurance is "inadequate." Such a ratio is a very crude index, indeed and results in a lower percentage than any other kind of measure, because every kind of expenditure that can be considered medical in any way is lumped into the denominator. Or the fact that some procedure, or drug expenditure, or outpatient treatment is not covered by an insurance or service benefit contract is cited as evidence that insurance is not "comprehensive enough."

There is no economic basis for judging or prescribing what proportion of total medical expenditures either of a society or of individuals and families ought to be paid in one way or another. If individuals are free to insure or not to insure, and if they place a relatively high value on certainty and a low value on uncertainty and risk, the proportion of total expenditures paid by insurance is likely to be high. On the other hand, the less dislike people have for uncertainty and risk, the smaller the proportion is likely to be. Small bills are relatively costly in the insurance process; the smaller they are, relative to an individual's income, the less willing he is likely to be to pay through insurance or prepayment for the added certainty and convenience achieved by transferring the risk to some insurer or purveyor of service. The more comprehensive the coverage, the higher the administrative charges and the more expensive the insurance coverage. Some people have confused bad contract design, where there is incentive to overhospitalization and uneconomic usage, with comprehensiveness of coverage.

It is important to realize that neither service benefit contracts nor medical care insurance contracts can be expected to cover all kinds and varieties of medical expenditures. To insist on an unattainable comprehensive payment of all medical expenditures through a third, fourth or fifth party to the payment process can only lead to the destruction of the voluntary health insurance structure and, ultimately, to abandoning the private practice of medicine by substituting a centralized, coercive system under which doctors become salaried employees of government.

Closely related to the question of comprehensiveness is the criticism leveled against contractual devices designed to ration scarce resources and to prevent uneconomical use of both resources and type of payment. These critics usually take exception to deductible and coinsurance features of contracts. The implication is that all expenditures, particularly the small ones, ought to be paid in some other way than out of current income or savings, that insurance, benefits or subsidies ought to pay everything—from first dollar to last dollar, as the phrase goes. Such an implication, of course, has no objective economic basis.

THE "HIGH COSTS OF MEDICAL CARE"

Certainly this is an issue involving economics and economic judgments! Unfortunately, the economist must invariably begin a discussion of the issue by calling attention to the misuse of words and the confusion of concepts. This misuse of words and confusion of concepts is not confined to the popular literature—which would be bad enough—but is also found in much of the medical literature and even in some technical economic articles written by persons who ought to know better. The essential nature of the confusion is a failure to distinguish clearly between *prices* of medical care goods and services, on the one hand, and total expenditures on medical care goods and services on the other. Price, of a good or service, whether medical or not, is a per unit concept; expenditures, on the other hand, involve both price per unit and the number of units purchased. Prices of medical services could rise while total medical expenditures declined, or fall while total medical expenditures increased. It is regrettable that the word "costs" is sometimes used to mean prices and at other times used to mean expenditures. Indeed, one can find "costs" used in two different ways on the same page or even the same paragraph. It is difficult sometimes, if not impossible, to determine what is meant when the words "medical care costs" are used.

Criticism is expressed often in the press that medical care costs are "too high" and are increasing. This can refer to prices per unit of medical services (whether in the form of physicians' fees, per diem hospital rates, drug prices or whatever) or it can refer to total expenditures in curing a specific illness or simply to total medical expenditures. Assume, for the moment, that the meaning of "costs" is prices per unit. There is no objective economic basis, in any absolute sense, for determining when any price, medical or other, is "too high" or "too low." Measurements are possible to show changes in prices, and the relation of changes in some prices to those in other prices or groups of prices or to total expenditure changes; but there is no "just price" or price level equilibrium.

One criticism, direct or implied, of physicians' fees and other medical care prices is that the existence and development of medical care insurance and service benefit plans are the cause of increased medical care prices. Although some further investigation of such implications is both necessary and desirable, the existing evidence neither proves nor disproves them. There is a correlation between the growth of the insurance devices and the increase in medical care prices. But logic strongly suggests that the increased use of insurance came about because of increased medical care prices and the likelihood of further price rises rather than that the price rises were caused by the system developed. The annual rate of increase in certain medical prices—surgical fees, for example—was substantially higher when the proportion of the population covered by insurance was lower. If "costs" mean expenditures rather than prices, the logical case is even stronger that expanded insurance purchases are the result of a desire to purchase increased quantities of medical care services of various kinds. This is reinforced by the general tendency toward a growing proportion of services in total consumer expenditures.

Comparative Rise in Consumer Prices

The behavior of medical prices over time is described by the medical care component of the Bureau of Labor Statistics Consumer Price Index. In the long period of rising consumer price levels since 1939, not all prices have risen at the same rate nor by the same amount. One would not expect such similarities. In all periods of this sort for which we have data, some groups of prices have risen more than others. There is little to suggest that any of these prices or groups of prices that have risen more than the general price level in the past twenty or twenty-five years have behaved significantly differently from other particular prices or groups of prices in previous inflationary periods. The evidence suggests, rather, that this is typical behavior, particularly when comparing the behavior of service prices relative to commodity prices. Where there is a tendency to reduce the proportion of total expenditures on commodities and increase the proportion spent on services (as has been happening), there is a tendency for service prices to rise more rapidly than commodity prices.

The facts of the matter are reasonably well known, although additional investigations can be very valuable in some areas. The upward movement of consumer prices has taken place for the most part since 1939: in medical care prices the result would not be appreciably different if the base of reference used were 1933 rather than 1939, although the data are not strictly comparable. In the most recent two decades the rise in the Consumer Price Index is slightly more than the rise in the medical care component of that index and considerably more than the increase in medical care prices other than hospital rates. The greatest increase, and in some ways quite remarkable increase, has been in hospital day rates although this is to some extent offset by the reduction in the average hospital stay—a factor the index does not take into consideration.

To look solely at nominal price changes in a period of substantial increases in both price levels and money incomes is, of course, decidedly misleading. One must consider both price changes and income changes in evaluating changes in terms of real prices and real incomes. Disregarding for the moment the rather spectacular changes that have been taking place over the past two decades in the quality of medical care, the real price of medical care, of the medical care complex of goods and services, is less today than it was in 1939. In 1959 it required fewer work hours, less labor time and effort, to purchase at a higher nominal price the same quantity of medical care that could be bought for a dollar or ten dollars in 1939. A factory worker in 1939 had to work 15 hours and 54 minutes in order to buy ten dollars worth of medical care. Twenty years later, for the same quantity of medical care, he had to work only nine hours and forty-two minutes—and this does not take into consideration that the ten dollars worth of care in 1939 was of decidedly poorer quality. At no time in the history of our society has the average person had as great an ability to pay for medical care as he has at present; and at no time has he been able to buy such excellent care as he can now (7, 9).

The Rise in Quality and Variety of Medical Services

In fact, of course, the quality of medical care has greatly improved over the past three decades. Some procedures are possible—whether the reference is to open heart surgery or polio vaccine—that simply were not available at all formerly; and some procedures formerly dangerous and expensive have been almost eliminated by the application of some of the newer drugs. Such increases in quality and in availability of procedures totally unknown in recent years are not taken into consideration when measuring price changes. These are two weaknesses in retail price index numbers in general—at least as they are presently computed. They are well-known to economists and statisticians, and it is widely recognized that they tend to give retail price index numbers an upward bias. Furthermore, it seems likely that the rate of innovation in medical care services is somewhat greater than the rate of innovation in most of the other components of the Consumer Price Index.

There is currently no index number for medical care that attempts to provide a "cost of illness" index. The various and sundry items going into the makeup of the medical care component of the Consumer Price Index are quite a hodge-podge with little reference to the relation of one to another, even in terms of total expenditure. It would be decidedly useful, if such an index could be devised and computed, to know whether or not it is becoming more expensive to treat specific diseases and to know those becoming more expensive, those becoming less expensive, and those remaining relatively unchanged. Such knowledge today is hit or miss, subjective and widely scattered.

If costs mean total costs or expenditures, the existence of rising medical care costs should be regarded less as undesirable than as decidedly desirable for our society—and for several reasons. The increased quality and variety of medical services available would be expected to bring about an increased demand for medical services. If, in addition, there is a growing realization of the importance of medical care to the individual and to his family; if there is a growing realization of the advantages of early diagnosis and treatment of disease, as well as immunization procedures—this tends to bring about an increased demand for medical care, an increased utilization of all forms of medical care services and facilities, and an increase in total expenditures on medical care. This has taken place to a substantial degree and such a development can scarcely be regarded by rational, responsible human beings as unfortunate.

Rising Incidence of Chronic Disease

There is a further aspect to this seldom discussed, even in medical circles. There is little doubt that the incidence of chronic illness as opposed to acute illness has been rising; the incidence of many forms of acute, communicable disease has been drastically reduced. Infant mortality, too, is much less important today than in earlier periods. Surely these and other accomplishments are meritorious. But we seem prone to forget, and this is one of the most intriguing parts of applying economic reasoning to medical care, that we must all die ultimately of something. Medical science seeks a goal it cannot possibly achieve—the immortality of the individual. In reality no doctor has ever saved a life, although many doctors undoubtedly have prolonged lives and, perhaps more important, have enhanced the dignity of living. Every successful medical innovation, every breakthrough, to the extent that it prolongs life also creates a new problem and, more often than not, it is a more expensive and more costly problem. If the lives of a significant proportion of the population are successfully prolonged, there will result either an increasing proportion of the population with chronic illness or a sharp shift in the nature of acute illness and its incidence. One or both these results must occur. Moreover, it seems likely that this will result in a greater total expenditure on medical care, over the life of the individual person, even if the prices of medical care services remain unchanged.

If one adds to these factors the very evident reluctance on the part of purchasers of medical care to accept the same quality of medical care they were getting ten or five years ago even at lower prices, the fact that both total medical expenditures and medical care prices are higher today than ten years ago, and are increasing, is scarcely something to marvel at.

Medicine as a Monopoly

The medical profession and its activities have been scrutinized, with unfavorable conclusions for the most part, by some economists largely on the grounds that the medical profession constitutes a monopoly of sorts. Doctors, it is sometimes said, utilize their monopoly power to restrict entry into the profession thereby enhancing monopoly gains. They practice price discrimination by charging differential prices for identical services (3, 8). Space does not permit more than a few remarks on these questions which have had devoted to them a rather substantial literature. Indeed, apart from the use to which the economic analysis is sometimes put by individuals interested in particular politico-economic proposals, there is much to be said for the economic description of the medical profession that they use.

The medical profession and other professions as well, by the nature of the case and not by virtue of the governmental licensing procedures involved, do in fact constitute monopolies of sorts. Where entry into the profession takes place on the basis of prescribed forms of education and approved standards of competence, the very nature of such a selection process restricts entry and results in a smaller number of practitioners than if there were no educational prerequisites and no standards of competence. But it is important to recognize that, so far as I am aware, the criteria employed that result in some restriction do not include indicators of the individual's monopolizing ability or adeptness in engaging in price discriminatory activities. Nor does there appear to be more than a rudimentary understanding of economic principles or method among the educational prerequisites and frequently not even this. This may be an unfortunate part of the process, responsible in part for the fact that members of the medical profession often find themselves caught in the cross-fire both from the left and the right.

Regrettably, to assert—as some members of the medical profession do assert—that the activities of the professions somehow make their members superior to other forms of economic endeavor because professionals do not strive for money is a form of intellectual snobbery that has hurt, and will continue to hurt, the members of the medical profession in their relations to government. An individual may be a very competent physician without having achieved substantial pecuniary success, but he is certainly not necessarily incompetent because he has prospered. Price discrimination, if it is practiced and to the extent that it is practiced, is not necessarily inconsistent with the profit motive. Nor is the profit motive inconsistent with the highest competence in the practice of medicine. On the contrary, I am prepared to suggest that the medical doctor who permits the market to ration his scarce services among the individuals who seek them will do more, in the long run, to promote individual freedom and responsibility than the one who does not. I suspect, after asking many doctors how their fees are determined for the performance of a given procedure, that this is an area where physicians talk like monopolists but behave like competitors.

The Doctor Shortage

It may be that, in the past, entry into medical schools was restricted on occasion, and to some extent that this restriction was motivated by a desire to alleviate an over-supply of doctors—as measured by the less than full employment of existing practitioners of medicine in the 1930's. This is hardly to be marveled at; new steel mills are not erected in profusion if current output is a small per cent of capacity. But it is very doubtful that such a policy exists today; to the contrary, the medical profession may be taking much too seriously some very superficial reasoning about the desirability of any given ratio of doctors to total population.

In any event, people who complain about a doctor shortage—past, present or future—are being somewhat illogical when at the same time they complain of the doctors' fees. Unless our society is willing to go the socialized, centralized, totalitarian route of coercing and compelling individuals to serve in various capacities, the supply of doctors will be adversely affected if doctors' incomes are lowered relative to those of physicists, biochemists or congressmen. This is not necessarily true if our society is willing to accept poorer and less competent physicians. If some writers argue that we should have more doctors who are paid less and are poorer in quality than we now have, they are at least consistent in their desires. But such a position is seldom taken; they expect as good or better doctors at lower cost—and this is not possible in a voluntary system.

MEDICAL CARE AS A POLITICAL ISSUE

More intriguing even than the medical care issues, primarily economic in nature, are those that are as much political issues as economic; issues that involve basic differences in ideological value judgments. Indeed, the very heat of current political discussions relating to medical care, and the vigorous political activities of various organized groups, suggest that there is not a clear recognition of the ideological spectrum. Differences of various kinds, particularly political and economic, can arise from several sources. One is the question of fact, of the extent of knowledge; this can usually be resolved rather easily by a pooling of knowledge or an extension of it. A second type of difference less easily resolved than the first results from unintentional, illogical interpretation of the facts or from the impossibility of obtaining them. For, as the famous British economist Alfred Marshall remarked, controversy "brings out the impossibility of learning anything from facts until they are examined and interpreted by reason; and teaches that the most reckless and treacherous of all theorists is he who professes to let facts and figures speak for themselves." Further complicating this wise observation is our tendency, and we are all guilty to some extent—consciously or unconsciously—to select and interpret the "facts" according to our desires. We frequently interpret them according to what we think *should* be rather than what is; and we desist too soon even in pursuing "scientific" studies. Particularly is this true in social sciences, although not confined to them, where objective measurement is more difficult than in the physical sciences and where the elaborately controlled experiment is difficult to apply.

But the third type of difference is the most difficult of all to resolve. Where there is no disagreement over the facts; where there is no error of logic in interpretation; then there is likely to exist diametrically opposed, antithetical ideological positions. To the extent that this type of difference exists, the matter cannot be settled by an appeal either to fact or to logic; it can only be resolved, if at all, by persuasion or by fighting it out, either physically or in the political arena, with the resultant coercion of some people by others.

Politico-economic controversies over medical care systems are not new, are not confined to the United States, and are unlikely to disappear even if the United States were to adopt a national health service similar to that in Britain—a highly unlikely development in the near future. Indeed, such controversy is likely to continue in Britain for quite some time to come. As long ago as 1884, Germany had a form of health insurance to which people whose incomes were below certain limits were required to subscribe, together with their employers and the government, in the purchasing of medical care. In England, low-income employees having less than $1,250 annual income were compelled to take part in a prepaid medical service by a National Health Insurance Act in 1912. Since that time almost every large, industrialized country has produced some kind of compulsory, or semi-compulsory, medical care scheme either through a national, governmental program or by compulsion to join private insurance or sickness funds. Right up to the present time, questions of prices, nature of service, proportion of resources to be devoted to medical and hospital service, resource allocation within the broad field of medical care—and so on—continue to be "hot" political issues in all these countries as well as our own (5, 11).

In the United States, during the formative years of the Social Security Act from 1934 to 1936, considerable agitation took place within the Roosevelt Administration for the adoption of a compulsory national health insurance program under Title II of the Act. Later several proposals were made to enact a limited version, which would extend hospitalization benefits to all those covered under Old Age and Survivors Insurance—in 1942, by Rep. Eliot; in 1943 and 1945, by Senator Green of Rhode Island. In 1948 the Wagner-Murray-Dingell bill touched off a vigorous political controversy by proposing, once again, a compulsory national health insurance program. In more recent years, a slightly altered version of the Eliot and Green proposals was dropped annually into the legislative hopper by Representative Aime J. Forand of Rhode Island, to which were added a large number of variations on the same theme by a number of other Congressmen and Senators. From these came the Kerr-Mills Act (Public Law 86-778), authorizing federal grants to approved state programs for providing medical care to aged persons of limited means but not the wider type program desired by Forand and others. The wider proposal was submitted in the House of Representatives and in the Senate, by Rep. King of California and Senator Anderson of New Mexico, early in 1962. It is to be expected that a bitter political struggle will follow once again in the legislative arena, and that it will not cease whether or not the legislation is passed.

The Ethics of Government Assistance

There are some interesting normative or ethical questions underlying such issues as medical care under the Social Security Act, compulsory health insurance for all, or for specific groups such as the aged—whether of the Kerr-Mills type, involving only aid to needy aged or aid to all, or to the entire group, paid for by payroll taxes. Basically, the normative questions are these: (1) To what extent, if at all, is it desirable for government to subsidize, by payment of money, large groups of heterogeneous, voting citizens? (2) To what extent, if at all, is it desirable for government to subsidize such groups by paying for, or providing directly, specific goods and services?

There are many other issues, in addition to those involving medical and hospital care, old age pensions, etc., to which these same normative questions apply. It should be apparent that a person may logically favor government intervention of the type suggested by the first question, while totally disapproving the type of intervention suggested by the second. To me, although both types of intervention seem undesirable and to be avoided if possible, the first type of subsidization is decidedly less evil than the second.

Positions taken in answering these two questions determine, to a great extent, the pressures for and against most of the activities that might be called collectively the "welfare state." Similarly, the nature of the political attitudes revealed by the various answers to these questions indicate the possible compromises among forces struggling in the legislative or political arena.

Alleviating the extremes of indigency, poverty or starvation has long been recognized as a moral obligation on the part of the individual and, with less general agreement, on the part of the community. The extent of the moral obligation on the part of family, friends and associates, upon local governments or national governments, or upon voluntary agencies or religious groups is not objectively determinable and frequently is subject to many interpretations.

Public assistance programs, for the most part, are modern adaptations of the poor laws; they are looked upon by many as necessary but temporary evils in the development and growth of the economy, necessary to aid the poor and unfortunate, the handicapped or even the improvident, until such time as rising living standards and educational achievement levels render such aid and assistance unnecessary.

Proponents of this view are likely to favor some level of government assuming this responsibility by direct monetary payments made to individuals or families on the basis of need, measured by some form of needs test—whether income, assets, net worth or subjective judgment.

Quite a different view will be put forth by others who regard the provision of social services, either directly or indirectly, as a permanent function of government—usually showing a preference for performing the function at the level of the national, central government rather than by states or localities. Instead of visualizing a temporary relief program, this view regards the provision of specific goods and services by government as a progressively expanding function, covering more and more goods and services, and entailing an ever-growing proportion of gross national product or national income or personal income. It regards as both necessary and proper the increasing employment of "experts" to set standards for goods and services and to ensure that there is a "proper" selection and distribution of such goods and services. Those who take this view are less concerned with poverty as such than with programs designed to increase the quantity and quality (frequently measured by the degree of equality in distribution) in the socially provided goods and services. They will not favor money distribution but rather will promote distribution of service benefits; they will fear that, if permitted to choose, the indigent or improvident or unfortunate will make choices of which the "experts" do not approve.

The entire spectrum of shades of compromise lies between these two viewpoints. Some may argue that there will always be a lower level to be treated as relatively poverty stricken— as in certain public housing developments that currently have an acceptable family income ceiling of $1,500 per year. Others may argue that the elimination of social expenditure programs, once embarked upon, is too difficult a political task to undertake and, therefore, that the existing level, expressed either as an absolute amount or as a proportion of the national income or other such measure, should be maintained but its expansion opposed or inhibited. The variety of compromise on an administrative level, devices for encouraging frequent reassessment of programs, seems practically unlimited.

Although these basic considerations apply to all welfare programs, their nature becomes clear when applied, for example, to such a program as medical care subsidies for the aged. The use of the payroll tax to finance aid to the entire group regardless of need is clearly the device preferred by those who regard the social services as a continually expanding function of society. A locally administered medical assistance program for the aged needy, as exemplified by the Kerr-Mills Act, is certainly the device preferred by those who regard the problem of poverty as a limited and temporary one.

The Medical Viewpoint

The American Medical Association, the American Dental Association and the American Hospital Association have vigorously opposed the provision of medical and health care benefits to the aged by means of the social security payroll tax. No such opposition took place against the Kerr-Mills Act providing aid to the aged indigent and near-indigent; indeed, these same organizations have been most active in implementing the legislation. Nor would the opposition of these organizations have been aroused by proposals to spend an equal amount of money in cash payments to the recipients within the existing OASDI structure. If, instead of subsidizing the purveyors of medical services by service benefit payments, dollar payments had been proposed sufficient to permit the aged citizen to buy health care insurance if he chose to do so, the purveyors of medical care would have had only a passing interest in the legislation. Underlying medical opposition to Social Security medical care is the belief on the part of the purveyor groups that the ever-expanding social service concept, with determination of standards by the "experts"—not necessarily doctors—rather than by market forces and individual choice, will ultimately lead to similar pressures for paying for the medical and health care of the entire population in a similar manner.

In a free society it is certainly the right of those who desire it to advocate the use of the Social Security system with its payroll deductions to provide medical care service benefits. But those who advocate it for particular groups, such as the elderly, cannot logically rest their case on the low financial status, indeed the poverty, of such groups. This is not so much the fact that the elderly are by no means a homogeneous group financially speaking. The emphasis upon poverty is a weak reed on which to rely. Poverty can be alleviated or modified in many ways—whether the poor are poor aged, poor farmers, poor negroes, poor urban slum-dwellers, or poor anything else. The medical profession is eminently justified in mistrusting the motivations behind the argument. If the Social Security device is a logical financial method for purchasing medical care for the elderly, it must also be suitable—probably more suitable—for the entire population and for the same reasons. Poverty is a false issue, if not a dishonest one.

The medical profession mistrusts the extension of governmental coercive powers into these various aspects of medical care. Doctors are becoming increasingly aware of the evidence that strongly suggests a general pattern. Governmental intervention into these areas tends to bring about a monopoly function of government and, in so doing, tends to destroy the freedom and the responsibility of the individual to provide for his own current and future health as well as for other elements of his well-being. Doctors are becoming increasingly aware that once such responsibility is lost, once such freedom is surrendered, the decision is well-nigh irreversible. The vast majority of medical doctors sincerely believe that only with individual freedom of choice, both of physician and of other things can the medical profession provide the highest quality of medical service. The House of Delegates of the American Medical Association has repeatedly expressed its position emphatically:

The American Medical Association believes that free choice of physician is the right of every individual and one he should be free to exercise as he chooses.

Each individual should be accorded the privilege to select and change his physician at will or to select his preferred system of medical care, and the American Medical Association vigorously supports the right of the individual to choose between these alternatives.

Lest there be any misinterpretation, we state unequivocally that the American Medical Association firmly subscribes to freedom of choice of physician and free competition among physicians as being prerequisites to optimal medical care.

The benefits of any system which provides medical care must

be judged on the degree to which it allows of, or abridges, such freedom of choice and such competition.

If one examines the various European systems of financing medical care, it becomes apparent that there are objectives in the systems going beyond that of providing such services outside the market—going beyond even a mistrust of the market structure. Perhaps these other aims are not a necessary part of such medical care systems, nor even of the welfare state itself. But the end result of almost every instance where non-voluntary systems have been established, medical care systems have developed in such a way that they can be employed as tools for the redistribution of income or even for attaining and retaining political power. Students of the effects of applying welfare instruments to medical care are impressed by the fact that there is usually some compulsion requiring everyone to insure against medical risks or to contribute to a system which purports to insure him against such risks. Almost invariably there is coupled with this a requirement that the individual insure through one unified government organization, and this is usually based upon assertions that this is necessary for efficiency, for economy and sometimes for equity. The net effect is virtually to make impossible the continuation of the voluntary method. The instrument produced, and a monopoly instrument at that, is certainly capable of doing things and providing things that the voluntary method could also provide. But it is also capable of becoming an instrument of social and political control and can be used for all sorts of ulterior purposes. Whatever aid, assistance, subsidization, is provided can be made dependent upon all sorts of special conditions and requirements. In other countries at least, in the course of time, this has often become the governing consideration.

Similarly, with reference to the boundaries of the professional independence of medical doctors, there are great dangers inherent in state intervention. Professor Hayek (4) has expressed it most eloquently; his statement should be read by every member of the medical profession:

There are so many serious problems raised by the nationalization of medicine that we cannot mention even all the more important ones. But there is one the gravity of which the public has scarcely yet perceived and which is likely to be of the greatest importance. This is the inevitable transformation of doctors, who have been members of a free profession primarily responsible to their patients, into paid servants of the state, officials who are necessarily subject to instruction by authority and who must be released from the duty of secrecy so far as authority is concerned. The most dangerous aspect of the new development may well prove to be that, at a time when the increase of medical knowledge tends to confer more and more power over the minds of men to those who possess it, they should be made dependent on a unified organization under single direction and be guided by the same reasons of state that generally govern policy. A system that gives the indispensable helper of the individual, who is at the same time an agent of the state, an insight into the other's most intimate concerns and creates conditions in which he must reveal this knowledge to a superior and use it for the purposes determined by authority opens frightening prospects. The manner in which state medicine has been used in Russia as an instrument of industrial discipline gives us a foretaste of the uses to which such a system can be put.

It is not possible to consider issues of this kind over any substantial period of time without adopting one position or another. The truly "objective" treatment of such issues can be undertaken in good faith only by an ideological eunuch. Therefore, stated unequivocally, this is my own position: I want to promote, to protect and to preserve the private—that is, the non-governmental—practice of medicine in the United States. I am unalterably opposed to any policy that threatens to obscure or to subvert that objective. If it can be proved beyond doubt, and to my complete satisfaction, that the best and most efficient medical care could be attained by some other system and at less cost, I should still prefer the private practice of medicine. In this matter, however, unlike some other questions, there is the probability that one can have one's cake and eat it, too. There is little evidence to suggest that the private practice of medicine is more expensive or less efficient. But even if this were not so, the voluntary, private practice of medicine makes possible the as yet unknown discoveries and developments of the future on which all true medical progress ultimately depends.

It is quite evident that some have different objectives. The most extreme among these wish to establish the practice of medicine as a monopoly of a group of salaried physicians, employees of government. Between these extremes, as usual, there are a variety of positions some of which have been touched upon above.

Is it possible to state objectively that there is one best method of providing medical care? Can we say how individuals should pay for medical care? Ought we to be able to prescribe how much each ought to buy, and under what circumstances he should be prevented from obtaining what he wants and is willing to pay for? Merely asking such questions reveals the complexity of the subject matter. People have different wants in medical care. Just as some people want white shirts, or plaid shirts or pink shirts, so people have different desires for medical care. To assert that people want the highest quality medical care as the oratorical phrase usually appears, or the best shirts, or the best transportation system, or the best government, all beg the fundamental questions involved. The public is a collection of individuals, and the whole is no greater than the sum of its parts. The ultimate wants in medical care are the wants of the individuals who form that public; there are no supra-individual wants or needs, values or ends. When one asks, what does the American public want in medical care, we are really asking what do individual people desire or want in medical care?

It is doubtful that there can be any single answer to such questions, or whether there should be. The "best" method of financing medical care or of purchasing such care will be the one best suited to the individual, considering all the varying aspects of an evaluation by the individual bearing on his case. The important thing is to permit the individual to have as much choice in selecting the type of medical care plan which he wants to receive as is possible under the circumstances.

In discussing the reasons usually put forth in favor of government intervention in medical care, D. S. Lees has this pertinent and cogent comment concerning individual choice (11):

There is then the general argument that if people are left to their own devices they will make the 'wrong' choices. The point would gain in cogency if only we knew what the 'right' choices were. It has long been recognized that children and imbeciles require special protection and that dangerous habits like drug-taking need to be restricted. But for the most part the 'wrong' choices are those which we ourselves disapprove of or which happen for the moment to be unpopular. In a free society these choices are shown a wide measure of tolerance and those who disapprove seek to change them by persuasion and not coercion.

It may be that some people do not want any medical care at all. I should prefer that they be permitted not to have any; or, at most, be required to furnish evidence that they have sufficient assets to assure themselves of reasonably satisfactory care if they change their minds. Even assuming that some people prefer some kind of insurance or service benefit plan to facilitate payment, there is available to them a wide variety of commercial health insurance or Blue Shield-Blue Cross plans a combination of which can satisfy almost anyone. In fact, the outstanding achievement of the voluntary system in medical care financing is the great variety of plans available for people to buy, using their own judgment in providing for their own well being in the purchase of medical care. Strangely enough, those who hold the social view consider this the great *dis*advantage of the voluntary system.

Whether we like it or not, all of us constantly have to make judgments that involve evaluating economic factors on the one side of the scale against non-economic factors on the other. These range from the most insignificant of items to the most significant evaluation in the world—our life—and they must be made whether one is wealthy or poor. When one says he cannot afford something, more often than not he means simply that he prefers other things more at their existing prices. What he is really complaining about is that he must make the choice at all. It may be that we don't like to make such choices; it may be that we would prefer to push them off onto somebody else, but the fact of the matter is that we cannot really avoid them. The important question is not whether the individual is competent to make medical judgments, but whether the evaluations that he must make are to be made *for* him by somebody else. Scratch the surface of almost any of the arguments against the voluntary method, or in favor of some impersonal, governmental, centralized mechanism for providing medical care, and you will discover that these do not reveal a dissatisfaction with the way in which the voluntary method functions. Rather the complaint is that the voluntary method works too well; it gives to people what they want rather than what some other people think they ought to have! At the bottom of most of the arguments against a system of medical care financed voluntarily is a lack of belief in individual freedom of choice.

Many writers have pointed out the inconsistency between freedom and security. Consider freedom *from* choice, rather than freedom *of* choice, and one comes close to a workable definition of slavery. Perhaps this author can be forgiven for quoting himself, but the following has the advantage of retaining its original passion, without being diluted by paraphrase or the passage of time (6):

> We live in a society still essentially free, one that gives to the individual the right not only to choose his physician but to make other choices as well. Indeed, we have even permitted the individual person to choose to use his capital and his services to advocate the abolition of freedom of choice itself. Throughout the history of mankind this sort of society has not been the general

rule but the exception. Perhaps this is inevitable. The totalitarian collectivist principle is straightforward; it appeals to those who say, "Do something now." The necessity of restraint, group and individual, the recognition of ignorance and the imperfection of human knowledge, and the denial of a millenium and the aim of establishing conditions that make life not perfect but workable— all these attributes of a free-choice society constitute highly sophisticated doctrine.

It is sobering to see the growing number of so-called leaders of political thought or politicians who advocate an ever-growing governmental assumption of responsibility for all sorts of complex economic and social problems—full-employment, care for the aged, care for the indigent, government health services, subsidized housing, and so on and on. Yet the moral ethic upon which our civilization rests emphasizes individual responsibility. Can such a civilization survive? Perhaps, but only if it recognizes the difference between freedom of choice and freedom from choice.

REFERENCES

1. Campbell, R. R., and Campbell, W. C.: *Voluntary Health Insurance in the United States* (Washington, D. C.: American Enterprise Association, 1960).
2. Follmann, J. F., Jr.: Trends in the future of voluntary health insurance, Proceedings of the Annual Conference of County Medical Society Officers (Los Angeles, Feb. 11–12, 1961).
3. Friedman, M., and Kuznets, S.: *Income from Independent Professional Practice* (New York: National Bureau of Economic Research, 1945).
4. Hayek, F. A.: *The Constitution of Liberty* (Chicago: University of Chicago Press, 1960).
5. Jewkes, J., and Jewkes, S.: *The Genesis of the British National Health Service* (Oxford: Basil Blackwell, 1961).
6. Kemp, A.: Freedom of choice, J.A.M.A. 172:943, 1960.
7. Kemp, A., and Livingston, W. R.: Medical care costs in an extended inflation, J.A.M.A. 174:1209, 1960.
8. Kessel, R. A.: Price discrimination in medicine, J. Law & Econ. 1:20, 1958).
9. Langford, E. A.: Medical care in the consumer price index, Monthly Labor News, Sept., 1957.
10. Lee, C. M., Jr.: The challenge of medical-care insurance, New England J. Med. 262:334, 1960.
11. Lees, D. S.: *Health Through Choice,* Hobart Paper No. 14 (London: Institute of Economic Affairs, 1961).

LOUIS A. BUIE, SR., M.D.

Long affiliated with the Mayo Clinic and Foundation, Dr. Buie is Emeritus Professor of Proctology at the Mayo Foundation for Medical Education and Research, University of Minnesota Graduate School. His lifelong concern with the proper conduct of medical practice is revealed in his participation in AMA affairs. He was a member of the House of Delegates from 1939 to 1957, on the Judicial Council from 1945 to 1960, chairman of the Committee on Constitution and Bylaws, 1950–1957, and a member of the Medical Disciplinary Committee. He has also served as Vice-Chairman of the Committee on Voluntary Health Agencies since 1952.

12. Medical Ethics of Today

Among the oldest systems of ethics is that of the medical profession, and the American Medical Association has been more than conscientious in accepting and preserving the responsibilities implied in such a system. Through the years the association has endeavored to engender and to enhance the proper behavior of all its members. Even a casual review of the Principles of Medical Ethics of the American Medical Association and the Opinions and Reports of the Judicial Council—hereafter referred to as the Opinions—by an impartial observer must inevitably convince him that no other body of men, whatever their calling, is guided by higher ethical standards.

The National Medical Association, which was the forerunner of the American Medical Association, appointed a committee at its first meeting in New York in 1846 to prepare a code of ethics. The proposed code was offered at a meeting which was held in Philadelphia in 1847, and it was patterned after the Principles of Thomas Percival, who had published 92 rules for the guidance of physicians of England in 1803. Percival's concept of ethics dealt chiefly with the relationship of physicians with each other, and the rules which he set down can account for the volume and some of the contents of the version of the Principles of Ethics which served as a guide for members of the American Medical Association for more than 100 years.

Until the revision was adopted in June of 1957, the accretions of many years had encumbered the Principles of Ethics by verbiage, ambiguities, pleonasms and qualifying constructions of dubious value, which, in themselves, engendered confusion and made straightforward interpretation most difficult. Hence, it became quite clear that the text should be altered to deal with broad basic principles which could serve as a ready reference for the busy practitioner and which would reflect the spirit of the modern age. Physicians had become accustomed to a lengthy document which never had encompassed fewer than 40 sections and which at one time (1903) contained as many as 53 sections. Just before the revised edition was adopted, the Principles were composed of a Preamble and 47 sections, amounting to more than 8,000 words. Some physicians, in fact, had never seen the Principles, and others had frankly despaired of ever getting through the massive text.

In June of 1952 the House of Delegates of the American Medical Association assigned the task of revising the Principles to its Council on Constitution and Bylaws, consisting of Warren W. Furey, Stanley H. Osborn, B. E. Pickett, Floyd S. Winslow, and Louis A. Buie, chairman. Accordingly, in December of 1955, an exhaustive analysis and tentative proposals were prepared. In this report, many of the complexities of the undertaking were revealed. A substantial portion of the text actually dealt with morals, manners and even economics. There were sections in which the fundamental concepts of ethics were entangled with the simplest propositions of etiquette and in which there was much overlapping and consequent confusion.

A new plan was presented to the House of Delegates in June of 1956. In view of the fact that few members of the medical profession had been afforded an opportunity to study the proposal, the Council requested that the new version be publicized and that action by the House of Delegates be deferred until the next annual meeting.

The brevity of this new version of the Principles attracted immediate attention and occasioned some doubt and even criticism. In my report, as chairman of the Council on Constitution and Bylaws, the fact was emphasized that there is nothing new or original about the quality of brevity. As examples, attention was called to the Constitution of the United States and, even more significant, to the Ten Commandments. As further proof, the members of the House of Delegates were reminded of the Oath of Hippocrates. This oath is the apotheosis of compact expression, and it established the pattern for all subsequent development of medical ethics. In some 300 words it outlines many of the basic principles on which have been built most ethical codes during the past 2,200 years. From the standpoint of integrity, no one has improved on the principles of this oath, but from the point of view of practical application, work has never ceased on the problem of adjusting them to the requirements of the contemporary scene. The new version of the Principles, which was ratified at the annual session of the American Medical Association in June 1957, consists of a brief Preamble and 10 sections, which in about 500 words succinctly express the fundamental ethical concepts embodied in the cumbersome document which had served for 110 years. Much of the prolixity and ambiguity which in the past had obstructed ready explanation, practical codification, and particular selection of basic concepts has been eliminated, yet the essence of every basic principle has been preserved. No fundamental concept of the original Principles has been omitted. It is intended that the new version will provide the physician with a permanent and readily accessible guide to ethical conduct.

THE JUDICIAL COUNCIL

To ensure that the Principles will be interpreted correctly and applied equitably, an appropriate deliberative body is necessary. The value of this arrangement is attested by courts of law, which perform a similar function in forensic matters, and by clergymen, who interpret theologic principles for their congregations. The judicial body of the American Medical Association is the Judicial Council. It is expected that the Principles will be supplemented by opinions and interpretations of this council, most of which are based on the early versions of the Principles, on past decisions and on pronouncements of the Judicial Council, which have been published for many years.

Thus far I have had nothing to say about the specific Principles. Let me begin by saying that these brief statements are intended to serve the physician as guides to ethical conduct, and that they are not immutable laws to govern him in the course of his professional activities. The Principles are written so that interpretations can be made by the Judicial Council to adapt them to particular factual situations.

THE PUBLIC DOMAIN

The young physician quickly learns that, in the practical affairs of life, ethics and economics often overlap. His idealism leads him to place ethics first, but economic needs often are responsible for a sharp conflict of purposes. Today, more than ever before, medicine is in the public domain. We see medicine as a leading motif on television; we hear much about medicine on the radio; and we read about it in the daily press in accounts by writers who specialize in the field. Much of this is good, but a certain amount is stimulated by aggressive, irresponsible individuals who would destroy the very system upon which the free practice of medicine is based. Thus, it is more important than ever that the physician adhere to his ideals and that his relationship with his patients should be his first consideration, after which come his responsibility to the public and to himself. There are ethical requirements as far as his relationship to so-called organized medicine is concerned, but this phase of his activities assumes a place of secondary importance when compared to his obligations to his patients.

1957 PRINCIPLES OF MEDICAL ETHICS*

Preamble.—These Principles are intended to aid physicians individually and collectively in maintaining a high level of ethical conduct. They are not laws but standards by which a physician may determine the propriety of his conduct in his relationship with patients, with colleagues, with members of allied professions, and with the public.

Section 1.—The principal objective of the medical profession is to render service to humanity with full respect for the dignity of man. Physicians should merit the confidence of patients entrusted to their care, rendering to each a full measure of service and devotion.

Section 2.—Physicians should strive continually to improve medical knowledge and skill, and should make available to their patients and colleagues the benefits of their professional attainments.

Section 3.—A physician should practice a method of healing founded on a scientific basis; and he should not voluntarily associate professionally with anyone who violates this principle.

Section 4.—The medical profession should safeguard the public and itself against physicians deficient in moral character or

*Ratified by the House of Delegates in June, 1957.

professional competence. Physicians should observe all laws, uphold the dignity and honor of the profession and accept its self-
imposed disciplines. They should expose, without hesitation, illegal
or unethical conduct of fellow members of the profession.

Section 5.—A physician may choose whom he will serve. In an
emergency, however, he should render service to the best of his
ability. Having undertaken the care of a patient, he may not
neglect him; and unless he has been discharged he may discon-
tinue his services oniy after giving adequate notice. He should not
solicit patients.

Section 6.—A physician should not dispose of his services
under terms or conditions which tend to interfere with or impair
the free and complete exercise of his medical judgment and skill
or tend to cause a deterioration of the quality of medical care.

Section 7.—In the practice of medicine a physician should
limit the source of his professional income to medical services
actually rendered by him, or under his supervision, to his patients.
His fee should be commensurate with the services rendered and
the patient's ability to pay. He should neither pay nor receive a
commission for referral of patients. Drugs, remedies or appliances
may be dispensed or supplied by the physician, provided it is in
the best interests of the patient.

Section 8.—A physician should seek consultation upon request;
in doubtful or difficult cases; or whenever it appears that the
quality of medical service may be enhanced thereby.

Section 9.—A physician may not reveal the confidences entrusted to him in the course of medical attendance, or the deficiencies he may observe in the character of patients, unless he is
required to do so by law or unless it becomes necessary in order
to protect the welfare of the individual or of the community.

Section 10.—The honored ideals of the medical profession
imply that the responsibilities of the physician extend not only to
the individual, but also to society where these responsibilities deserve his interest and participation in activities which have the
purpose of improving both the health and the well-being of the
individual and the community.

Some Major Questions

A few points in the Principles have led to confusion, and I
should like to consider some of them briefly. Probably those

in which difficulty has been encountered most frequently are free choice of physician, fee-splitting, rebates, advertising and solicitation and purveyal of medical services.

The 1955 Principles and the Opinions bear an equally significant relationship to the Preamble and the ten sections of the present Principles. We will examine several of these sections and try to determine in what manner they can be utilized, while interpreting ethical problems in the light of basic opinions established by the accepted older Principles and the pronouncements of the Judicial Council.

Fee-Splitting

As has been mentioned, some of the provisions of the 1955 Principles are confusing. From many sources, in past years, while the early editions of the Principles were in force and even after the 1957 version was adopted, demands were made that all Principles be elaborated so that all situations could be covered. An attempt was made to respond to these demands and the result was the confusing, cumbersome document mentioned in the report of the chairman of the Council on Constitution and Bylaws at the time the abbreviated version of the Principles was presented to the House of Delegates in 1957.

There is no better example of this than Section 6 of Chapter I of the 1955 Principles, entitled Payment for Professional Services (see Addendum 1). Through the years the demand that the Principles be "spelled out" had its effect; we find, in the last modification of Section 6 of Chapter I before adoption of the present Principles, four paragraphs consisting of 271 words. In these paragraphs it states that "the ethical physician . . . limits the sources of his income . . . to services rendered the patient." Then it goes on to say: "Remuneration . . . should be in the form and amount specifically announced . . . at the time the service is rendered or in the form of a subsequent statement." Another paragraph discusses unethical methods of inducement to refer patients and says that deception and coercion often are practiced. It describes prevalent ways of dividing fees. In the third paragraph it is said that both "offering" and "receiving" inducement are unethical, and a list is added of unethical inducements, such as split fees, rebates, "kickbacks," discounts, loans, favors, gifts and emoluments. Then this profound observation is added: "Fee-splitting violates the patient's trust that his physician will not exploit his dependence upon him . . . [and it asks physicians to avoid] placing the desire for profit above the opportunity to render appropriate medical service."

In the final paragraph billing procedures are discussed, and the evils of "combined billing" are revealed. They limit the opportunity for understanding of the financial arrangement between the patient and the physician, and joint billing may interfere with free choice of consultants, which is said to be "contrary to the highest standards of medical care."

In the 1957 edition of the Principles, Section 7 deals with the problem of fee-splitting. You will observe that it consists of seven and a half lines and only 78 words.

In the Opinions it is stated that Section 7 "embraces the spirit and intent of the following sections of the 1955 edition of the Principles." Then it lists: Chapter I, Section 6, entitled Payment for Professional Services; Chapter I, Section 8, entitled Dispensing of Drugs and Appliances by Physicians; Chapter I, Section 9, entitled Rebates and Commissions; and Chapter VII, Section 1, entitled Limits of Gratuitous Services.

The Opinions continue with "excerpts from Reports and Opinions of the Judicial Council which are applicable in interpreting Section 7."

No less than 31 opinions of the Judicial Council are quoted, going all the way back to 1924. Some of these opinions cover as much as a page and some as few as two lines. Seven of these pronouncements deal with fee-splitting specifically. Despite the fact that old Section 6 of Chapter I stated a number of situations which involved fee-splitting, there were still some indecisive areas that needed clarification. Thus, most of the reports of the Judicial Council dealt with problems arising from former unclear pronouncements or changing concepts of medical practice. Among problems which required interpretation were:

1. Rebates and commissions on the sale of optical and surgical appliances.

2. Joint stock companies of physicians organized for the purpose of operating clinics or laboratories with the stock owned in part or entirely by physicians connected only as stockholders. The Judicial Council refused to give its approval to this arrangement in 1926.

3. Dispensing of drugs by physicians, physician ownership of pharmacies and other relationships of physicians with pharmacies. These were discussed in reports of 1947, 1957 and 1958; on September 3, 1960, three pronouncements were made: Rental of space to a pharmacy on a percentage basis was declared unethical. Another stated that "drugs, remedies or appliances may be dispensed or supplied by the physician, provided it is in the best interests of the patient." Another affirmed that a physician, as a citizen, has the right to make investments according to his best judgment, and the fact that he is a physician does not preclude him from investing in the stock of a pharmaceutical company. Furthermore, the Council expressed the opinion that "it is not, in itself, unethical for physicians to own pharmacies, provided there is no exploitation of the patient."

4. Division of income by members of a group. This action must be based on the relative amount and value of the services rendered by each member. In 1946 the Judicial Council said that the practice of dividing the income of a group equally, after deducting expenses, is unethical. This statement was revised in August 1959 to provide that the division of income among members of a group may be determined by the mem-

bers and "may be based on the value of the professional medical services performed by the member and his other services and contributions to the group."

5. Billing procedures and payment by the surgeon for assistance by physicians. The policy maintained by the Council is revealed in the following statement made by the Judicial Council on March 30, 1957:

When two or more physicians actually and in person render services to one patient they should render separate bills. It is contrary to the traditions of the Association and spirit of the Principles for the surgeon to bill for the total surgical procedure and pay an assistant from the amount so received. . . . The patient should also be advised that the assistant will earn and charge a fee for his services and will send a bill for his services direct to the patient, which the patient should pay to the assistant.

The entire subject was brought into focus again by Resolution 11, introduced into the House of Delegates in December 1960, aimed at having a surgical assistant's fee included in schedules of allowances of health insurance companies and prepayment plans. The ultimate recommendation was that a plan be developed to include surgical fees for assistants in *all* fee schedules. It was revealed that during recent years a proposal of the American College of Surgeons had been studied and reported to the Board of Trustees by the AMA Council on Medical Service acting jointly with the Judicial Council. The entire subject was concluded in a statement of the Board of Trustees of the AMA to the House of Delegates during the annual meeting of June, 1961. Owing to the important bearing of this pronouncement on modern day relationships of surgeons and general practitioners, it will be quoted verbatim.

The following principles are stated as representing the policies of the American Medical Association:

1. Each member of the AMA is expected to observe the Principles of Medical Ethics in every aspect of his professional practice.

2. Each doctor engaged in the care of the patient is entitled to

compensation commensurate with the value of services he has personally rendered.

3. No doctor should bill or be paid for a service which he does not perform: mere referral does not constitute a professional service for which a professional charge should be made or for which a fee may be ethically paid or received.

4. It is ethically permissible for a surgeon to employ other physicians to assist him in the performance of a surgical procedure and to pay a reasonable amount for such assistance. This principle applies whether or not an assisting physician is the referring doctor and whether he is on a per-case or full-time basis. The controlling factor is the status of the assisting physician. If the practice is a subterfuge, to split fees or to divide an insurance benefit, or if the physician is not actually employed and used as a bona fide assistant, then the practice is contrary to ethical principles.

5. Under all other circumstances where services are rendered by more than one physician each physician should submit his own bill to the patient and be compensated separately.

The above Report was referred to the Reference Committee on Insurance and Medical Service which reported it is fully in accord with the Report and with the five Principles and recommends their approval. The Report of the Reference Committee was adopted by the House of Delegates.

Ghost surgery.—The ethical objection to fee-splitting is based on the fundamental principle that whatever weakens the confidential relationship between patient and physician is likely to make diagnosis more difficult, treatment less effective and recovery less prompt. No patient would choose to be the unwitting victim of secret negotiations when his health, and even his life, may be in the balance. Frank and open relationship with the patient is destroyed when the specialist secretly rebates a portion of his fee to the referring physician.

If a surgeon has a patient who requires a surgical operation which the surgeon cannot perform, it is his duty to refer him to a colleague of his choice or if he has no choice, then he is duty bound to select a physician who he believes can perform the operation more capably. It is unethical for the original surgeon to accept a referral fee. It is unethical for him to arrange for hospitalization, schedule the operation, or call on another surgeon to perform the operation without the patient's knowledge that the operation is being performed by someone other than the original surgeon. If, in addition, he sends a bill for the entire service, he is guilty of what is known as "ghost surgery." This type of deception is always accompanied by payment of a fee to the "ghost surgeon." It is also unethical merely to "stand in" at the time of the operation in order to assure a fee for supposed assistance which actually is not rendered.

On the other hand, if he participates in the care of the patient before or after operation, or both, it is proper for him to collect a fee, but the fee must not be paid to him by his colleague to whom he has referred the patient. One of the most important features of this entire scheme is the method of billing. Each independent participant in the care of the patient must render a separate bill and the patient must utilize separate checks when making the payment. Of course, an employee does not submit a bill.

There are many ways of splitting fees. For example, a druggist may offer to pay the office rent of a physician in return for an agreement that all prescriptions of the physician will be referred to that particular druggist.

A group of physicians, or a clinic owning a building, may rent space to a druggist on a sliding scale, the amount of the rental charge depending on the profit made by the druggist on the prescriptions sent him by the group. Or the druggist may pay a certain percentage of the net profit of his business to the group which owns the building. In establishing a contract of this kind, a fixed rental charge is the only arrangement that can be considered ethical.

An optical establishment which grinds lenses and makes glasses may give a rebate to an ophthalmologist who prescribes glasses. In like manner, the orthopedist who prescribes braces and corsets, artificial limbs, crutches and the like may receive rebates from the appliance manufacturer. All these practices are unethical because they tempt the physician to send his patients to the individual or the company most liberal with its insidious remuneration of the referring physician and not necessarily to the source of the best service.

Free Choice of Physician

This is an expression used to reflect both an economic and an ethical principle. The phrase simply means that the patient has the right to choose his physician, but application of this right is by no means absolute. For example, the physician also has the right, except in emergencies, to choose his patient. However, arbitrary or economic limitations on the patient's exercise of his inherent right to choose his physician are detrimental to the patient's welfare and should be kept at a minimum.

Many industries choose certain physicians to care for their employees. Often this practice is necessary because of the demands of employees for so-called fringe benefits. A good quality of medical care is not always provided by this arrangement, but often it is difficult to prove the deficiency because of the attitude of the patient. Sometimes he simply does not care, or he is impressed by the fact that the medical attention he is receiving appears to be inexpensive. Members of the medical profession do not believe that their professional services can be bought, sold, packaged and delivered as a commodity in trade. To them, "free choice of physician" is a fundamental issue, as it should be to every citizen. By some public figures this principle is said to be an ancient shibboleth to protect selfish ends, and some commercially minded interests ridicule the concept. Yet experience has shown that the quality of medical care deteriorates when a third party chooses the patient's physician and pays the bill. This arrangement disrupts the intimate personal relationship which is so important to the art and science of medicine, and destroys the very source of the patient's confidence in his physician.

There was a time when the physician had to concern himself only about the care of the infirm. His professional activities were conducted on a purely personal basis with his patients. Although his outward life was that of a man of the world, his duties often resembled those of the minister or the priest. His life was dedicated, first of all, to the service of others. Third party participation was limited to charity cases, compensable industrial patients and services provided by local and federal governments for indigents, inmates of institutions and military personnel. Health and accident insurance was purchased by the patient himself and he was indemnified in accordance with provisions of the policies.

Today medical care is administered on a large scale by physicians selected by the patient and they are compensated by Blue Shield or commercial insurance company plans. Medical care is also administered under other programs. Labor unions, industry and so-called consumer groups furnish medical services directly rather than by indemnification for cost of such services (1). Usually these plans are administered by "closed-panel" medical groups in which physicians are compensated by a salary rather than a fee-for-service basis. The degree of freedom of choice of the physician in such plans varies widely. The patient may be allowed to choose his physician from a large or small group, or he may be required to accept the services of a physician assigned to him by the plan. Usually where these third party plans are in operation, the principle of free choice of physician is fragmentary or entirely absent.

The medical profession is dedicated to the principle that the interests of the patient are served best when he may select his own physician and the physician may enjoy a similar privilege with regard to selection of his patients. It is a personal liberty to which both are entitled, just as much as their right to choose the manner in which they worship God. Theoretically, a citizen need not accept medical care administered by labor unions or government, but his rejection of either does not relieve him of his share of the financial burden that supports the system.

Section 6 of the 1957 Principles warns the physician against disposing of his services under conditions which interfere with the free and complete exercise of his professional activities or cause their deterioration. It is this Principle which covers the oft-discussed subject of free choice, although free choice is also discussed in the Opinions under Section 1 (see Addendum 2). According to the Opinions, Section 6 embraces the spirit and the intent of four sections of Chapter VII of the 1955 Principles.

Section 2 (1955) says that conditions must not interfere with rendition of adequate medical care.

Section 3 (1955) defines contract practice and says that it is unethical if it permits of features that are declared unethical by the Principles or if the contract or any of its provisions causes deterioration of the quality of medical services.

Section 4 (1955) defines free choice of physician and says that it can be exercised under "usual conditions of employment between patients and physicians." A third party with a "valid interest" may intervene between the patient and the physician. He has a valid interest if he assumes legal responsibility and provides for the cost of medical care and indemnity for occupational disability.

Section 5 (1955) concerns a subject that has caused much discussion, despite the fact that it leaves little doubt about its meaning. It reads as follows:

A physician should not dispose of his professional attainments or services to any hospital, lay body, organization, group or individual by whatever name called, or however organized, under terms or conditions which permit exploitation of the services of the physician for financial profit of the agency concerned. Such a procedure is beneath the dignity of professional practice and is harmful alike to the profession of medicine and the welfare of the people.

It is an accepted principle that the only commodity that a physician may sell is his medical service. The Principles state unequivocally that physicians must not sell spectacles, instruments or appliances *at a profit,* or receive emoluments from their sale by others. He engages in unethical practice if he "hires himself out" to an institution (e.g., a hospital), accepts a salary and agrees to allow the hospital to bill patients whom he has served, collect the fees and utilize the profit to defray the general expenses of the hospital.

Pathologists, radiologists and anesthesiologists, more than any other members of the medical profession, have become involved in difficult situations because of failure to observe this principle.

Long ago it was agreed that the practice of law by a corporation is against public policy and in many, if not all, states it is prohibited. This sentiment was expressed in a report of the Judicial Council that was made in 1922 and it is more significant now than it was then, because the tendency toward such practices is so much greater. In medicine the relationship between the physician and his patient is much more intimate and more important than that between an attorney and his client. It is not possible for the intimate, warm and friendly associations of the physician with the patient to exist between a patient and a corporation. Certainly if it is against public policy for a corporation to practice law, how much more so must it be for a corporation to practice medicine.

Undoubtedly, the chief source of contention in the entire subject of free choice of physician centers around problems caused by the practice of medicine by lay organizations. Many of the opinions and reports of the Judicial Council have dealt with this subject. Despite the fact that the position of the medical profession has always been clear on this subject, as shown in these pronouncements by the Judicial Council, problems have arisen repeatedly that have required analysis and explanation.

A review of the pronouncements, included in the Opinions, reveals that there has been no equivocation regarding the attitude of AMA. In its report of 1947 the Judicial Council interpreted "free choice of physician" to mean "not only the patient's right to choose any physician desired but also, conversely, the physician's right to accept or reject any patient requesting his services. . . ." When applied to voluntary health plans, the qualified, licensed physician residing in the area must be allowed to participate. If he possesses proper qualifications, it is stated specifically that he is not *required* to be a member of the American Medical Association. It is, however, required that he "accept and obey the terms of the contract offered by the plan, and on violation of the terms he may be dropped from the rolls, if the violation seems sufficiently grave for such action." The report continues:

It is needless for us to remind members that any violation of this provision would indeed deprive the public of the choice of a great many physicians. As the voluntary plans are intended to cover and supply medical care of a high quality for the whole country, with no feature of a compulsory system, it is necessary that the principle be strictly observed. . . . These basic points also require that the medical profession determine the adequacy and character of the hospitals. All hospitals approved by the local physicians and willing to accept the terms of the plan should be allowed to participate. In order that a high standard of medical service be maintained, hospitals may limit somewhat the number of physicians who deliver medical service in their institutions and even assign a physician to certain definite fields in accordance with his training and experience. . . . Under no circumstances shall doctors working under this plan be forced to send patients to a particular hospital unless it is the only one approved in that area.

In another report (June, 1959, supplemented in December, 1959) we find:

The American Medical Association believes that free choice of physician is the right of every individual and one which he should be free to exercise as he chooses. . . . Each individual should be accorded the privilege to select and change his physician at will or to select his preferred system of medical care.

In the same report it is stated unequivocally that

the American Medical Association firmly subscribes to freedom of choice of physician and free competition among physicians as being prerequisites to optimal medical care. The benefits of any system which provides medical care must be judged on the degree to which it allows or abridges such freedom of choice and such competition.

Contract practice (Chapter VII, Section 3, 1955 Principles [see Addendum 2]).—When a contract denies "a reasonable degree of free choice of physicians to those cared for in a community where other competent physicians are readily available," physicians who are parties to the contract are engaging in unethical practices. The Principles of Medical Ethics, in this connection, are concerned with the form of the contract and the conditions under which it is made. There are many circumstances under which contract practice is legitimate and ethical. In fact, there are occasions on which it is the only way in which competent medical care can be administered. Examples of this situation are encountered where workmen are employed in remote communities where appropriate medical services can be provided only by contracting with competent physicians to do the work. Sometimes legal requirements demand that large employers of labor provide medical services for their employees under certain conditions which can be secured only by some form of contract. Another instance in which contract practice can be considered ethical is when a community is so small and so free of desirable cultural advantages, that some form of contract or agreement as to compensation is required to induce a competent physician to assume responsibility for the health of its citizens. In other words, whether or not a contract is ethical depends on its form and its terms, as well as the circumstances under which it is made.

In 1926 the Judicial Council provided a definition of contract practice which has remained unchallenged:

By the term "contract practice," as applied to medicine, is meant the carrying out of an agreement between a physician or group of physicians as principals or agents and a corporation, organization or individual, to furnish partial or full medical services to a group or class of individuals for a definite sum or for a fixed rate per capita.

In this definition no mention is made of ethics because contract practice per se is not an unethical question, ethics being concerned with the form of the contract and the conditions under which it is made.

As far back as 1913 the Judicial Council made this comprehensive and informative pronouncement:

All medical practice is contract practice either implied or expressed between the physician and the patient if the patient be of legal age, or between the physician and the parent or guardian of a minor. There is no reason in law or morals why a physician should not enter into a contract with an individual, firm or corporation, provided that the contract be an honorable one for the performance of any honorable act and not interfering with the rights of others. Lodge practice and the industrial insurance work stand out as being distinctly on a different basis from the other contracts with economic corporations. The contracts made between physicians and economic corporations are necessities in our present stage of economic development. Surgeons and physicians are employed by these corporations partly as a matter of self protection—to properly care for the accidents occurring in the transaction of their business and that they may be well protected against unjust damage suits that are likely to occur. Besides this self defense of the company there is a growing appreciation by large corporations that the better the health of their employees is protected the better will be the results obtained in their work, and hence while it may tend toward benevolent and socialistic ideas, it is really a question of economic efficiency.

Five circumstances under which contract practice would become unethical were listed in the 1927 report of the Council.

1. When, based on the "usual fees paid for the same kind of service and class of people in the same community," the compensation is considered to be inadequate,

2. When compensation is so low that competent service becomes impossible,

3. When physicians underbid their colleagues in an attempt to secure the contract,

4. Where a reasonable degree of free choice of physician is denied the patient for whom the services of other competent physicians are readily available, and

5. When there is solicitation of patients.

Other Problems Applicable to Section 6

Hospital and health associations.—The Judicial Council regards as unsound, unethical and inimical to the public interest, schemes in which organizations controlled by groups of laymen, or by individuals, offer medical and hospital service to anyone who will buy "membership" and pay a nominal sum each month as "dues."

Practice under compensation laws.—Provisions of law which appear to encourage the practice of medicine by corporations, to curtail the privileges of the individual employee with respect to free choice of his medical attendant, and interfere with the rights and privileges of physicians not connected with corporations are frowned upon by the medical profession. Compensation acts of the various states differ widely in the provisions affecting these questions. Some of these laws are manifestly inequitable as they affect the practice of medicine and the best interests of employees and the public. The individual state medical associations are importuned, inasmuch as they hold original jurisdiction in such matters, to consider these questions and to deal with them in the light of the law and to effect needed corrections through the state legislatures concerned.

Periodic health examinations and vending medical services. —This problem concerns the question of whether the medical profession shall vend its products directly to the consumer or sell them to a middleman or a third party. The medical profession, obviously, favors periodic health examinations. However, it cannot condone such practices by commercial organizations that have entered the field of medical practice as middlemen, or jobbers, offering to furnish periodic medical examinations to the public, generally for a stated sum per annum and sending reports of findings to the examined. It is known that some of these organizations even give advice to the examined as to what they should do for the conditions found. The examinations can be made only by physicians and these companies sign up contracts with physicians to make the examinations and send the reports directly to the company instead of the patient. The company pays the physician a definite price and sells the results of the examination to the individual examined at a profit. Under such circumstances the physician is selling his independence. If this were a case of the good of the public versus the good of the profession, there would be no question at issue because the profession always has and always will yield its own interest to that of the public good; but this happens to be an instance in which the public good can be served best by what is best for the profession.

The relation between the patient and the physician is an individual matter, and anything that disturbs this relationship is detrimental to the best interests of the patient. . . . The service of periodic health examinations, as conducted by commercial institutions, must inevitably result in the undermining of the confidence of the people in the ability of the practitioner. . . . No organization is medically qualified or, in our opinion, justified in issuing to individuals applying for examination a routine statement of the results of the examination (1924 report of the Judicial Council).

Health associations.—This problem arises in the practice of so-called health associations or hospital associations which obtain "members" (prospective patients) through the services of paid solicitors or otherwise. The plan used by these groups is to collect minimal membership dues, for which medical and surgical services are promised when needed. The Judicial Council believes that, in some instances, promises are made that cannot be carried out because it is unlikely that adequate medical service, often requiring hospitalization and a surgical operation, can be delivered for the sum realized from collection of nominal membership dues. This principle is wrong and physicians are warned against aligning themselves with organizations which practice it. The Judicial Council has acknowledged that the cost of medical service has increased, but the increase has not "by any means" been proportionate to the increased cost of living commodities, of labor, or of services rendered by other professions. The Council has issued this statement:

The individual physician who drags pure commercialism into the practice of medicine or who extorts undue fees from his patients brings reproach on the whole profession and should receive the censure that is due him; likewise, he who furnishes medical service to groups at rates below a fair value of the services rendered. The honest and competent physician who is interested in maintaining honored traditions and who is in the practice of medicine as a profession should receive such compensation for his services as will enable him to maintain himself and his family in comfort and to make provisions against the time when he cannot keep up professional activities (1926 and 1931 Reports).

Purveyal of medical service (Chapter VII, Section 5, 1955 Principles [see Addendum 2]).—Only those who are licensed by the state and are properly qualified should enjoy the privilege of healing the sick. This privilege belongs only to the medical profession. In its 1932 report the Judicial Council said:

In increasing numbers, physicians are disposing of their professional attainments to lay organizations under terms which permit a direct profit from the fees or salaries paid for their services to accrue to the lay bodies employing them. Such a procedure is absolutely destructive of that personal responsibility and relationship which is essential to the best interests of the patient.

The practice of medicine by corporations is becoming more of a problem as time goes on. Such practices are detrimental to the best interests of the patient. When medical service is made impersonal, when the humanities of medicine are removed, when the coldness and automation of the machine are substituted for the humane interest and intimate counsel inherent in individual service and when the professional and scientific independence of the individual physician is sacrificed, the quality of medical service and with it the health of those served will decline. Any attempt to make the conquest of disease subordinate to economic considerations violates the fundamental principles of medical ethics and is degenerating to the individual as a physician.

Instances of intrusions by lay organizations into the practice of medicine include the following:

1. Insurance companies which administer workmen's compensation. Here the compensation paid to the physician by the company is much less than the legally approved fees on which the premium paid by the industry is based, thus allowing the insurance company to make a profit.

2. Certain hospitals which forbid their staff physicians to charge fees for their professional services to "house cases" but collect such fees themselves and absorb them in hospital income.

3. Some universities which employ full-time hospital staffs and open their doors to the general public. Then they charge such fees for the professional care of the patients as to net a profit to the university. They make a direct profit from the professional care by a practice of questionable legality, according to the Judicial Council, and are in direct and unethical competition with the profession at large, as well as with their own graduates.

Hospital insurance should not include the sale of medical services.—Regardless of whether group hospitalization insurance is or is not financially sound, the furnishing of medical service should not be included in the sale of insured hospital accommodations. In its 1936 report the Judicial Council called attention to the fact that some hospitals were invading the practice of medicine, sometimes with approval of members of the medical profession, and sometimes without it, saying that

in this time of extensive changes in hospital economics the point has arrived at which further marriages between hospitals and staff physicians that make the doctor of medicine the servant of the hospital should be stopped and a series of attempts at divorce among marriages that have already taken place should be instituted.

Anesthesia a medical service. We emphasize our insistence that anesthesia is a medical service and therefore should always be under the direction and supervision of a physician who assumes the responsibility and who should present his bill for services. No hospital or individual without a license to practice medicine should be permitted to collect the fee for anesthesia.

Advertising

The question of advertising presents another problem. But the attitude of the medical profession in this regard is different from what it used to be. For example, there was a time when an ethical physician felt that he had to avoid the questions of a newspaper reporter. Today it is recognized that the public is entitled to know about certain advances made by the medical profession and that the physician is the one best qualified to appraise these advances. Advertising and solicitation are so inseparably a part of modern economic life, however, that it requires continuous vigilance to guard against the intrusion of these dynamic forces into the field of medicine. Solicitation of patients is prohibited by the Principles of Medical Ethics.

Physicians generally recognize that in an age of scientific wonders there is a constantly increasing body of news and information concerning disease which is helpful to the public. Yet it is also true that exploitation of such news for financial profit may harm the public. It is common knowledge that sensational publicity of cures for cancer, tuberculosis, "rheumatism" and other diseases has resulted in unnecessary suffering and false hopes of relief. This, to any reasonable man, is cruel and reprehensible.

The ubiquity of radio and television broadcasting has brought with it new advertising problems. Quacks, patent medicines and all kinds of cures thrust themselves into millions of homes. There is no way to measure the injury to public health that has resulted from selling such medical services without appropriate evaluation and supervision.

The Principles of 1957 deal with the subject of advertising in Section 5. The final sentence consists of five words: "He [the physician] should not solicit patients." The entire subject of advertising is covered by these few words.

Let us compare this brief statement with Section 4 of Chapter I of the 1955 Principles (see Addendum 3). This Principle begins with these words: "Solicitation of patients, directly or indirectly, by a physician, by groups of physicians or by institutions or organizations is unethical." Next is the statement that this Principle protects the public from the advertiser and the salesman of medical care by establishing an "easily discernible" distinction between him and the ethical physician. It continues that unethical devices, which are not always obvious, may be employed to inspire newspaper and magazine comments about physicians or institutions.

For many years it has been traditional to include in this Principle these oracular words: "Self laudations defy the traditions and lower the moral standards of the medical profession; they are an infraction of good taste and are disapproved." Finally, it is explained that the most worthy and effective advertisement is accomplished by establishment of a good reputation, and the warning is added that "disregard of local customs and offenses against recognized ideals is unethical."

This comparison provides an example of the verbiage of the early form of the Principles. As a matter of fact, although Section 4 is entitled Advertising, Section 5 (see Addendum 3.) of the same issue deals partially with the same topic under the title The Relationship of the Physician to Media of Public Information. This lengthy dissertation, consisting of five paragraphs, explains how far a physician can go with medical writing and news releases without becoming involved in the unethical practice of advertising.

Although complaint was lodged against the early versions of the Principles because of their excessive volume, they have not been rescinded. Consequently, the wordy discussion of various items applicable to Sections 4 and 5 of Chapter I of the 1955 Principles will serve as valuable reference material. This section is quoted verbatim in the Opinions and it is said that its spirit and intent are embraced in Section 5 of the 1957 version. As far as advertising is concerned, this is the only part of the 1955 Principles mentioned in the Opinions. Perhaps this is why all the interpretations of the Judicial Council included in this portion of the document are devoted to various problems connected with advertising.

Some of the pronouncements on this topic are as follows:

Advertising by groups.—In 1922 attention was called to advertising by "groups" and it was said that "some of these groups are advertising in a manner that would be considered most reprehensible if done by an individual physician." The Council could not see any difference between a group of physicians "advertising themselves under whatsoever title they may assume and an individual physician advertising himself."

Form letters on periodic health examinations.—"It is the opinion of the Judicial Council that the sending out of any circular letter or any form of printed or written matter which may be construed as advertising or as soliciting patronage by the individual physician or by any group of physicians is unethical" (1928 report).

Commercial medical directories.—In the report of 1936 it

was stated that it is unethical to list physicians, by specialty, in directories published by commercial concerns. This practice was termed "subtle ways of avoiding the pronouncement of the Principles of Medical Ethics concerning solicitation of patients, under a guise of buying a directory when the real intent is the purchase of the publication of the buyer's name in the directory for the purpose of obtaining patients."

Solicitation by individuals or groups.—In this report (1946) the Council reminded members of the medical profession that while solicitation of probable insurers or insurees is necessary to the success of medical insurance plans and is permitted, the solicitation of patients, either by individuals or by medical groups, is forbidden.

Use of proper advertising media.—Disregard of local customs and offenses against recognized ideals are unethical, even in the case of publication or circulation of simple professional cards. In Section 1 of Chapter III of the 1955 Principles the physician is held to be obligated to uphold the dignity and honor of his profession. This is undoubtedly one of the most profound and far-reaching of the Principles. Probably there is no instance of unethical behavior in which this Principle will not be violated. If a physician upholds the dignity and the honor of the medical profession, it seems unlikely that, at the same time, he can commit an unethical act.

The Judicial Council has held that the component medical societies must determine what practices are in accord with local customs. At the same time, such societies must exercise sufficient caution to ensure full compliance with the spirit and the intent of the Principles. Furthermore, it has maintained that the practice of medicine should not be commercialized or treated as a commodity in trade. Respecting the dignity of their calling, physicians should resort only to limited use of advertising and then only to the extent necessary to serve the common good and to improve the health of mankind. This sentiment was expressed in the report of 1955.

Distribution of reprints of articles.—Ethically, a physician will not mail reprints indiscriminately and without sufficient reason. It is impossible to define categorically what constitutes a sufficient reason. No one will deny that

it would not be ethical for a physician to mail reprints if his intent was to solicit patients directly or indirectly or to attempt to bring undue attention to himself. The practice, therefore, cannot be recommended. This is not to say that the author of a medical article may not honor requests for copies of his article (J.A.M.A., March 30, 1957).

What the public is entitled to know.—Certainly the public should be informed about public hygiene and preventive medicine. The public should know the names of physicians, the type of their practices, the location of their offices, their office hours and the like, and physicians may furnish this kind of information through acceptable news media without fear of criticism. Telephone listings, office signs, professional cards and dignified announcements all are acceptable means of making factual information available to the public. But the particular use of any ethical advertising medium to solicit patients is unethical.

The Physician and the Sectarian (Cultist)

Only the physician, the doctor of medicine, possesses that high degree of education, training and experience required to comprehend and to utilize the remarkable store of information which has accumulated regarding the care of the infirm. Only the physician can keep abreast of the remarkable advancement in medicine and surgery which is being made continuously. He and his colleagues of the medical profession are the acknowledged custodians of the accumulated knowledge of medicine and medical practices which should be used for the benefits of humanity. Despite the fact that all this is true, the Judicial Council, in its 1936 and 1945 reports, admitted that no one is compelled to choose only physicians, properly educated and trained, when selecting "medical attendants."

The individual may elect to receive his medical care from himself, his neighbor, osteopathy, chiropractic, naturopathy or Christian Science, but he is not entitled while under the care of such irregulars to demand that the man educated in scientific medicine furnish opinion and advice to one so far deficient in education that he cannot so understand and apply that opinion and advice as to be able to make satisfactory use of it.

Definitions of sectarian and physician.—In its 1924 report the Judicial Council defined a sectarian as applied to medicine as one "who in his practice follows a dogma, tenet or principle based on the authority of its promulgator to the exclusion of demonstration and experience." In the same report a physician was defined as "one who has acquired a contemporary education in the fundamental and special sciences, comprehended in the general term 'medicine' used in its unrestricted sense, and who has received the degree of Doctor of Medicine from a medical school of recognized standing."

Section 3 of the 1957 Principles embraces the spirit and the intent of Section 1 of Chapter II of the 1955 version (see Addendum 4) which reads, in part, as follows:

In order that a physician may best serve his patients, he is expected to exalt the standards of his profession and to extend its sphere of usefulness. To the same end, he should not base his practice on an exclusive dogma or a sectarian system. . . . A sectarian or cultist as applied to medicine is one who alleges to follow or in his practice follows a dogma, tenet or principle based on the authority of its promulgator to the exclusion of demonstration and scientific experience. All voluntary associated activities with cultists are unethical. A consultation with a cultist is a futile gesture if the cultist is assumed to have the same high grade of knowledge, training and experience as is possessed by the doctor of medicine. Such consultation lowers the honor and dignity of the profession in the same degree in which it elevates the honor and dignity of those who are irregular in training and practice.

Optometry.—Although the comprehensive statement just

quoted would seem to cover all problems that might arise with regard to sectarianism, there have been occasions on which current situations have required clarification. In the Opinions we find that the relationship between doctors of medicine and optometry was discussed in meetings of the House of Delegates and action was taken in 1934, 1936, 1950, 1951 and 1955. During most of that period, voluntary association, professionally, with optometrists was considered to be unethical. A partial exception to this policy was established in 1950, when "lectures, etc., to 'nonmedical groups' were permitted if they were designed to prevent blindness." This action was rescinded by a resolution that was adopted in 1955.

An unusual feature of the controversy regarding optometrists is that they have never been declared sectarian or cult practitioners. Indeed, there is room for doubt that optometry should be considered a sectarian practice comparable to osteopathy or chiropractic. Optometrists are licensed to practice in most, if not all, states, but their practice is limited to diagnosing and correcting mechanical defects of the eye. To remedy these conditions they may prescribe proper lenses, but they are neither qualified nor licensed to do more. On the basis that it is a futile gesture for physicians to consult on a professional level with one who does not possess the same knowledge, training, experience and ideals as the doctor of medicine, it was decided, in 1955, that voluntary professional association with optometrists is unethical. However, it is not unethical for a doctor of medicine to hire a technician who has been trained or has a degree in optometry as long as the technician does not hold himself out to the public as an optometrist. In other words, a physician may hire one who is trained or licensed in optometry but, by this association, he must not raise the practice of optometry to the same high level as medical practice.

Osteopathy.—The Principles provide that "a physician should practice a method of healing founded on a scientific basis; and he should not voluntarily associate professionally with anyone who violates this principle." For many years, the Judicial Council interpreted this principle to apply to all osteopaths regardless of training, practice or experience.

The broad application of this principle was brought under review on several occasions. A committee of the Association after having spent three years studying relations between osteopathy and medicine recommended a revision of AMA policy in 1955. This recommendation was not accepted and a similar recommendation made by the Judicial Council in 1959 met the same fate.

However, the Judicial Council in June, 1961 again recommended a change in application of AMA policy. Its report to the House of Delegates called attention to the transition of osteopathy into osteopathic medicine, to the almost exclusive use of osteopathy of medical literature and the "unmistakable" fact that many osteopaths are practicing medicine. The Judicial Council said that in the past policy had been applied collectively. Now, it suggested, policy should be applied individually at local level: if the individual bases his practice on the same scientific principles as do members of the American Medical Association, voluntary professional associations with him are ethical.

The Council suggested that the same criteria that are employed to evaluate the professional, ethical and scientific competence of doctors of medicine can be utilized to determine the qualifications of doctors of osteopathy. In addition, it might be possible to evaluate the professional and scientific competence of a doctor of osteopathy according to his professional education, the type of examination given, and the license granted by the state in which he practices. Or it might be possible to establish these standards through local liaison committees of doctors of medicine and doctors of osteopathy. In some states it might be possible to duplicate what is being done in California.

Finally, the Judicial Council recommended that the House of Delegates declare that:

1. It shall not be considered in itself unethical for members of the American Medical Association to associate professionally and on a voluntary basis with doctors of osteopathy who base their practice on the same scientific and ethical principles as doctors of medicine in order that patients may have the full measure of the benefits of the objects of this Association as stated in Article II of its Constitution: to promote the science and art of medicine and the betterment of public health.

2. It is the prerogative and the obligation of each constituent medical association to implement this policy on a state or local basis.

The recommendations were adopted by the House of Delegates and constitute present policy in regard to relations between doctors of osteopathy and doctors of medicine.

The Physician's Responsibility

The common good of mankind is the "avowed objective" of the medical profession. Physicians are the trustees of medical knowledge and skill, they dedicate themselves to the alleviation of suffering, they share their knowledge and discoveries with their colleagues, they recognize their useful rank among the citizenry of their country, and in their relationships with their patients and their colleagues they maintain the most inflexible standards of personal honor. These are some of the Principles involved in Section 2 of Chapter I of the 1955 Principles (see Addendum 5), probably the most profound of all the Principles of Medical Ethics, and they are embraced in the brief statement of Section 2 of the 1957 Principles.

Patents and copyrights.—Also covered by this section is the principle that a physician may obtain a patent on surgical instruments and appliances or medicines and he may obtain a copyright on publications, methods and procedures, as long as it does not retard or inhibit research or restrict the benefits derivable from the patented article.

This is a new concept that was recognized by the Council on Constitution and Bylaws and the Judicial Council in 1954 when it was decided that the Principle that had governed patents and copyrights ever since the Principles took form was based on a faulty notion. Section 7 of the 1954 Principles classed patents and copyrights with the sale, for profit, of instruments, appliances and drugs. In the 1953 version, Section 6 of Chapter I went even farther and dealt with Patents, Commissions, Rebates and Secret Remedies. The prime evil was thought to be the receipt of remuneration for anything other than the medical service that the physician could render. The idea involved was somewhat obfuscated because, if physicians had to observe this Principle "to the letter," they would not be considered ethical if they made profits from investments, rental or sale of property and so forth.

The entire subject was brought into focus while the question of drugstore ownership by physicians was under consideration. It was felt that a physician who participated in the ownership of a drugstore in the area of his practice might be prejudiced when dispensing prescriptions. It was conceivable that only inferior drugs might be available at the drugstore in question and, in consequence, the patients might suffer. The ultimate test—the concern of the ethical physician—always was the effect that any procedure under consideration would have on the patient. Thus, it was determined that although the instance just described would have to be considered unethical, there was no reason why partial ownership by a physician, of a drug firm far removed from his area of professional activities, should be considered unethical. It was established that remuneration received from items other than the sale of his services could be accepted ethically. The proscription against a physician's engaging in "barter and trade in the appliances, devices or remedies prescribed for patients" was maintained, but obtaining patents and copyrights, and receipt of remuneration from them, were not unethical procedures as long as those factors concerned in the delivery of an appropriate quality of medical service were not hindered.

Experimentation

Although no specific stipulation concerning animal experimentation can be found in the Principles of Medical Ethics, many pronouncements dealing with the subject have been made and resolutions have been passed by the House of Delegates. It is covered in Section 2 of the 1957 Principles by the statement that "physicians should strive continually to improve medical knowledge and skill."

As early as May, 1884, the House of Delegates approved appointment (2) of a Committee on Experimental Medicine to be "charged with the duty of opposing, by all legitimate means, any interference with the progress of medical science by unwise or ill-considered legislation."

Animal experimentation.—During the same session,

The House of Delegates adopted a resolution expressing the convictions: (1) that experimentation on animals is a most useful source of knowledge in medical science; (2) that it is the means by which many valuable discoveries, both practical and scientific, have been accomplished; (3) that its direction and supervision can be properly entrusted only to members of the medical profession, and that its restriction and prohibition by law would inevitably retard the advancement of medical science and the improvement of the medical art (J.A.M.A. 2:572, 1884).

In May, 1945, the House of Delegates approved a report of the Board of Trustees which called attention to the fact that:

Much propaganda against animal experimentation has been fostered and disseminated by various poorly informed groups.

The benefits of medical research through animal experimentation have reached a majority of the people of the United States. Many lives have been saved during the war primarily by animal experimentation in research on blood plasma and various drugs.

The benefits to mankind and to the animal kingdom have been great through the animal research in surgery and medicine, particularly related to rickets, hypertension, lockjaw, hookworm, rabies, diphtheria, diabetes, and distemper.

Interference with animal experimentation would cause medicine to cease to progress in many ways.

Because there has been a determined attempt by groups to prevent further experiments on animals, the House of Delegates of the American Medical Association approves the education of the public in the benefits both to men and to animals from animal experimentation and urges that the people of the United States be completely and thoroughly informed as to these benefits and as to the effect on further progress in research on various diseases, should such animal experimentation be forbidden in any state.

The House instructed the Board of Trustees to prepare for distribution an illustrated booklet outlining the benefits of animal experimentation to mankind (Dec. 1945:37, 90).

Human experimentation.—Further reports were made in December, 1946, June, 1948, and in 1952 (December, 1952: 91–92, 109, 110). After discussing a resolution from Illinois on Experiments on Convicted Persons, the House of Delegates adopted this resolution:

Resolved, That the House of Delegates of the American Medical Association express its disapproval of the participation in scientific experiments of persons convicted of murder, rape, arson, kidnapping, treason or other heinous crimes, and also urges that individuals who have lost their citizenship by due process of law be considered ineligible for meritorious or commendatory citation; and be it further

Resolved, That copies of this resolution be transmitted to the surgeons general of all federal services, the governors of all states, all officials of state and federal penal institutions and parole boards.

Ladimer (4) in 1955, discussing Permissible Medical Experiments, called attention to the fact that

The great weight of the evidence before us is to the effect that certain types of medical experiments on human beings, when kept within reasonably well-defined bounds, conform to the ethics of the medical profession generally. The protagonists of the practice of human experimentation justify their views on the basis that such experiments yield results for the good of society that are unprocurable by other methods or means of study. All agree, however, that certain basic principles must be observed in order to satisfy moral, ethical and legal concepts.

Ladimer referred to a statement made by General Telford Taylor, chief of counsel for war crimes, before the Nuremberg Military Tribunals in the "Medical Case" judgments rendered August 19, 1947, which "resulted in death sentences for seven medical officials of the German Reich, seven acquittals, and sentences of confinement for nine others under indictment charging war crimes and crimes against humanity as outlined in Control Council Law No. 10 enacted in December of 1945."

Ten basic requirements were outlined for human experimentation:

1. Voluntary consent of the human subject is absolutely essential. The person involved should have legal capacity to give consent freely and without coercion. He should have comprehensive knowledge of the elements of the subject matter involved, including the nature, duration and purpose of the experiment, all inconveniences and hazards and the effects of the experiment on his health.

2. The experiment should yield fruitful results, unprocurable by other methods or means of study.

3. The experiment should be based on results of animal experimentation and a thorough knowledge of the problem under consideration.

4. The experiment should be conducted so that there would be no unnecessary physical and mental suffering and injury.

5. No experiment should be conducted if there is reason to believe that death or disabling injury will occur; with the possible exception of instances in which the experimental physicians also serve as subjects.

6. The degree of risk should never exceed that determined by the humanitarian importance of the problem to be solved.

7. Proper precautions should be taken to protect the experimental subject against even the remote possibility of injury, disability or death.

8. Those conducting the experiment should be qualified scientifically and should possess the highest degree of skill.

9. The human subject should be at liberty to terminate the experiment at will.

10. The scientist in charge must be prepared to terminate the experiment at any stage if he believes its continuance is likely to result in injury, disability or death of the experimental subject.

The report of Dr. A. C. Ivy, who appeared at the Nuremberg Trials as the representative of the United States Government to review the war crimes of a medical nature committed by the Germans, was referred to the Judicial Council. In 1946 the following report was made to the House of Delegates by the Judicial Council:

Your reference committee finds that the experiments in Doctor Ivy's report are opposed to the Principles of Medical Ethics of the American Medical Association, which have three basic requirements: (1) the voluntary consent of the individual on whom the experiment is to be performed must be obtained; (2) the danger of each experiment must be previously investigated by animal experimentation; and (3) the experiment must be performed under proper medical protection and management.

This pronouncement was published again in the *Journal of the American Medical Association* on March 30, 1957 .

MEDICAL DISCIPLINE

Realizing that some manner of discipline is required if the Principles are to be effective, the Board of Trustees of the American Medical Association authorized the appointment of a committee, known as the Medical Disciplinary Committee, in November, 1958. Its investigations were conducted with the assistance of the staff of the Legal and Socio-Economic Division of the American Medical Association and an examination was made of the disciplinary rules, laws and procedures as applied to medical practice licensure and medical society membership with particular regard for the degree to which efficient discipline is maintained among medical practitioners.

During the course of the investigation, which was completed in 1960, four regional meetings were held which were attended by representatives of 27 state medical associations and 24 state boards of medical examiners.

Questionnaires were sent to all state medical societies, all state boards of medical examiners and to several of the larger county medical societies. Members of the staff of the Legal and Socio-Economic Division personally interviewed officials of 15 medical societies and 15 state boards of medical examiners.

The committee met with representatives of the National Association of Blue Shield Plans, the Health Insurance Council, the Association of Casualty and Surety Underwriters and the Association of American Railroads.

The report of the Medical Disciplinary Committee was approved by the Board of Trustees on June 24 and by the House of Delegates on June 29, 1961, after which the committee was discharged and its functions were assigned to the Judicial Council as one of its continuing activities. The results of the committee investigation revealed that, by and large, adequate medical disciplinary mechanisms do exist and that they are used. The frequency and effectiveness of their use, however, are less impressive.

In its Conclusions and Recommendations the committee directed proposals to medical schools, state boards of medical examiners, state medical associations and the American Medical Association.

Medical schools.—Present methods of instruction are inadequate and a greater effort should be made to teach ethical and proper socio-economic principles during the period of schooling.

Medical schools should provide a required course in these

principles and they should cooperate with state boards of examiners and state medical associations to ensure that students become acquainted with practical problems and socioeconomic principles and learn their proper solutions.

State boards of medical examiners.—There should be closer cooperation between state boards, medical schools and state medical societies and certain procedural changes should be made.

All state board examinations should include questions on medical ethics and proper socio-economic practices, and state boards should cooperate with medical schools to enhance the knowledge of ethical and proper socio-economic principles by medical students during the period of formal schooling.

State boards should examine the records of the American Medical Association, the Federation of State Medical Boards of the United States—hereafter called the Federation—and, if possible, all other state boards before issuing any applicant a license to practice medicine.

Each state board and state medical society should examine the disciplinary provisions of its state's medical practice act and try to establish changes where indicated. "A Guide to the Essentials of a Modern Medical Practice Act," adopted by the Federation of State Medical Boards of the United States in February, 1956, is included in the report of the Medical Disciplinary Committee.

The Federation should appoint a committee to draft model rules of procedure in disciplinary procedures for state boards and the American Medical Association should provide staff assistance.

State boards should make discipline their prime responsibility, make annual reports to the governors of the states, and send copies of reports to state medical associations, the American Medical Association and the Federation. They should obtain legal assistance to develop disciplinary mechanisms, recommendations and procedures and, by legal consultation, avoid chances of litigation.

A central source should be established to provide information on disciplinary procedures and on licensing and disciplinary actions taken by all state boards.

State medical associations.—By limiting their concern to matters that are appealed to them from the local level, state associations have not been as effective as they could be in the area of medical discipline. There are defects in basic mechanisms and "considerable apathy" at the county and state level.

State medical associations should develop greater interest in activities of their component societies in the discharge of disciplinary obligations. Changes are required in disciplinary mechanisms at state and local levels. Indoctrination programs should be provided to acquaint new members of component societies with ethical principles and proper socio-economic practices. The services of grievance committees should be made more widely available. More interest should be manifested in complaints of overcharging, advertising and solicitation of patients, abuse of prepayment and insurance plans and so forth.

Grievance committees should be utilized as "grand juries" to initiate action against an offender and thereby obviate the necessity of an individual member's suffering the embarrassment of making a complaint against a fellow member.

Bylaws of state societies should be amended to provide for disciplinary action at the state level when required and after proper action has *not* been taken by the county society.

All members of the state medical association should use their influence to improve financial aid for the state board and interest themselves in assuring capable membership for it.

The state society should establish a review committee to enhance good relationships between insurance companies and physicians.

The American Medical Association.—A more aggressive attitude should be assumed by the American Medical Association. It should supply advice and assistance to state boards and state and county medical societies in all aspects of medical discipline.

The American Medical Association, in cooperation with the Federation, the Council of State Governments and other interested groups should draft a model medical practice act. It should encourage each state society and each state board to report annually all major disciplinary actions taken within its jurisdiction. It should distribute annually the Principles and the Opinions of the Judicial Council to all senior medical students. It should prepare a syllabus or lecture guide on medical ethics, medical practice acts and proper socio-economic conduct for physicians charged with the responsibility of giving lectures on these topics. The American Medical Association Bylaws should be changed to confer original jurisdiction on the Association to suspend or revoke American Medical Association membership of a physician guilty of violation of the Principles of Medical Ethics, regardless of positive or negative action of the state or county societies. It should seek to have the Joint Commission on Accreditation of Hospitals require, for accreditation, lectures, within the hospital, on ethics and proper socio-economic practices.

REFLECTIONS ON PUNISHMENT

If all the recommendations of the Medical Disciplinary Committee are consummated, it is likely that fewer violations of the Principles of Medical Ethics will go unpunished. Probably the most effective form of punishment is to deprive a physician of his license to practice medicine. Prominent among those who have to be disciplined severely are the abortionists, narcotic addicts, alcoholics, the mentally incompetent and the professionally incompetent. Others requiring less severe punishment are those who overcharge, those who charge higher fees when patients are insured, those who perform unnecessary surgery, those who consort with quacks and faddists, those who advertise and solicit patients, covertly or openly, those who split fees and those who accept rebates.

Infractions of tax laws have nothing to do with professional competence, which is the important consideration. On the other hand, there is no doubt that the license of a physician should be revoked if he is incapable of practicing medicine because of his addiction to narcotic drugs.

Fundamentally, punishment is the natural retribution exacted of a wrongdoer by his fellowmen. Despite this obvious fact, it cannot be denied that foreknowledge of the effect of punishment often serves as a deterrent, not only to the offender, but to others who might be tempted to violate the law or depart from ethical and moral principles. In fact, it will be acknowledged that rehabilitation of the wrongdoer is just as important as the imposition of penalties. The exactment of a fine or the imposing of a jail sentence is by no means an infallible deterrent of misconduct. For the benefit of the physician and, what is probably more important, for those who are the recipients of his professional ministrations, it would seem that a happy balance could be established at some well-reasoned point between the imposition of a penalty and rehabilitation of the offender. By use of the instruments of probation and suspended sentences this eminently desirable objective might be accomplished. In order to realize this, adequate investigations are required. They must be assayed and used as a basis for the measuring out of just and effective penalties when punishment is due. At the same time, they will help to prevent egregious injustices against a temporarily confused physician and his patients. In this manner the welfare of the public will be protected against the permanent loss of the services of a physician who may possess adequate or even superior professional capabilities.

A dependable safeguard reposes in the fact that the extending of probation or the suspending of a sentence does not prevent a board or a medical society from taking drastic action whenever strong measures are required. Legal opinion considers this line of action, fortified by the safeguard I have mentioned, an effective means of punishment which possesses the enhancing virtue of opportunity for the tempering of justice with mercy.

So long as the medical profession is composed of organizations of voluntary membership, its members are obligated to keep their house in order. If this obligation is not fulfilled, there is always the threat of a government that is ever ready to step in and take over. If a physician's license is revoked for good cause and if revocation becomes final, there is little doubt that the medical society concerned is obligated to expel the culprit, who, by his own act, has removed himself from the ranks of the honorable members of the medical profession. On the other hand, what action should be taken by the county medical society if the offense has not been punished by suspension or revocation of a license? Suppose the physician has been convicted of driving while intoxicated. Obviously, whatever action is taken would depend upon the nature of the offense, and this can be decided only by careful determination of the facts in the case.

What should be done when a physician deliberately and repeatedly submits false or fraudulent claims to his Blue Shield plan or to a commercial insurance company? Let us assume, for the moment, that the evidence is insufficient from a legal point of view to warrant revocation of his license by the state board. Should the medical society, with evidence in its possession sufficient for reprimand, censure or suspension, proceed to exercise its authority? Here the facts and circumstances of the case assume major importance. If the offense is grave enough and if incontrovertible evidence is at hand, the medical society has no alternative. It should suspend, or at least reprimand, the physician who will not abide by the rules and regulations and who will not respect ethical principles of the medical profession.

But the world in which we live is imperfect and it is regrettable, to say the least, that at times we have to fear the interposition of the law as we attempt to govern our professional conduct and to maintain our ideals. Legal involvement is indeed a threat which cannot be brushed aside lightly.

If we have within our ranks one who is unworthy of membership and hence association with upright practitioners of unquestioned probity, if we honestly believe he should be expelled and if we have evidence to support our belief, we should take action, despite the threat of legal reprisal from him. We should not be reduced to inertia by the fear of legal action attendant upon a decent and deserved act of discipline. We should not sacrifice principles of rectitude because of consequent costs of time, money and effort. If we hope to maintain the dignity, honor and integrity of the medical profession, we can do no other than to take prompt, specific and even drastic action whenever the case warrants it.

However, I believe that intrinsically the physician is a conscientious man who asks no more of public renown than that which the respect and good will of his fellow citizens can confer upon him. After serving for many years on the Judicial Council of the American Medical Association, I have become convinced that there are few unregenerate, malicious wrongdoers in the medical profession. I have never believed that offenses such as fee-splitting, advertising or solicitation of patients, practices which are encountered most frequently, have been committed with criminal intent. A young physician may commit such an infraction unintentionally. Even if he does it carelessly, I doubt that it warrants a denial, suspension or revocation of his license to practice medicine. In this respect medical societies would do well to provide for the issuance of a warning, a censure or a reprimand, rather than what might be compared with a capital penalty.

A profession imbued with such warm fraternal relationships and such impressive honor and dignity should be able to establish or evolve a means of punishment which will accomplish these three worthy and efficient objectives, namely, (1) to impose a penalty which is just and proper, (2) to develop chastening measures which will exert a deterrent effect upon others who might become involved as well as the offender, and (3) to ensure that the potentialities for rehabilitation are never absent. It should resort, more efficaciously, to these implements of counsel, admonition, censure and warning. Based on my conviction that most offenses are not committed intentionally, that physicians rarely are malicious and that by training and tradition they have an inherent disposition to conform to every ethical principle, much can be accomplished by explaining why a given conduct was wrong, by issuing a warning against its continuance or repetition and by administering a good "bawling out."

I have observed the salutary effect of such treatment. The young physician who erred was thereby taught respect for his profession and its honor, dignity and integrity and he did not err again. Denial, suspension or revocation of his license to practice medicine would have accomplished only a part of the objective.

Had the course of action taken a harsher form, the offense charged to him certainly would have been explained, but much worse, his own destiny would have been destroyed and a useful and valued practitioner would have been removed from a community which might have been hard put to it to find his successor or his equal.

To deny a physician his license, or to revoke it, is the severest penalty that can be imposed upon him. Obviously, such devastating punishment should be reserved for application in only the gravest infractions of law or good conduct, and should not be inflicted when there is any chance for rehabilitation of the person affected.

In the administration of disciplinary procedures and in the entire scheme of medical ethics, members of the medical profession have a heavy responsibility. Whenever the ethical conduct of a physician is questioned, not only is his personal reputation at stake, but the dignity of the medical profession is challenged. The serious nature of a charge of unethical conduct demands judicious management. Adequate appraisal, mature, objective and discreet preliminary investigation are imperative. When it is being demonstrated that ethical principles have been violated, the principle of local autonomy should always be paramount and facts should be determined at the local level. County medical societies should perform this function and, following the advice of the Medical Disciplinary Committee, county societies should make adjustments, where required, to handle this responsibility with efficiency. It should always be remembered that it is the responsibility of the accuser to determine that an unethical act has been committed and it is always advisable to consult the Judicial Council before hastily considered or precipitous action is taken.

As stated in the Preamble of the Principles of Medical Ethics, the Principles "are not laws" and no thoughtful man would regard them as such. Perhaps, because of the very fact that they are not rigid laws, ethical principles can penetrate within areas in which laws must stop short for want of jurisdiction. There is no law, for example, which enjoins a man from being a vain, strutting, boastful individual who is proficient in nothing but the easy vice of proclaiming his own virtues, skills and spurious learning. No magistrate in a constituted court possesses the authority to chastise such a person, but if the offender is a physician, his colleagues do. Physicians like to dwell together in amity and accord, and when a colleague transgresses the precepts of probity or violates the maxims of professional decorum, the way of the transgressor is hard, indeed. Based on the ancient Anglo-Saxon concept that a man is entitled to be judged by his peers, the ethical practitioner, wherever he may be, has no reason to fear his colleagues, but the man who deliberately ventures into the twilight zone of dubious practices and questionable conduct has good reason for extreme concern. No amount of devious statecraft, ponderous deliberations or solemn covenants can save him from the just retribution of his fellows if, knowing better, he embarks on a course of error and deceit.

ADDENDA

Very soon after the 1955 Principles were replaced by the new version in June, 1957, the Judicial Council issued the following pronouncement:

The 1957 edition of the *Principles* was not intended to and does not abrogate any ethical principle expressed in the 1955 edition of the *Principles of Medical Ethics of the American Medical Association.* The format and language of the 1955 and 1957 editions differ; certain items dealing with professional manners and etiquette have been eliminated. However, the basic ethical concepts they include are identical. Therefore, no opinion or report of the Council interpreting these basic principles which were in effect at the time of the revision has been rescinded by the adoption of the 1957 edition.

With this statement the medical profession was informed that many of the provisions of the early version of the Principles will continue to be utilized in interpreting ethical problems. Many of these provisions have been mentioned and brief quotations have been made in my discussion of their application to the 1957 Principles. In order to afford an opportunity for a more complete understanding of the principles involved, the following principles are quoted in their entirety from the 1955 version.

ADDENDUM 1. PAYMENT FOR PROFESSIONAL SERVICES

Fee Splitting

Sec. 6.—The ethical physician, engaged in the practice of medicine, limits the sources of his income received from professional activities to services rendered the patient. Remuneration received for such services should be in the form and amount specifically announced to the patient at the time the service is rendered or in the form of a subsequent statement.

Unethical methods of inducement to refer patients are devices employed in a system of patronage and reward. They are practiced only by unethical physicians and often utilize deception and coercion. They may consist of the division of a fee collected by one physician ostensibly for services rendered by him and divided with the referring physician or physicians or of receiving the entire fee in alternate cases.

When patients are referred by one physician to another, it is unethical for either physician to offer or to receive any inducement other than the quality of professional services. Included among unethical inducements are split fees, rebates, "kickbacks," discounts, loans, favors, gifts, and emoluments with or without the knowledge of the patient. Fee splitting violates the patient's trust that his physician will not exploit his dependence upon him and invites physicians to place the desire for profit above the opportunity to render appropriate medical service.

Billing procedures which tend to induce the physician to split fees are unethical. Combined billing by physicians may jeopardize the doctor-patient relationship by limiting the opportunity for understanding of the financial arrangement between the patient and each physician. It may provide opportunity for excessive fees and may interfere with free choice of consultants, which is contrary to the highest standards of medical care.

Rebates and Commissions

Sec. 9.—The acceptance of rebates on prescriptions and appliances or of commissions from those who aid in the care of patients is unethical.

ADDENDUM 2. CONDITIONS OF
MEDICAL PRACTICE

Sec. 2.—A physician should not dispose of his services under conditions that make it impossible to render adequate service to his patients, except under circumstances in which the patients concerned might be deprived of immediately necessary care.

Contract Practice

Sec. 3.—Contract practice as applied to medicine means the practice of medicine under an agreement between a physician or a group of physicians, as principals or agents, and a corporation, organization, political subdivision or individual, whereby partial or full medical services are provided for a group or class of individuals on the basis of a fee schedule, or for a salary or for a fixed rate per capita.

Contract practice *per se* is not unethical. Contract practice is unethical if it permits of features or conditions that are declared unethical in these Principles of Medical Ethics or if the contract or any of its provisions causes deterioration of the quality of the medical services rendered.

Free Choice of Physician

Sec. 4.—Free choice of physician is defined as that degree of freedom in choosing a physician which can be exercised under usual conditions of employment between patients and physicians. The interjection of a third party who has a valid interest, or who intervenes between the physician and the patient does not *per se* cause a contract to be unethical. A third party has a valid interest when, by law or volition, the third party assumes legal responsibility and provides for the cost of medical care and indemnity for occupational disability.

Purveyal of Medical Service

Sec. 5.—A physician should not dispose of his professional attainments or services to any hospital, lay body, organization, group or individual by whatever name called, or however organized, under terms or conditions which permit exploitation of the services of the physician for the financial profit of the agency concerned. Such a procedure is beneath the dignity of professional practice and is harmful alike to the profession of medicine and the welfare of the people.

ADDENDUM 3. ADVERTISING

Sec. 4.—Solicitation of patients, directly or indirectly, by physicians, by groups of physicians or by institutions or organizations is unethical. This principle protects the public from the advertiser and salesman of medical care by establishing an easily discernible and generally recognized distinction between him and the ethical physician. Among unethical practices are included the not always obvious devices of furnishing or inspiring newspaper or magazine comments concerning cases in which the physician or group or institution has been, or is, concerned. Self laudations defy the traditions and lower the moral standard of the medical profession; they are an infraction of good taste and are disapproved.

The most worthy and effective advertisement possible, even for a young physician, especially among his brother physicians is the establishment of a well merited reputation for professional ability and fidelity. This cannot be forced, but must be the outcome of character and conduct. The publication or circulation of simple professional cards is approved in some localities but is disapproved in others. Disregard of local customs and offenses against recognized ideals are unethical.

The Relationship of the Physician to Media of Public Information

Sec. 5.—Many people, literate and well educated, do not possess a special knowledge of medicine. Medical books and journals are not always easily accessible or readily understandable.

The medical profession considers it ethical for a physician to meet the request of a component or constituent medical society to write, act or speak for general readers or audiences. On the other hand, it may often happen that the representatives of popular news media are the first to perceive the adaptability of medical material for presentation to the public. In such a situation the physician may be asked to release to the public some information, exhibit, drawing or photograph. Refusal to release this material may be considered a refusal to perform a public service, yet compliance may bring the charge of self seeking or solicitation.

An ethical physician may provide appropriate information regarding important medical and public health matters which have been discussed during open medical meetings or in technical papers which have been published, and he may reveal information regarding a patient's physical condition if the patient gives his permission, but he should seek the guidance of appropriate officials and designated spokesmen of component or constituent medical societies. Spokesmen should be empowered to give prompt and authoritative replies and a list should be issued which identifies them and discloses the manner in which they may be reached. These provisions are made with full knowledge that the primary responsibility of the physician is the welfare of his patient but proper observation of these ethical provisions by the physician concerned should protect him from any charge of self-aggrandizement.

Scientific articles written concerning hospitals, clinics or laboratories which portray clinical facts and technics and which display appropriate illustrations may well have the commendable effect of inspiring public confidence in the procedure described. Articles should be prepared authoritatively and should utilize information supplied by the physician or physicians in charge with the sanction of appropriate associates.

When any sort of medical information is released to the public, the promise of radical cures or boasting of cures or of extraordinary skill or success is unethical.

An institution may use means, approved by the medical profession in its own locality, to inform the public of its address and the special class, if any, of patients accommodated.

ADDENDUM 4. STANDARDS, USEFULNESS, NONSECTARIANISM

Sec. 1.—In order that a physician may best serve his patients, he is expected to exalt the standards of his profession and to extend its sphere of usefulness. To the same end, he should not base his practice on an exclusive dogma or a sectarian system, for "sects are implacable despots; to accept their thralldom is to take away all liberty from one's action and thought." A sectarian or cultist as applied to medicine is one who alleges to follow or in his practice follows a dogma, tenet or principle based on the authority of its promulgator to the exclusion of demonstration and scientific experience. All voluntarily associated activities with cultists are unethical. A consultation with a cultist is a futile gesture if the cultist is assumed to have the same high grade of knowledge, training, and experience as is possessed by the doctor of medicine. Such consultation lowers the honor and dignity of the profession in the same degree in which it elevates the honor and dignity of those who are irregular in training and practice.

ADDENDUM 5. THE PHYSICIAN'S RESPONSIBILITY

Sec. 2.—The avowed objective of the profession of medicine is the common good of mankind. Physicians faithful to the ancient tenets of this profession are ever cognizant of the fact that they are trustees of medical knowledge and skill and that they must dispense the benefits of their special attainments in medicine to all who need them. Physicians dedicate their lives to the alleviation of suffering, to the enhancement and prolongation of life, and to the destinies of humanity. They share whatever they have learned and whatever they may discover with their colleagues in every part of the globe. They recognize instinctively that the need for improvement of medical knowledge and skills is never at an end, and while they strive toward satisfaction of this need they are zealous in making available to physicians of good character who possess the desire and the ability to learn the aggregate of progress in medical education, research, and discoveries as they may exist at the time. They do not remain content to limit their activities to the care of the infirm, since they recognize also their useful rank among the vast concourse of citizens on whose shoulders the destiny of our nation rests. At the same time they will resist attempts to debase their services by diverting them to ignoble purposes. In their relationships with patients, with their colleagues, and with the public, they maintain under God, as they have down the ages, the most inflexible standards of personal honor.

REFERENCES

1. Hirsch, B. D.: Personal communication to the author.
2. American Medical Association: *1846–1958, Digest of Official Actions,* vol. 1 (Chicago: American Medical Association, 1959) pp. 153–154 and 612–617.
3. Osteopathy: special report of the Judicial Council to the House of Delegates, J.A.M.A. 177:774–776, (Sept.) 1961.
4. Ladimer, Irving: Ethical and legal aspects of medical research on human beings, J. Public Law 3:488, 1955.

Index

347